A PRESIDENTS STORY

A Novel of Power and Personality

Brad McKim

HPC Global Fiction
History Publishing Company, Palisades, NY

ISBN 9781940773360 electronic e-book

ISBN 9781940773391 Quality Paperback

For information regarding special prices for bulk purchasing contact History Publishing Company LLC info@historypublishingco.com

SAN 850-5942

Published in the United States of America by History Publishing Company LLC

To Kay, Love of My Life who never tires of how much I never tire of Presidents, Baseball, Guitars and Trout.

Cast of Characters

John Adams: Massachusetts, Second President. Co-author of the Declaration of Independence and first Vice President. Vain, jealous and spiteful, he never received the recognition he considered his due. He was probably right.

Thomas Jefferson: Virginia, Third President. Co-author of the Declaration of Independence, founded the University of Virginia. Devoid of pretense, he received the recognition and adulation that John Adams craved…and found it wanting.

James Madison: Virginia, Fourth President. Drafter and principal advocate for the Constitution, he became known as the "Father of the Constitution." By the time he died, his progeny was becoming unrecognizable to him.

James Monroe: Virginia, Fifth President. Revolutionary war veteran that served under George Washington and went on to serve as Minister to Great Britain, Secretary of State and Secretary of War under Jefferson and Madison. He disappointed them all, yet still followed them into the White House.

John Quincy Adams: Massachusetts, Sixth President. Son of John Adams, much more a citizen of the world than of Massachusetts, he carried his father's intransigence and antipathy for political parties into an era where they were anachronisms.

Andrew Jackson: Tennessee, Seventh President. Military hero known as "Old Hickory", he dueled, bullied and fostered a cult of personality that made him the idol of the "Common Man." The first living proof that *anyone* could grow up to be President.

Martin Van Buren: New York, Eighth President. The architect of the Democratic Party, he created the political organization known as the "The Albany Regency." Patronage and politics became synonymous thanks to the efforts of "The Little Magician."

William Henry Harrison: Indiana, Ninth President. The hero of the Battle of Tippecanoe, Harrison was never as successful battling politicians as he was battling Indians.

John Tyler: Virginia, Tenth President. The son of a man who was more popular than Thomas Jefferson in Virginia and a signer of the Declaration of Independence. Like John Quincy Adams, Tyler's attempt to maintain his father's world left him out of step and out of office.

James Knox Polk: Tennessee, Eleventh President. The protégé of Andrew Jackson who became Speaker of the House of Representatives by mastering the most arcane rules of Congress. Impatient with those who refused to work as hard as he did…which was everyone.

Zachary Taylor: Kentucky, Twelfth President. A career military man who was a hero in the Mexican War. Known as "Old Rough and Ready," he was considered ready to be President, despite never having voted in his life.

Millard Fillmore: New York, Thirteenth President. Handsome and affable, he was a key cog in the New York political machine that Thurlow Weed built to compete with Martin Van Buren's Albany Regency. Until he decided to be his own man.

Franklin Pierce: New Hampshire, Fourteenth President. Congressman and Mexican War veteran, he was the son of another hero of the Revolution. Unlike Adams and Tyler, he was less concerned with carrying on his father's legacy. His father, however, *was* concerned.

James Buchanan: Pennsylvania, Fifteenth President. Brilliant lawyer who served in Congress, as Secretary of State and

Minister to Great Britain. The "bachelor" President was more ambitious than romantic, and more prone to accommodation than confrontation.

PROLOGUE: December 14, 1799

Dr. Dick shook his head slowly as Dr. Craik inserted the lancet into the old man's arm and again allowed the blood to ooze. Along with Dr. Brown, the three men had agonized over whether to bleed the patient further. Dr. Dick urged that further bleeding meant certain death but the older doctors were not persuaded. So, the fourth bleeding of the night began...

The rain and snow had finally stopped but it remained bitterly cold. With the pall of death hovering over the dark room, even the fire crackling in the hearth failed to prevent the tremulous shivering of the prospective mourners. The old man groaned and spit into the brass pan at his side. Dr. Dick clenched his fists and held his tongue; the old man trusted Craik, not him. He already urgently argued that the old man was choking and more bleeding would only weaken him and, obviously, not make it easier to breathe. But Craik had been friends with that fool Brown for more years than Dr. Dick had been alive. Brown would bleed a hemophiliac.

Even in the faint light Dr. Dick could clearly see the pale white face of the old man across the room. The blisters Dr. Craik made were the only color left on a body that Dr. Dick knew to be beyond salvation. Ironic, he thought, that one could weather musket balls, cannon fire, bayonets, plague and other curses of life and, in the end, be killed by his physician. But at least Craik was a friend that gave the old man comfort in his last hours. Maybe that counted for more than rational medicine at a time like this.

The old man seemed not troubled in the least by his mortality that he perceived with an astounding degree of clarity. He already had his wife retrieve two wills from his parlor and directed that one of them be burned. This was being done. The other testament lay teetering on the end of the bed in front of his wife. She sat quietly much like she apparently did her whole life with the exception that this time she did no needlepoint, knitting or other handiwork. She simply watched in subdued horror as the blood and breath lurched from her husband.

Dr. Craik signaled to Brown and then Dr. Dick to convene again outside the room as the old man's condition worsened. The old man saw this gesture, however, and hailed Craik to stay. As Craik leaned down to him he said he wanted no more done. He wanted to be allowed to die if that was to be. Much to Dr. Dick's surprise, Craik turned, sat down in a chair near the fire and said no more. Brown took Dr. Dick by the arm and led him from the room. There were Negro slaves, young and old, that remained with Craik and the old man's wife. But Dr. Dick understood, the moment for memories had come and he had no memories to cherish of the old man.

As Brown and Dr. Dick stepped to the bottom of the stairs, the younger doctor started, "To draw blood from one so old is pure-", but Brown's pained gaze held Dr. Dick and his medicinal theories at bay. Dr. Dick crossed the room and stared out the window at the vast entrance to the old man's home. Brown was right; hell, the old man was the one who asked to be bled in the first place. He had already been bled by his caretaker when the first doctor arrived. The caretaker trembled and disclaimed that he didn't want to but the old man insisted and that he just "felt somethin' had to be done to ease all that sufferin'". Craik, being wiser and less quick to condemn than Dr. Dick, told the caretaker that he did the right thing. Dr. Dick cringed at his own callous comment that the caretaker really should not practice medicine on his own volition and the caretaker's sorrowful response, "I'm truly sorry Doctor" as he slumped in his chair. Before Dr. Dick could apologize for his pettiness, Craik summoned him to the old man's side.

The old man was bleeding and his breathing was labored when Dr. Dick first saw him. Shortly he started to gag and Dr. Dick quickly thrust two fingers into the old man's throat to unblock it. The old man's breathing became more regular but he appeared annoyed at the doctor for undignified way he was saved. Craik quickly assured the old man that Dr. Dick was one of "the brightest young doctors" he knew and so on and so forth...

It was not long, however, before the breathing again became difficult and lurched with the opening and closing of the passages. After getting more blankets to keep the old man warm and dry, Dr. Dick caucused outside the room with the other doctors who were already discussing how the next bleeding should proceed. Dr. Dick laughed derisively and blurted, "So you can kill him quickly? He is not choking in his arm. We must open the throat and allow him to breathe and regain his strength. Then, if you must bleed do so but he'll never survive without more." Craik nodded but recanted under the illusory weight of Dr. Brown's ancient arguments on the merits of bleeding.

As he watched the old man's horses huddle against the cold and the last light flicker out in the slaves' quarters, Dr. Dick wondered aloud about the time to Dr. Brown. "It's close to midnight" came the reply and Dr. Dick yawned reflexively. He had not noticed how long he was at the old man's home and now did not relish the cold ride back to his own humble dwellings. The roads were muddy and hard to negotiate in the daytime, much less at night. He began to gather his thoughts for a courteous adieu to Dr. Brown.

As Dr. Dick turned to say goodnight he saw the caretaker descending the stairs with Dr. Craik. Without hesitating, he rushed forward to apologize to the caretaker for his prior thoughtlessness. He started to elaborate on the vanity of doctors, the pressures of his profession and his neglect of the caretaker's depth of feeling for the old man when Craik held up his hand. At the same time his other arm enveloped the caretaker. The servant began to weep. Craik said slowly with a profound break in his voice, "General Washington is dead."

As Dr. Dick watched the caretaker and the old doctor shuffle to the door he gripped the railing of the stairs. He realized that he was not prepared for this moment though he knew it was upon him. Nor was his country which did not yet know that it would, for the first time, face the future with only the *legend* of George Washington.

With ominous timing, the first President's clock chimed twelve as Dr. Dick closed the door behind him and braced himself for the cold.

PART I

THE VIRGINIANS

(1801-1825)

Chapter 1:
Thomas Jefferson

Washington: March 1801

By this, the last night of his term as President of the United States, John Adams' palsy was worse than ever. As he bent over the small desk scribbling the names of relatives, friends and political allies, he struggled mightily to keep his hand from trembling long enough to string together the necessary letters. The palsy was always aggravated by tension and cold weather and, at this moment, these agents were both present.

Cold weather was all Adams knew since he came to this half-finished "President's House" in the middle of the Virginia wilderness the preceding November. The roads leading to and from the house and "Washington City" (as the General had called it) were muddy quagmires most of the time when they were not frozen, rutted trenches. In Adams' four long months he tried to acclimate both to the house and the "town," but failed miserably. He was delighted to be spending his last night in this mansion of 36 half-finished, freezing rooms.

If polar temperatures were a source of constant bedevilment for Adams the last four months, tension was a life-long malady. His parents virtually dragged him to Harvard when he was sixteen years old despite his desire to work the land like his father. After four years of modest academic progress and cascading introversion, Adams graduated and became a teacher. He approached teaching with the same grim acceptance which he displayed at Harvard. It was not long, however, before Adams' young pupils began to rejoice at the thought of another school day--not because of their intrinsic love of learning or the gripping erudition of their instructor but because of the rollicking sport they were having with the young tutor. After two years of snakes in his desk and mocking depictions of him drawn by young artists greeting him every morning, Adams took the bar exam and became what every young man with a longing for importance but an uncertainty as to vocation had become for years before and for at least 250 years hence: A lawyer.

Unlike so many who stumble into the law for lack of a better alternative, Adams was ideally suited for the job of a barrister. Quick-witted, single-minded when faced with a task, pugnacious and often mean-spirited, the life of advocacy suited him to a tee. He soon became the bane of the other counselors in and around Braintree, Massachusetts. Baiting, deriding and consistently out-flanking his foes, these were Adams' happiest days.

Ambition soon enveloped Adams as he tired of the mundane triflings of his existing clientele and began to assist (and ultimately assumed) the fight of James Otis against the British Writs of Assistance. From this battle against King George's authority to send troops into private colonial homes without notification or cause, Adams embarked on a stormy course destined for independence. He began to consort with his cousin Samuel and soon was taking on any case that might lead him to engage the Crown. His penchant for the great cause of independence brought him three things which would dominate his life--independence, paranoia and poverty.

In the early 1770's Adams made a name for himself in several court cases that challenged the authority of the British Crown. By 1774 he was chosen as a delegate to the First Continental Congress. In 1775 he nominated for Commander-in-Chief of the rebel army the man who would overshadow every act that Adams would undertake for the next twenty-five years: George Washington. Adams worked on no less than ninety committees in the Continental Congress culminating in the signing of the Declaration of Independence. Typically, on the day he signed the Declaration with his fellow founding fathers, rather than rejoicing in the bold move he played such a large part in fostering, Adams sulked. His colleagues' failure to recognize his extensive efforts to the point of crediting Thomas Jefferson with a greater share of the praise for drafting the Declaration than himself was more than Adams' immense ego could absorb.

During the next ten years Adams spent the majority of his time in Europe. He went abroad with the hope that he might escape the shadow of General Washington in particular, and others whom he considered inferior to him intellectually but who had blocked him from the notoriety he was not sure he wanted but that he *was* sure he deserved. He was, to say the least, disappointed when he arrived in France only to be greeted by an aging, lazy, lascivious and, alas, famous, Benjamin Franklin. For an intermittent five of the next ten years Adams negotiated, wrote and extracted concessions from the French and other European powers while Franklin flattered, drank, whored and took the credit. Adams left England in 1788 with the grave confidence that he had worked mightily for twenty years carving himself an impenetrable wall of obscurity.

While Adams' enemies were many, they also tended to be his admirers. They found it easy to belittle his vanity and railing at those he believed stupid, but they found it hard to deny his dedication and intelligence. As a result, in 1789 he became Washington's Vice President despite a smear campaign led by Alexander Hamilton which would leave the two men implacable foes. While Adams was ideologically aligned with Hamilton in many respects he would, in the ensuing years, tell many a man that Hamilton was "an intriguant and a bastard".

Thus, after eight boring years as Vice President and four unrewarding years as a President that nobody seemed to like or want, Adams sat at his desk by candlelight scratching down the names of relatives and those few friends still loyal to him (at least in his own mind) to fill federal judgeships throughout the land and local posts in Washington City. This action was motivated by three different causes. First, Adams viewed himself as a bastion of virtue in a sea of swine. He had never shown favoritism or compromised his beliefs in the public service. Even in France when the senile Franklin and his bawdy French friends had tempted him with wine and unchaste young mademoiselles he had resisted not because he was disinterested but because it was not the proper behavior for a man serving the public good. After thirty years of being "good", however, Adams had nothing to show but a mountain of debt, an army of detractors and a disdain for the American public he had been so "good" for. Adams was going to engage in cronyism while he still had a few cronies to engage.

Second, Adams knew that his appointments would hurt Hamilton who almost single-handedly kept Adams from being elected to a second term by publishing a pamphlet about Adams called "The Public Conduct and Character of John Adams." Hamilton intended the pamphlet for circulation only within his Federalist party but Aaron Burr, Hamilton's Republican foe, obtained a copy and saw to it that it received wide publication among his party and the public at large. Hamilton's work was typical for Hamilton--Adams was branded as petty and egotistical--which he was--but those who served with him also knew him to be unwaveringly honest and forthright, characteristics that Hamilton failed to point out. The American people decided against being led by a chubby egomaniac with a volatile temper. Adams did not smile, but as he wrote he relished the thought of Hamilton attempting to build support for his Presidential aspirations with a vast number of judicial and electoral districts controlled by the man Hamilton destroyed.

Finally, though he bore him no ill will, Adams could not allow his successor, Jefferson, to monopolize the country's political thought through appointments of his own. Here was the purest of Adams' motives. Hamilton and Jefferson emerged as the leaders of two competing factions, the Federalists and the Republicans. By 1800, one was either a Jeffersonian or a Hamiltonian, a situation Adams considered fraught with danger. Political parties were inimical to Adams' grand view of representative government and its inherent call for compromise and cooperation. A party system could only lead to rankest forms of favoritism, corruption and political "whoresmanship" as Adams liked to say. With his life-term appointments in place, maybe Hamilton and Jefferson might be stymied in their quest for a universal ideological view.

So, Adams wrote one familiar name after another, many

with little or no judicial experience. As he neared the end of his list he leaned back and did something rare for John Adams--he dwelt briefly on the positive. He thought about the woman he missed almost continuously for ten years in Europe but he now vowed to never miss again. Abigail Adams was the one person who understood John Adams and, consistent with his view of himself, probably the only one who loved him.

Abby had been a catch for John Adams not so much for her beauty but because of her wit and even-tempered manner. Self-effacing and secure, the only real impediment to her marrying Adams after a three-year courtship was Abby's minister father. With Adams being nine years older than his daughter, the Preacher Smith bellowed that he would see no girl of his marry a son-of-a-farmer lawyer that seemed to prefer non-paying cases. As she would do so often in the years ahead with her often-bellicose husband, Abby calmly pointed out that she loved her plump beaux and did as she pleased.

Throughout his political career, Adams had relied on Abby for advice more than any other person. Often her vision proved to be clearer than the "leaders" that comprised Adams' contemporaries. Of course, Abby had causes that Adams was not prepared to posit as goals for his career such as female suffrage, abolition of slavery and criminal penalties for wife abuse. Although he agreed with her that she was certainly capable of intelligently casting her ballot, he pointed out that she was an anomaly among those of the fairer sex (to which she always rejoined that he was the archetype for his sex!). And Adams also agreed that it was reprehensible for a man to beat his wife but he could not lead the campaign to imprison half the male population.

It was Abby's abhorrence of slavery that left Adams in a quandary. Her mocking tone when she scorned Adams' contemporaries' independence celebrations while they acquired and bred more Negroes stung more than any of Hamilton's ill-intentioned barbs. More people in the Northern part of the new country seemed to agree with Abby but not enough to banish slavery yet. The South was more agrarian. Adams held little hope that slavery would wane there anytime soon. But the last four months in this miserable wilderness had not only left him cold physically, but perhaps, morally. Here he saw the poorly shod and disheveled blacks that did their masters' bidding on a constant basis and Abby's protestations grew more frequent and poignant. Another four years in this place could not have passed without Adams giving voice to his wife's dismay.

Adams recalled his wife's last words before she left two weeks ago to return to Massachusetts when she scolded her husband for saying he would not stay to witness Thomas Jefferson's inauguration. He muttered aloud and to no one in particular, "I have not changed my mind Abby--I cannot stay and watch Jefferson become President."

All of his belongings were packed. Adams gave strict orders that all of his entourage was to be ready to depart at 4:00 the next morning, some eight hours before Thomas Jefferson was to be sworn in as John Adams' successor. He was humiliated by the indifference shown to him at the General's farewell which also happened to be Adams' inauguration and Adams was not about to be snubbed by the likes of the "common man" that formed Jefferson's devoted following. He had drafted his resignation when he found out that Jefferson was elected but Abby had dissuaded him from going through with his plan.

Ostensively, Adams argued that he must resign or there would be violence at the inauguration between his followers and Jefferson's. Abby had stroked his bald head and told him that that might have been true among the followers of Burr had the House broken the tie with Jefferson in Burr's favor, but Thomas Jefferson was far too much of a gentleman to allow that to happen. She grew more tender and said that Adams was simply overwrought from the death of their son Charles a few months before. And she was right. An incorrigible gambler with a fondness for rum and brothels, Charles still was Adams' favorite, perhaps because he was so unlike Adams. Even thinking of him now caused the President to shudder with a grief that left him melancholy for Abby who shared his pain so kindly.

What Abby did not say to Adams was that Adams did not have enough followers left to cause violence at the inaugural. He had not yet admitted to himself that between his rift with Hamilton and the Federalists and his fundamental disagreement with Jefferson's Republicans, Adams was a man without a party. Because of this Adams had spent his last six months as President lecturing all who would listen about the evils of party politics sounding all the while like the bitter old man that he was. This grieved Abby almost as much as the death of her son. Her husband was gruff, impatient and stubborn but he held his lofty achievements very dear. To see him so rudely cast aside had left her with the impossible task of bandaging the country's most fragile ego.

Adams summoned a messenger, bundled up his list of appointments and directed the boy to waken the Secretary of State at his home and deliver the commissions Adams had signed with the names of most of Adams' last devotees. The Secretary of State also happened to be the Chief Justice of the Supreme Court, John Marshall. By law, he was required to carry out the President's judicial appointments. In this particular instance, Adams chuckled softly at the thought of Marshall's likely reaction to these "midnight judges" as they would come to be called. Marshall would smile wryly at Adams' clever parting shot that would infuriate Hamilton because the appointments were Adams' Federalists, not his; they would infuriate Jefferson simply because they were Federalists. It was Adams' ringing last cry against party politics.

As Adams heard the boy run down the stairs and out into the frosty night he remembered that he also promised a few justice of the peace appointments for Washington City as well. He would have to have the courier take those to Marshall in the morning before Marshall was no longer Secretary of State, but only Chief Justice.

Adams picked up his quill again and jotted down a note to the messenger instructing him that these were additional appointments that he failed to send to Marshall the night before and the boy must deliver them before that "son of a bitch" Madison became Secretary of State. On a separate page Adams wrote several names along with his designated job for each-- "political plums" in the strictest sense. He concluded with the name of a man he did not know well but who often appeared at Adams' levees and who, as Adams understood it, pulled a few political strings to throw a vote or two Adams' way in the last election. Considering Adams' poor showing, he mused that here was a man with little, if any, political clout. Nonetheless, in a developing system of patronage Adams needed one more justice of the peace and William Marbury suited him as well as the next currier of favor.

* * *

Thomas Jefferson folded his inaugural address while he stared absently out the window and placed the speech in his vest pocket. He was pleased with the fluidity of the message and, as always, silently proud of the eloquence of his writing. At the same time, however, he checked his enthusiasm. Too many times he was infatuated with his own prose only to have his words ring hollow with his less than compelling oratory. This he had come to accept.

What he could not accept was the news that the boy who frequented the tavern downstairs told him late the night before. Adams had left him a judicial system filled with judges hostile to his new administration and then left the Capital at four o'clock in the morning. Jefferson's reaction to this news was outwardly non-committal but inwardly it was typical Jefferson. He was not particularly troubled by the judges--if they were Adams men then at least he could rest assured that they were not Hamilton men and that meant that they were likely to have some moral fiber-- and it was probably for the best that Adams was gone. Everyone would be more comfortable. Even in the best of his moods, Adams was an annoyance to have at your side in public.

Nonetheless, Jefferson's primary reaction to the messenger's news was embarrassment and sorrow. Although he was publicly among Adams' most visible detractors and political foes, Jefferson admired and liked Adams. True, Adams was stubborn and often mean-spirited, but he was fiercely dedicated to his young country and was the perfect balance for Jefferson in those heady first days of the republic. Adams' shortcoming, in Jefferson's view, was not one of intelligence or honesty or diligence, it was one of paranoia. Adams' whole career was spent looking for ambushes and hidden daggers that did not exist. His lack of trust was clear to all who served with him and, eventually, to the people who voted him out of the Presidency.

Jefferson still shuddered at the scene not a month before when Adams accosted him in front of this tavern and bellowed that Jefferson had thrown him out of office. Jefferson reminded him that it was not he, but the system that he and Adams created that "threw" him out. Adams was pacified but not content.

This incident and Adams' obvious maneuvers to embarrass Jefferson caused Jefferson pain on a personal level more than political. For whatever political storms Jefferson might encounter, his most debilitating episodes inevitably involved his highly-valued friendships. And his long fellowship with Adams was clearly imperiled. Abby was the more level-headed of the two (if not the more intelligent!) and Jefferson sighed with the hope that Adams' wife might prevail on her husband to set aside political animosities in favor of the fondness that Jefferson was sure Adams still held for him.

"Mr. Jefferson, I'll bring your horse around--you best get going..." shouted Captain Hoban from down the stairs at Conrad & McMunn's Tavern. Hoban had been drilling his small artillery all morning below Jefferson's window much to the next President's dismay. Hoban firmly believed that rioting and demonstrations were inevitable on this day, the first inauguration day for a president other than a Federalist. Jefferson was sure, however, that there would be no such uprisings and, to prove this, he crossed quickly to the door and called down from the top of the stairs to Hoban, "Thank you Captain but I think it is a far better day for a walk."

Jefferson smiled as he heard Hoban's perplexed reply, "But Mr. Presi..., I mean Jeffers..., excuse me sir but it is probably not wise, not that I presume to...well, if the Federalists were to...I would be..."

"Captain, if they wish to attack me they can equally do so whether on foot or on horse and I really do think it is a fine day for a walk."

Hoban confidently rebutted, "On horse you can escape easier than on foot."

Jefferson shook his head and descended the stairs until he reached the bottom step where he stopped and sat at Captain Hoban's feet. The Captain often heard about Jefferson's proclivity for enervating his subordinates by assuming an awkward relative physical position. Usually, unassailable logic followed. Hoban felt sure that he was about to experience this phenomenon first-hand as he desperately searched for some means of getting lower than the man who would be the new President within the hour. As he shifted he realized that the patrons of the tavern as well as a few of his own troops were staring at this odd scene of Hoban towering over the drafter of the Declaration of Independence, the first Secretary of State and second Vice-President who sat on the last step with his arms resting on his knees and his hands folded together as though he were about to tell his grandchild a story.

"Captain, no one is going to attempt to harm me or allow harm to come my way for at least four years, I promise you."

Hoban did not want to ask the obvious question but realized that none of the onlookers would and that Jefferson himself would rot on that bottom step before volunteering his reasoning. Hoban attempted to cleverly avoid hearing Jefferson's explanation, "Well I wouldn't be too sure of yourself on that count...sir."

"Sound advice my friend but, in this case, unwarranted," Jefferson taunted Hoban.

Hoban retreated slightly and avoided the issue by pretending to be concerned with the orderliness of his troops outside. He scowled at a lieutenant and ordered him to "make sure they're ready to escort Mr. Jefferson in five minutes." As the lieutenant turned to obey Jefferson laughed purposefully and said, "Captain, again my warmest thanks but I would rather walk alone." The young lieutenant stopped in the doorway and watched Hoban try in vain to not show his irritation with the nonchalant Virginian.

"Mr. Jefferson, it is my job to see that no one harms you. If you are hurt, I will be disgraced," Hoban pleaded.

"No one will raise a hand against me," Jefferson chided.

At last Hoban asked the inevitable question. "How do you know?"

To Hoban's relief, Jefferson finally rose, placed his huge hand on Hoban's shoulder and said, "Because, as undesirable as I may be for a President, I'm not Mr. Burr." As the tavern erupted in laughter, Hoban watched as Thomas Jefferson turned and walked out the door to be sworn in as President of the United States. Hoban made no attempt to hinder him because he knew that Jefferson was right. No matter how one felt about the tall red-head from Virginia, few were comfortable with the thought of Jefferson's Vice President, Aaron Burr, leading the country.

Jefferson's party, the Democratic Republicans, backed Burr for President with the express understanding that Burr would come in second and serve as Jefferson's Vice President. Yet when the final electoral votes were counted, Burr was tied with Jefferson. It was fully expected that Burr would concede to Jefferson and assume his agreed upon duties. But Burr succumbed to ambition and refused to acknowledge his promise. After the House of Representatives broke the tie in Jefferson's favor and named Burr Vice President, Jefferson vowed that Burr would never have his trust again. Jefferson's supporters were so incensed at the New Yorker that Burr soon displaced Alexander Hamilton as the object of their wrath and, as a result, was smeared unmercifully.

So, while Jefferson barely beat his new Vice President, he now walked with quiet confidence to the Senate knowing that the treacherous Burr was not only *not* a physical threat, but was about to be sworn in as the world's most impotent man--the Vice President of the United States. And Jefferson intended to make sure that Burr's Vice Presidency would be even more dull and agonizing than his own tenure in that insufferable job...and that it would be memorable compared to the rest of Burr's career after that.

* * *

"This must be a very proud day for you Mr. Madison!"

The shrill voice of Margaret Smith jolted James Madison from behind. Madison turned and started to stand but then thought better of it. At 5 foot and 4 inches and barely 100 pounds

11

Madison had become adept at avoiding comical scenes such as standing next to the immense figure of Mrs. Smith that hovered over him presently. Always the gentleman, however, Madison invited Mrs. Smith to sit next to him.

As the newspaper editor's wife settled in next to him in the Senate chamber to watch the inauguration of Thomas Jefferson as the nation's third president, Madison replied to her original proclamation, "I am very happy to see a friend and highly capable man like Tom Jefferson become president." While this statement was true, both Madison and Mrs. Smith knew it was disingenuous. The matronly woman ignored Madison's comment, however, and stated the obvious point that was on every person's mind in the room if not the city.

"This shows that the Constitution you wrote and convinced us to adopt works. Never has civilization seen a leader take power with so much opposition yet with no bloodshed. It is a mark of the viability of your work and foresight that..."

"You must be Margaret Smith!"

Thankfully, Dolley Madison returned to her husband's side and saved him from one of Margaret Smith's verbose ingratiations before it went any further. As passionate as Madison could be on any subject he turned his mind to, the rudder which controlled his brain was, if powerful, also very cumbersome. He had never been skilled at chit-chat or at accepting praise, especially where it was feigned. Thus, he had never been able to start a conversation or end it. He merely contributed, albeit weakly, to the interlude between the two.

Dolley, on the other hand, was different. The very essence of "buxom", she was sixteen years younger than Jemmy Madison and the opposite in not only disposition but appearance. While Madison was dour and pensive with a dry but infrequent wit and a look that combined anemia and emaciation, Dolley was vivacious with a rollicking sense of humor. And, quite simply, Dolley was beautiful.

At thirty-two years old, Dolley had a flair for fashion that accentuated her rosy countenance and splendid figure. Her penchant for pearls and turbans was already well known and, soon, would set the trend for Washington socialites. She moved with a confidence and grace that was the envy of all Washington wives.

But while Dolley was envied for her beauty, grace and aplomb; she was universally well-liked. Lacking any sense of spite or malice, it was impossible to not adore Dolley and, if one attempted criticism of Mrs. Madison, ostracism was sure to follow. The closest she came to being reproved was the general public's consternation as to why she married Jemmy Madison. The grandest catch in the city was enamored with this sallow gentleman old enough to be her father. Those who speculated that she was after money were clearly uninformed that Madison was hopelessly in debt.

The answer lay in Dolley's past and Madison's future. At twenty-one Dolley married a young lawyer named John Todd. Both were Quakers and Dolley settled into her role of devoted wife and mother uncomfortably. She had just come to realize that her intelligence and wit needed a greater outlet than her confining life allowed when John Todd died from yellow fever in an epidemic that also claimed one of her two babies. Left with her son Payne, the widow became the belle of Philadelphia. While she did nothing to sully her character, she set out deliberately to find a husband that would recognize her abilities, yet also give her security. After rejecting the married Aaron Burr's advances, Mr. Burr introduced her to Jemmy Madison.

If Madison lacked size and charisma, he was open-minded, indulgent and beyond the state of "being destined for"--he *was* immersed in "great things." While their love was far from spectacular in a physical sense, it was intense and passionate in the devotional context. Madison often lamented the fact that he was unable to father a child with Dolley but that was the only aspect of their marriage that bordered on a lack of fulfillment.

It was at moments such as this that their relationship was at its symbiotic denouement: Dolley interloping to rescue Jemmy from the trauma of dealing with Mrs. Smith while Dolley genuinely welcomed the opportunity to meet and charm someone new. Mrs. Smith departed the Madisons making a mental note to include a reference to the "delightful Mrs. Madison" in her column in her husband's paper the following day.

As Mrs. Smith left, Dolley winked at her husband with a twinkling but knowing smile and he looked at her with unspoken but unmistakable gratitude. At that moment the soon-to-be-third President of the United States entered the Senate Chamber. Madison laughed and commented to Dolley, "For a man who professes to have no political instincts our friend is doing quite well." Indeed, the shy Jefferson was smiling at friends and detractors alike as he made his way to the podium floating slightly above the crowd. His unusual height and his red mane normally set him apart anyway, but on this day, for once, he seemed to have taken care to appear presidential.

As Jefferson reached the Madisons he stopped to acknowledge his choice for Secretary of State who also happened to be his best friend. Jefferson bowed low and kissed Dolley's hand and embraced "Jemmy" warmly. Jefferson whispered to Madison, "Well old friend now that we've finally got the country, what do we do with it?"

Madison laughed lightly but he did not respond. He simply smiled at his old comrade and gently pushed him toward his destiny. The Presidency was Tom Jefferson's destiny as far as Madison was concerned. While many felt that Madison was the obvious heir to the throne, Madison had no such illusions. Leadership was not built on a record of drafting intricate documents and serving on innumerable committees as Madison had done in framing and sponsoring the Constitution; it was a combination of accomplishment and visual advocacy as Jefferson did. His breadth of interests and unique presence were what set leaders apart.

Madison was content to serve with his friend and, where necessary, lend his assistance. But there was one thing that was clear--Jefferson knew exactly what he wanted to do with the country. More than anything else, Jefferson's election was causing Alexander Hamilton and his cronies to realize that the United States really was a democratic republic and political enemies like Jefferson could not only grab the reins of government, but do it with no sign of a struggle. Madison and Jefferson's idealized dream of a country that allowed its people to choose its representatives in an organized and civilized fashion was today a reality.

While Madison agreed with Jefferson's critics that the new President sometimes took his "man of the people" image too far with his slovenly dress and disdain for formality, Madison could not agree that this was merely Jefferson's political hook to garner grass roots support. That was simply Jefferson. He did view himself as a man of the people. He was a typical genius eccentric in Madison's view. And Madison derived no small amount of pleasure at Hamilton's and his Federalist crowd's discomfiture with Jefferson's mockery of form.

Now as Jefferson climbed the podium and prepared to take the oath, Madison knew that by this very afternoon Jefferson would be working tenaciously to uproot as much of Alexander Hamilton's influence in the government as possible. Hamilton's Bank and the absurd army it supported would be the first targets in Jefferson's drive to steer the country back to its agrarian soul. Jefferson's recurring nightmare of a United States industrialized and miserable like Great Britain would allow him no other course. And if Madison could help, so be it.

Not that Madison had any illusions about the contribution he would make to Jefferson's administration. While Madison was highly capable and an almost peerless statesman, Secretary of State was the one Cabinet position for which he was ill-suited. Having never been out of the country, Madison would be forced to rely on others for insights on how to deal with the French and British primarily and lesser powers secondarily. Of course, that would not often be necessary since Jefferson was clearly inclined to handle foreign matters himself. Although no one had the temerity to suggest the notion aloud, it was an unspoken truism that Jefferson was grooming his friend to be his successor as President. The State Department was the one area where it was plain that Madison needed to serve an apprenticeship.

Madison had no qualms about his figurehead status since it really did not matter who was Secretary of State; Jefferson would be in control. Jefferson was no power monger but, despite his reputation as the champion of the farmer and domestic tranquility, he was fascinated by intrigue abroad. Thus, Madison would help as he was needed, learn all that he could and enjoy

Tom Jefferson's companionship.

Jefferson concluded taking the oath from John Marshall who Madison now replaced as Secretary of State. Adams' recent appointment of Marshall as Chief Justice was particularly troubling to Jefferson. Even though Jefferson and Marshall were distant cousins, they were bitter political rivals. Jefferson saw the jurist as an aristocrat while Marshall saw Jefferson as a disingenuous crusader for the rights of the "common man" while consorting with the elite of his own country and other countries, especially the French. Madison smiled at the ironic way this young republic went about transferring power. Few could have been more pained than Marshall at Jefferson's election, yet here he was anointing him with the power that Marshall's political allies coveted.

As Jefferson began his inaugural address all those around Madison strained to hear. Madison did not even try. He had known Tom Jefferson long enough to know that there was little hope of him delivering a speech in audible tones. As Madison had the same incapacity for public speaking he was not annoyed.

Madison gazed at the gathering of prominent Federalists who sat together straining to hear. Jefferson was apparently discussing the need for a sense of unity within the country among men of all political persuasions for Madison did hear Jefferson's one attempt at forceful speaking when he raised his voice and declared, "We are all Republicans, we are all Federalists." This statement had no discernible effect on the impassive Federalists; they knew as well as Madison that Jefferson had no intention of bringing them into the fold but instead intended to lead them to political slaughter.

As the Madisons made their way out into the crisp Washington afternoon they were accosted by the short, bald figure of Albert Gallatin. A Swiss immigrant whose financial maneuvering made him rich many times over, Gallatin was the heir apparent to the Treasury department. Madison, on the other hand, *knew* that Jefferson fully intended to hand the keys to the vault to Gallatin after he settled into office.

"Ah, my friend, it is always a pleasure to see you accompanied by Mrs. Madison. I'm afraid that alone you are not as enticing." Gallatin still carried his French accent but his English was impeccable.

Madison had grown used to greetings such as Gallatin's since he married Dolley. "Perhaps you would like to escort her to our lodgings in aid of your attractiveness Albert. I have a new office that I have not seen yet and I'm sure that Mr. Jefferson will soon be expecting great things!" The two men chuckled as Dolley interceded,

"Mr. Gallatin do you have any word from my family?"

Gallatin and Dolley were both from Pennsylvania. He often made a point to stop and see if Dolley's Quaker parents and other relations had any messages or packages for delivery when he was on his way to Washington.

"Indeed I do. I have a gift that your Aunt sent for you which we can pick up along the way. James (Gallatin always called Madison by his formal name), we will talk later I presume?"

Madison smiled and nodded. He knew that Gallatin desperately wanted the Treasury job and was puzzled why Jefferson had not yet appointed him when he was the most obvious choice. Unlike Gallatin, Madison knew that Jefferson would reward his friends and supporters with posts but was uncomfortable with the specter of one mass distribution of favor. Jefferson was not above political patronage, he was just more careful than most.

As Madison watched the soon to be Secretary of the Treasury set off with the Secretary of State's wife on his arm, Madison was struck by how odd Dolley looked strolling alongside a man who was an inch or two taller than Madison. How peculiar I must look next to her he thought, not for the first time.

There was a horde of "common men" who descended on the city to witness Jefferson's assumption of power. As the drunk fast began to outstrip the sober, Madison was offered libations and temptations of every sort as he picked his way along the muddy backstreets of the capital. With each polite refusal he was accused of being a Federalist, monarchist or other foe of Republicanism before someone would recognize him and correct their inebriated brethren. Madison would nod with a kind and grateful smile and step over the next reveler that had finally succumbed to sleep in the middle of the street.

Madison was remarkably unperturbed by the street scene or any of the more menacing tipplers. He long before stopped worrying about the possibility of him being a party to physical battles. With his small frame and reserved manner, Madison knew it was impossible to assault him without looking like a bully. Someone always stepped in on his behalf.

He arrived at the State Department and rapidly went to his new office. It was immaculate, John Marshall having moved out when he was appointed Chief Justice. After that, Marshall was Secretary of State in name only, just presiding over the office enough to fulfill cursory and non-controversial details. He did not want any of his activities in that office to impact his status as a lifetime judicial appointee, the position he long aspired to and valued.

There was a short stack of papers waiting for Madison to handle. On the top of the stack was a list of commissions for judicial appointees in John Adams' flamboyant handwriting. Madison had heard about the list that was delivered to Marshall the night before but this was not it. None of the names were those of the more notorious appointees that he was told about. He saw different writing at the bottom of the page noting in unfamiliar writing:

"Supplement to appointees confirmed March 4.
Deliver."

Madison quickly surmised that these appointments were not delivered by Marshall in the rush of the inauguration. It was assumed that Madison would carry out his duty as Secretary of State and deliver the President's appointments for execution. Madison, however, had another view. He was duty-bound to carry out the instructions of *his* President, not Marshall's. Adams got his ounce of flesh with the appointments that were delivered.

Madison sat down and read the note just above William Marbury's name once more. Then he folded the paper in quarters, opened the empty bottom drawer to his new desk and slid the paper to the back. He noiselessly closed the drawer.

* * *

Tennessee: August 1801

Rachel Jackson stared with wonder through the front window as she watched her husband briskly approaching with the mulatto child. She shook her head, smiled and murmured, "My dear hard-headed, soft-hearted Mr. Jackson. What hath ye wrought this time?"

Judge Andrew Jackson was soon in the door and handed the child over to his wife. He proceeded to tell the whole sordid story to her. A farmer raped his neighbor's slave and then tried to disavow the resulting child. The neighbor (who the farmer had been feuding with for many years) brought charges of theft over the abduction of his slave. Lost in the maelstrom was the welfare of the child. Judge Jackson dispatched the quarreling farmers with a withering torrent of invective and assumed custody of the child.

Rachel listened with no visible sign of dismay but ached as she heard of the slave's and her child's travails. As a devout Christian, she vowed to pray for the black girl's soul. It was not unusual for Rachel to seek out the benevolence of God. She was not always so spiritual though.

The same age as her husband, Rachel was still a striking woman with auburn hair and dazzling green eyes that radiated from a face that seemed to have tanned at some point and never paled. At 17 she married Lewis Robards, a man of means but with an indefatigable jealous streak when it came to his beautiful young bride. He took Rachel to Kentucky after they married but it was not long before her gay young spirit and his pathological suspicions collided.

After accusing her of various affairs which he drove home with his fists more than once, in a fit of rage Robards commanded Rachel to go home to Nashville. Rachel seized the opportunity and raced back to her mother's boarding house. It was not long before Robards was begging her to rejoin him and, at her mother's urging, Rachel went back. But things did not change. Soon Rachel did not wait for Robards to request, she simply went home. Robards followed Rachel back to Tennessee and moved back in with her under Rachel's parents' roof. By this time Rachel's mother had a new boarder: Andrew Jackson. For once, Robards' jealousy was justified. The playful interplay between Rachel and Jackson fast became an embarrassment to Rachel's family and an all-consuming irritant to Robards. Robards finally told Jackson that he was to stay away from Rachel or he would seek satisfaction. Jackson, in turn, promised Robards that if Robards ever implied that Jackson was consorting with a married woman again, he would slice off Robards' ear. Upon receiving this threat Robards pressed charges against Jackson for assault. On the day of his arraignment, however, Jackson sat in the courtroom waiting for his case to be called and slowly sharpening a large knife. Robards fled and the judge dismissed the case for lack of a complainant.

By 1790 Robards had grown tired of his wife's frivolity and knew that he could hardly rebuke her in the presence of her mother and older brothers. So, he took her to Mississippi. They were not there long when Robards gave her a thrashing to make up for the "fun" she had in Nashville. Of course, the call went out to her brothers in Nashville to bring her home.

But her brothers did not come. They had grown tired of their sister's stormy marriage and, after watching her flirt with Jackson, felt that Robards was within his rights in taming his undisciplined bride. Rachel lingered for a time under her husband's tyrannical hand until Andrew Jackson heard of Rachel's plight. He also heard that Robards was suing for divorce. Immediately, Jackson went to Mississippi, rescued Rachel and married her.

There was one problem though. Robards had not been granted a divorce. The Tennessee legislature had merely passed an act, at Robards' request, allowing a man to sue for divorce if sufficient grounds could be proven. It was only after two years of "wedded bliss" that Andrew and Rachel learned that Robards finally sought and received a "legal" divorce. Rachel's family and the couple's friends all urged a remarriage to attempt to minimize the stain of sin that already permeated their relationship. Andrew Jackson scoffed at the notion that there was anything improper about his marriage but when Rachel pleaded that she too felt that they must remarry, he relented. In 1794 they remarried.

Despite the unchivalrous manner of making his point, Rachel realized that Robards had a point. She *had* flirted mercilessly during her first marriage and, indeed, fell hopelessly in love with Jackson while she was still married. More than once she stayed up into the wee hours sitting on the front porch of her mother's home coquettishly talking with the young lawyer while her husband lay in their bed smoldering with anger. By the time of her "legal" marriage to Jackson she began to heed the cries of her mother that she had disgraced herself and her family. And Rachel reacted by becoming pious to the point of fanaticism--a radical shift by anyone's measure who knew Rachel before. And so, as she listened to Andrew Jackson's story of the farmers and the slave, she feared for their souls as she always feared for her own.

She asked at the end of the tale, "What is to become of this sweet child?"

Jackson looked at the baby and became grim. "His beginnings are already too notorious and although his coloring clearly favors his father, there is no doubt that he is mulatto. I must take him away from here if he is to have any hope of a peaceful life."

"But where?", Rachel queried.

"I have to go to Kentucky next week to discuss a debt that I am owed by a widow woman. The debt is small; perhaps if she agrees to take the child in I will forgive the debt."

"Forgiving a small debt is not a fair bargain for agreeing to raise a child."

Jackson reflected momentarily. "You're right, of course. I will need to make provision for the child."

And Jackson did this. The widow gladly accepted the child in exchange for the debt and, from time to time over the years, gladly accepted Mr. Jackson's financial assistance in raising her own children and Judge Jackson's "child."

* * *

Indiana Territory: April 1803

Governor William Henry Harrison was astride his favorite horse, a powerful sorrel with an imposing presence. In two days this magnificent steed carried Harrison from his headquarters at Vincennes to the banks of the Mississippi River. He snapped a question at his aide, Colonel Weatherspoon, whose horse had fared badly and would have to be replaced for the trip home.

"Will they come to us or should we go to their camp?"

Weatherspoon did not hesitate. "They will send a messenger to us."

Harrison leaned on the bowed neck of his horse. "And what if they decide they don't want to talk after the messenger tells them why we are here?"

"Oh, they'll talk. The messenger only comes to see if there are more than a few visitors. And he will only have so long before he must be back. If he doesn't return or comes back and says that there are many whites, they will get ready to defend themselves." Weatherspoon stared ahead watching for the approach of the "messenger."

"They" were the Meskwakihuk or "Red-Earth People." Harrison and his fellow white settlers in this wilderness that was being called the Northwest Territories referred to "them" as the Sac and Fox tribes. The tribes were separate but, after battling the French to the north, they consolidated and moved south. Here they came to control vast areas along the Mississippi.

Harrison had instructions, however, to get control of this land from the Indians--at virtually any cost. The instructions came from President Jefferson himself. Harrison was a lieutenant under General Anthony Wayne and fought at the Battle of Fallen Timbers along the shores of the Great Lakes where some of these same Indians and other tribes were subdued in 1794. A year later the Indians were forced to sign the Treaty of Greenville ceding enormous territory to the United States. Out of these lands the new state of Ohio was formed and admitted to the Union, just one month before Harrison came to this lookout over the Mississippi.

But even as Ohio was going through the birth of statehood, settlers were clamoring for more acreage. All that stood in their way were Indians. Harrison did not question Jefferson's rationale that it was the white man's duty to develop the West, he just hoped it could be done without another Battle of Fallen Timbers. He did not feel any great animosity toward these savages. He felt it was not his fault that they were too ignorant to insist upon greater compensation for their lands. But he did feel some remorse about the Battle of Fallen Timbers and the killing of the Indians for the land. This would not, however, stop him from warring with the "Red-Earth People" to get their lands and carry out his orders. While Harrison valued his appointment as Governor of the Territory, he knew that territorial governors did not command the respect that state governors did. And Harrison intended to create a state for himself.

As Harrison watched the sun set in the dusky haze on the far side of the river, he and Weatherspoon saw an Indian horseman making his way through the trees and brush below them. Just as Weatherspoon predicted, the messenger headed for the two white men. He did not hurry in his approach though. From the time Harrison first saw him until he came to a halt before them, close to a half hour elapsed. It was almost dark.

Harrison was surprised to see that "the messenger" was at least his own age if not older. He was thin like Harrison too. But where Harrison was delicate in appearance with his soft features and hair that was barely parted on the right side of his head and combed almost straight down, the Indian was chiseled bronze. His lean body was acutely muscular with a series of bulging veins that accentuated his sinewy sculpture. His shaved scalp with a bristling feather of hair at the back of his head told Harrison and Weatherspoon that he was a Sac warrior.

Weatherspoon began speaking in Alonquian tongue informing the Indian that Harrison wished to meet tribal leaders and to purchase some of his tribe's lands. The warrior listened impassively and said nothing when Weatherspoon finished. He turned, looked at Harrison and his eyes narrowed. Harrison shifted uncomfortably and faced Weatherspoon. "Ask him his name." Weatherspoon complied but the Indian remained silent.

Harrison snapped at Weatherspoon, "Tell him that his people can only benefit by talking with us. Tell him that we mean no harm." Again, Weatherspoon complied.

The Indian finally spoke, devoid of expression only gesturing once toward the Mississippi. When he finished he turned his horse and headed back to his tribe at the same slow pace with which he had approached. Harrison watched him go for some time before looking back at Weatherspoon who was clearly hesitant to relay the messenger's message.

"Well?"

Weatherspoon did not look at Harrison. As he translated he watched the Indian ride away. "He said that his tribe has no interest in speaking to us."

Harrison knew there was more. "And what else?"

Weatherspoon looked at him now and spoke quickly. "He said that a murderer at Fallen Timbers who drove his people from their home cannot speak now of not harming his people any more than the River can flow to the North--harm is inevitable."

Harrison meditated momentarily on the unfortunate recognition. Finally, he asked, "Was he the chief?"

Weatherspoon replied, "No, not yet. From his horse and his weapons though it is clear that he is a powerful member of the tribe...What do we do now?"

Harrison wheeled his horse around and headed for home. As he did so, he answered in a quiet and dispirited voice, "We get them drunk." He then stopped and turned in his saddle and asked, "Did he say his name?"

"Yes. It is Makataemishkiakiak."

Harrison smiled. "And what does that mean?"

"Black Hawk."

***

New York: July 1804

Most of the lawyers at the State Bar of New York meeting that year were surprised to see Aaron Burr in attendance. His reputation had long been established and it was not as though appearing at such a meeting would result in any greater notoriety. For however much lip service was paid to the need to exchange ideas and foster a sense of collegiality among the lawyers of the state, most of the attorneys were here to be met and, somewhere down the road, be remembered sufficiently to have a case or two referred to them when some other attorney was too busy or had a conflict of interest.

Certainly, that was why Martin Van Buren was now standing sipping madeira and making small talk--two areas of expertise to be sure. But Van Buren's hope of a quiet evening of business generation faded with the entrance of the Vice President. Burr wasted little time in greeting those near the door and heading across the room toward Van Buren.

Van Buren's warm salutation and low bow disarmed Burr and the Revolutionary war hero had no choice but to return the civilities. The difference was that Burr, a master of flattery and deception, was genuinely displeased with Van Buren. Van Buren, or "Matty" as he was called, on the other hand, bore no animus toward Aaron Burr. Indeed, he actually liked and, in certain respects, admired Burr.

The present tension grew from the exercise of Van Buren's first vote that he cast in his life. Not quite 22 years old, Van Buren was sponsored by the politically powerful Van Ness family in serving his legal apprenticeship in New York City prior to returning home to upstate New York to practice law with his half-brother, James Van Alen. Peter Van Ness saw in Van Buren the makings of not only an outstanding lawyer but a charming manner perfectly suited for political deal-making. In all of this Van Ness was correct, but he did not plan on Matty developing a political mind of his own.

Like Van Ness, Van Buren was Dutch. And like Van Ness, Van Buren was affable but stubborn. Not three months before the state of New York held its election for governor with the Van Ness family supporting Colonel Burr while their arch-rivals the Clinton and Livingston families supported the weak but non-controversial Chief Justice of the state supreme court, Morgan Lewis. Both Burr and Lewis were Democratic Republicans which demonstrated the degree to which Alexander Hamilton's Federalists had fallen out of favor in both New York and nationally. But Hamilton still had sufficient clout to swing the vote in Lewis' favor and away from his long-time antagonist, Burr.

Van Buren voted for Lewis. While he was by no means pivotal in the outcome, Matty's vote was disturbing for two reasons. First, he already established that he was a talented and industrious attorney and was growing more popular on a daily basis in his home district. He was clearly a force that would have to be reckoned with in the future.

Second, Van Buren had violated the time-honored tradition of dancing to the tune of his mentors, the Van Ness family. Peter and William Van Ness' fury at hearing of Van Buren's lack of allegiance was unbounded. But Van Buren stoically stayed his own course not because he was a great fan of Morgan Lewis, but because he saw Aaron Burr as a bad deal for the state of New York.

After Burr failed to bridle his ambition and accept the Vice Presidency willingly after tying Jefferson in electoral votes for President in 1800, his political fortunes plummeted. Jefferson's wrath was parlayed into a concerted effort to discredit and ignore Burr. The Vice President was still popular in this, his home state, but the rest of the country saw him as the living antithesis of Jefferson whose popularity was soaring with the announcement of the Louisiana Purchase.

Martin Van Buren was a Jefferson devotee but, to a greater extent, was a devotee of the States rights ideology of Jefferson's Democratic Republicans. It pained him to cross his mentors but, even at his young age, Van Buren knew that power resided not in the individual but in the party. Aaron Burr could wield great power within New York, but not in Washington and certainly not in his party.

After he exercised his right to vote by overcoming the protestations and threats of the Van Nesses, Matty explained to them that he was first and foremost his own man; but second he was a party man and Aaron Burr meant certain disaster for the Democratic Republicans of New York. With Burr as Governor, the state would have no leverage in Washington. Though not mollified, the Van Nesses had to respect the young lawyer's analysis.

And now Matty faced Burr for the first time since word had been relayed to the City that he broke with the Van Ness camp. Van Buren recognized that Burr had an insatiable ego and a passion for power that few could match, but he always enjoyed Burr and supported him. He was in the awkward position of having to tell Burr that his personal admiration was undiminished but he did what he felt was best for the state.

As they stood face to face they were able to look one another in the eye. Their opposing figures could have been caricatures of one another. Each was short but held his chin aloft to compensate. Each was fastidiously dressed, even for this formal setting. And each was solid, if not muscular. The only difference was that Burr, at 48, had a full head of hair while his young counterpart was already balding.

Burr dispensed with pleasantries in short order and said, "I was disappointed to hear of your disaffection for me." Burr phrased his challenge carefully. It would have been uncouth to publicly question a man's vote, just as it was uncouth to publicly seek a man's vote.

Matty was ready for Burr and, more importantly, he was sincere. "On the contrary, Colonel (Burr was vain about his military career and Van Buren knew it), my esteem for you has not diminished in the slightest. I still believe that your vision of westward expansion and development is the future of this country. My hope is that the President has seen fit to forget his previous silliness and draw upon your talents."

Burr was diverted. "I'm afraid Tom Jefferson does not lightly forget and I am not seeking forgiveness. Unlike his mentor General Washington, Jefferson is set on being the head of his party and making sure that his party is the only party. If he can continue to smother me and Hamilton, he will have his way."

Van Buren could not disagree with this characterization of the President but he seized Burr's reference to the third member of the power triumvirate struggling to gain supreme control of the nation's political reins, a struggle that Jefferson was clearly winning. "I was distressed to hear of your interview with Mr. Hamilton." Van Buren intentionally left out any reference to Hamilton's military title to further comfort and flatter Burr.

Burr nodded grimly. "I am sorry it has come to this but I have no choice but to defend my name."

Van Buren's euphemistic reference to an "interview" concerned Burr's challenge of Hamilton to a duel. During the campaign for the governorship, Burr was subjected to the usual barrage of smear tactics that had become typical for the young country's elections. The stories printed about Burr, however, bore Hamilton's distinctive rancor which was all the more accentuated by his intense dislike for Burr. Hamilton did not deny being behind the stories and so Burr demanded satisfaction.

The irony of the situation was that, for once, Hamilton had not strayed far from the truth. The tales of Burr's sexual escapades and corrupt dealings were common knowledge. But it was a tribute to his skill and charm that these blemishes did not thwart his rise to the ranks of the political elite. Hamilton, on the other hand, had little room for besmirching a man for his sexual forays. Between the two, Hamilton and Burr had a flock of illegitimate children that few could match.

No, thought Van Buren, this duel was not about Colonel Burr's "good name"; it was about Burr's demise. Burr's only damaging mistake was not one too many brothels or bribes, it was failing to accept the Vice Presidency graciously. Even then, the tie with Jefferson might have been broken in Burr's favor but for Hamilton's intercession on Jefferson's behalf. Hamilton could not abide Jefferson, but he detested Burr.

Then, less than four years later, Hamilton again swung the day for a man for whom he had little regard but who had the good fortune to be opposing Aaron Burr. After this, Burr claimed slander based on perilously near-truths. In two days would meet Hamilton.

Van Buren pitied Hamilton in a way. He had no choice but to meet Burr. Hamilton's dwindling influence would be immediately and irrevocably sapped if he refused. Unfortunately for Hamilton, Burr was an expert gunman while Hamilton had spent more time organizing finances and equipment in the

Revolution than fighting. He was no match for Burr's prowess with firearms. Either way, Hamilton was dead. The choice was obvious. Survive as a ridiculed coward with no political life or die a martyr, of sorts. But Van Buren knew Hamilton well enough to know that he was probably praying that Burr's gun would misfire at this very moment.

Van Buren shook his head grimly and told Burr, "I do hope that misfortune does not befall one who has so much more good to do for his country." With this, Van Buren caught the eye of a colleague and moved away from Burr to engage in a seemingly important discussion. As Burr rode home that night he smiled as he realized how easily Van Buren had distracted him from his intended reprimand of the young Dutch attorney.

Three days later, as Van Buren climbed into a carriage to return to his home in Kinderhook with his law partner, a boy from William Van Ness' office called to him to wait. When the boy reached the carriage he delivered his message, "Mr. Van Buren, Mr. Van Ness said to let you know that he received word last night. Colonel Burr killed Alexander Hamilton yesterday."

Matty sighed. "Please let Mr. Van Ness know that if what you say is true, Mr. Burr has also killed Mr. Burr."

* * *

Washington: January 1805

Thomas Jefferson emerged from the water closet as a slave that he brought from his home, Monticello, immediately entered the enclosure to retrieve his waste and dispose of it. As always, the chore was even more revolting with the President's ubiquitous runny bowel. Despite his calm, almost nonchalant demeanor, Jefferson's intestines were in a constant state of irritation. Since becoming President his diarrhea had become almost crippling.

He was especially irritated this day as he clutched the Washington paper where he spotted the following news:

Charges against Vice President Aaron Burr
were dismissed in New Jersey for the killing

of Alexander Hamilton. Prosecution cited a
lack of sufficient evidence to convict and
overcome Colonel Burr's plea of self-defense
and reasonable justification....

This was the first bad news Jefferson had to deal with for a long time. In the last year his political fortunes boomed. After successfully capitalizing on John Adams' efforts and avoiding war with France, he then proceeded in October 1803 to consummate the purchase of millions upon millions of western acres from that same country. Only intending to try and purchase the port of New Orleans at any cost, Jefferson was stupefied when the maniacal Napoleon offered not only New Orleans but an area as large as the existing United States for an absurdly low price.

But Jefferson did not remain in his stupor for long. Disregarding his criticisms of George Washington and Alexander Hamilton for what he felt was open neglect of the mandates of the Constitution, Jefferson declined to seek Congressional approval and sent instructions to his French emissaries to accept the offer without delay. In one cavalier stroke, Jefferson added over 800,000 square miles of land to the country's possessions. Congress' first reaction was indignance and rage at the slight to its authority but it soon became clear that the public was thrilled with the Purchase. Jefferson's popularity soared and it became politically suicidal to decry his handling of the "Louisiana Purchase."

In the wake of the Purchase, Jefferson commissioned his private secretary, the twenty-nine-year-old Meriwether Lewis, to explore the new lands. His adventure with his friend William Clark captured the imagination of not only Jefferson but the whole country. Jefferson kept his political crown jewel fresh in the public's collective mind by making sure that the regular reports from Lewis and Clark were published in as many newspapers as possible.

During his ascendancy, Jefferson was buoyed further by the news of Aaron Burr's fateful duel with Hamilton. Always a vigorous opponent of dueling, Jefferson was unable to suppress a rapturous smile at his ironic good fortune. He thought to himself at the time that if two people were going to duel, he could not think of two men he would rather have do the honors. Outwardly, however, he gave the full appearance of dismay and regret over the situation.

And recently, if it was not already a foregone conclusion, it was becoming clear that he was overwhelmingly reelected as President. The votes from the November election were almost all counted and word was that he virtually swept the country. The President personally saw to it that the twelfth amendment to the Constitution was passed to make sure that no overly ambitious scoundrel like Burr could double-cross the party's true candidate for the presidency. Each candidate for President now had his own companion candidate for Vice President. The Federalists offered up the bland and chubby Charles Pinckney, but without Hamilton to create the illusion of competence, Pinckney was simply washed away by the Jefferson tide. In March, Jefferson and his Vice President (the anti-Jefferson-but-still-a-Republican-from-New York-that-assured-Northern-votes George Clinton) would be sworn in together.

But today Jefferson rubbed his temple and reclined in his office trying to stem the onslaught of a migraine headache. He long suffered from the devastating pain that chose a spot within his skull and proceeded to concentrate its full complement of throbbing, piercing and torment. When these headaches came, Jefferson ultimately relented and withdrew to his room for a day or two until blessed relief came. The wait for this temporary end was invariably agonizing and all-consuming. For one or two days, Jefferson thought not of his country, his family or even his beloved Monticello--he focused only on the pain and offered all possible promises to the Almighty for any relief no matter how transient.

And now, along with the reprehensible Burr being free, he had not received any word from Lewis and Clark for over a month. If they were lost, the country's ardor for westward expansion would be stymied by fear and Jefferson's grand Purchase would be called into doubt. And, to Jefferson's mind, if Burr still had the clout to wriggle out of a cold-blooded murder charge, he still had the clout to cause Thomas Jefferson political trouble.

As he dwelt on these problems, blackness began to shade the perimeters of his eyes and the pain burst in a spot slightly above his right eye where it became entrenched for a particularly sadistic siege.

* * *

That night as Jefferson writhed above them immersed in his agony, James and Dolley Madison hosted a dinner party for the Justices of the Supreme Court. Dolley was, for all practical purposes, the official hostess of the President's House. Jefferson's own wife died over twenty years before and his daughter Martha lost all interest in presiding over the innumerable fetes that insidiously propagated themselves no matter how much Jefferson tried to avoid such formal gatherings. But every diplomat or new arrival in Washington expected some sort of suitable recognition by the President or dire reports returned with the "scorned" dignitary.

This is not to say that Jefferson failed to create more than a few political storms by his disdain for his office's requirements of form. He had already welcomed the new British minister to the United States by appearing before him in his bathrobe and slippers. Later, he had, intentionally, committed another faux pas by escorting Dolley, who he adored, to the dinner table rather than the British minister's wife as called for by custom. This touched off a marathon chess match among the foreign ministry in Washington for escorting the wrong woman to the dinner table for the "right" reasons, i.e., to see which country could deliver the ultimate insult to the other and demonstrate its supremacy. To Jefferson, this was tangible proof that form begets form. So,he came and went as he pleased at these parties, spoke to who he wanted to when he wanted to and dressed as comfortably as he desired. And, if not for Dolley's skill at diffusing the President's effrontery, Jefferson might have been in physical danger.

After Jefferson's youngest daughter Maria died in 1804 giving birth to his granddaughter, both Jefferson and his only remaining child, Martha, lost all patience with the "frivolous" demands of the Presidency. While Dolley could sympathize with Jefferson's reaction, having lost a child of her own, she knew that a good dinner party could exert as much political influence as any of Jefferson's reams of written works. Accordingly, Dolley subtly, but firmly, took over the hostess duties.

James Madison already knew that this night would not be easy after Jefferson's servant came down and told him that "the Darkness" had taken the President and he would not be down for the dinner. He relayed this message to Dolley who, characteristically, smiled, paused long enough to take a pinch of snuff from the snuff box that Jefferson brought her from France and laughed. "Oh well, what would we do if somebody was not offended by Tom Jefferson's hospitality?"

But Madison knew that there was little chance for offense. People no longer came to the official dinners for a chance to speak with the President since they knew he rarely listened or committed to a position at such functions anyway. They came to delight in Dolley's company. And tonight, after some initial grumbling about the President's audaciousness, the evening would level out.

Dolley's charm would be put to the ultimate test with the Chief Justice on this evening. This would be the first reception for the Court in almost two years. Jefferson refused to hold the "annual" honoring of the Justices a year ago after the decision in *Marbury v. Madison* was issued in late 1803.

Madison winced as he thought about Chief Justice Marshall's political master-stroke. After Madison casually "forgot", and then refused, to deliver John Adams' last minute judicial commissions (with Jefferson's whole-hearted support and encouragement), William Marbury went directly to the Supreme Court asking for a writ to require Madison to deliver Marbury's commission.

Madison gave the case little thought until Marshall published his decision. A staunch Federalist, the Chief Justice dealt his cousin the President a firm blow by turning William Marbury's trifling five-year justice of the peace commission into a trenchant political tool. Instead of deciding whether Madison was obligated to deliver Marbury's commission and award him his post, Marshall ruled that the Act that required the delivery of the commission by the Secretary of State was unconstitutional. So, Madison could not deliver the commission because the law that required delivery was invalid.

Jefferson and Madison were immediately inflamed by Marshall's "twistifications" as Jefferson put it. In a technical sense Marshall ruled in their favor by holding that Madison was correct in not delivering the commissions. But, just as Madison failed to deliver the commissions to keep Federalists out of office, Marshall came up with the theory that his Court could hold a law to be in violation of the Constitution so that he could exercise control over the Republicans and the laws they passed.

The irony of the situation was not lost on Madison, the so-called "Father of the Constitution" who never envisioned such an application of his progeny. Marshall, a healthy lifetime appointee, secured himself a political veto that would undoubtedly outlast his cousin, Madison and their followers. While this sobered Madison, at the same time he was mildly amused by Marshall's failure to mention that not more than twenty-four hours before Madison's decision to not deliver the commissions, Marshall delivered Adams' other appointments in his capacity as the outgoing Secretary of State. And Marshall did nothing to command that those predominantly Federalist appointments be overturned because Marshall's authority was "unconstitutional."

So, after receiving *Marbury v. Madison*, Jefferson refused to receive the Court in 1804. Madison knew that this was almost as big a political blunder as the *Marbury* case because it gave Marshall the assurance that he had beaten Jefferson and Madison at their own game. But Jefferson was too enraged in early 1804 to consider holding the annual dinner. This offended the rest of the Justices but delighted Marshall.

This year Dolley convinced Jefferson that holding the dinner was politically expedient not for its influence over Marshall, but for the other eight Justices. Now, as Marshall arrived with several of his colleagues Madison braced himself for the caustic remarks that were sure to fill the air when they learned of the President's "headache". Few besides Madison knew about the magnitude of Jefferson's headaches since the President did his best to conceal their existence. When an occasion did arise where Jefferson was so incapacitated that he could not attend, his guests were invariably suspicious that the President chose to avoid them. His usual easygoing manner belied any hint of the tension that brought on "the Darkness."

Madison marveled at how adroitly Dolley delivered the news of the President's condition with sufficient gravity to preclude any question of her candor while shepparding the jurists into the drawing room where Jefferson's latest eccentricity, an Italian Marine Band, prepared to play for the Court. Only the crusty but harmless Alfred Moore commented that "at least the President got out of bed to meet the British minister." But the Justices' wives had looked forward to an evening of Dolley Madison entertainment too long to allow the President's absence to present any sort of impedimenta to the evening.

Madison squeezed his wife's hand with deep affection as the last drunken Justice left the President's house at 2:30 the next morning.

* * *

An hour and a half after the Madisons bid farewell to their last guest, Senator John Quincy Adams of Massachusetts sat down to make an entry in his diary. Although he had no particular regimen for writing in his diary, he did attempt to keep a daily record which consisted more of reflections than simple reporting.

Senator Adams was like his father the second President in almost every material respect. Each was irascible, stubborn, haughty, diligent, intelligent, tenacious, annoying, arrogant, unpopular, revered, colorless, paranoid, short and bald. And, like his father, he was a Federalist who found himself agreeing more often than not with the anti-Christ of his party, Thomas Jefferson.

First he supported the Louisiana Purchase when none of his Federalist brethren did for no other reason than the fact that it would be an open political concession that the President had pulled a major coup. Adams could not abide this sort of reasoning when it was clear that the Purchase was of indisputably colossal benefit to the nation.

Now Adams pondered Jefferson's most recent proposal in the musings of his diary:

The senator from the President's state
delivered the President's solution to
the impressment problem yesterday and I am
truly vexed. The British continue to
behave rudely to our seamen who have been
subjected to the most heinous of insults
and unwarranted seizures. The Anglos have
taken no less than fifty American sailors as
virtual slaves under a variety of pretexts.
The President's southern constituents would
make war in their next breath but he knows
too well that we could not fight the King's
militia any more than Daphnis could have
resisted Chloe. We must take a stand in
some fashion though or we will forever
be a colony for the European bullies that
have grown accustomed to our timidity. So
Mr. Jefferson has posited a cancellation of
trade with the Brits until they are amenable
to a cessation of their cavalier behavior.
I cannot see where we have an alternative
course upon which to right ourselves but
more than a few imbecile merchants in my
constituency would place their trade
concerns before the welfare of their sons.
My support of Mr. Jefferson's embargo
will certainly be criticized
but we cannot maintain a cowardly
posture while the Anglos and French make hay
with our sailors. Mr. Jefferson has
decimated our own militia to such an extent
that economic warfare is all we can wage.

Adams went on to note a couple of letters he had received and then re-placed the diary among the mounds of important debris dominating his desk. It would be light in an hour. Adams prepared for his one real regimen which was some form of invigorating exercise each day before dawn. In the summer he skinny-dipped in the Potomac; on these cold winter mornings he preferred a brisk walk or a horseback ride through the woods surrounding this wilderness that doubled as the Capital of a burgeoning empire.

On this morning, he opted for a walk. The air was nippy, but the ground was dry. Unlike so many of his northern colleagues, Adams rather liked Washington. While he tried to avoid the tropical, mosquito infested summers, he found the spring and fall to be a cornucopia of flora and fauna such as he never experienced in his well-traveled thirty-seven years.

This was hardly faint praise coming from a man who spent his childhood traveling the length and breadth of Europe learning at the feet of the masters. Then, at the age of twenty-six George Washington (who held the son in greater esteem than he did the father) appointed John Quincy as Minister to the Netherlands. After three years in this post Washington asked Adams to go to Portugal as the U.S. representative to that country. But before he could make his way to Lisbon, his father became President and immediately installed his son in the critical Prussian ministry.

While his father fretted about charges of nepotism, the son went about his business and forged commercial treaties with the Prussians that were already paying impressive dividends. The senior Adams need not have worried about any question of favoritism. It was almost universally recognized, albeit in some instances begrudgingly, that John Quincy Adams was not only qualified to serve abroad, but perhaps was more qualified than anyone else. Irrespective of one's view of his politics, he was undeniably brilliant.

But he was a little too brilliant for Thomas Jefferson. Although the two men shared similar views on most issues, Jefferson guarded his power over foreign matters jealously and Adams was clearly a threat to his omnipotence. Still stinging from the second President's "midnight judges," Jefferson called

John Quincy home and replaced him with a southerner who had never been north of Virginia or east of Carolina.

This proved to be the fatal blow in John Adams' and Thomas Jefferson's friendship. John Quincy knew they had not spoken or written to one another in over four years. He found this particularly painful not only because of his natural affinity for his father but because he studied for a time under Jefferson's tutelage. Jefferson offered these services to Abby and John as a favor in the days before Federalists and Republicans.

John Quincy was hurt by Jefferson's recall but he also expected it. He figured that Jefferson could not risk leaving a highly visible Federalist in the distinguished Prussian ministry without alienating his following. Unlike his father, Adams did not take the recall personally, he knew it was just sound politics.

The move did signal the beginning of Adams' concurrence with his father that political parties were a cancer infecting the country. He knew that Jefferson would not have been able to effectively push any of his programs if he did not establish quickly that his administration served Republicans first, Federalists second. But Adams knew that it was preposterous for anyone to believe that the nation was better served with him out of the foreign service.

As Adams wrapped a scarf about his neck and the lower part of his head and proceeded out into the chilly morning, he headed away from the Capitol building which was lurching toward completion and away from the President's House. He walked instead toward the frozen Potomac where he hoped to again swim in the spring when the woods would be teeming with blooms and newborns. Likewise, the November elections of 1804 and 1806 would be sufficiently distant to allow men to think about policies and programs rather than party exigencies. He stumbled momentarily and cursed the relentless darkness of January.

* * *

Tennessee: May 1806

Jane Polk continued to fold clothes after she got done nursing Marshall, the newest addition to her growing brood. Little Marshall was her fifth child but she was pregnant with her sixth as she moved herself, her husband and her children into their new home just southwest of Nashville.

She halted momentarily as another wave of nausea gripped her. She was in her second month and knew already that she was carrying a boy. With Jane and Lydia she had barely paused to stop and deliver--and she had not been sick. But with her three boys she woke up vomiting and continued to retch until she gave up and went to bed for a day or two. Then she generally had about a day and a half before she would commence throwing up again. She had spent the last two days on her back recovering from her most recent bout of all-day morning sickness.

Unfortunately, she had not spent the last two days on her back in bed. Instead she was in the back of a wagon traveling over either little or no roads as her family made its way from Mecklenburg County, North Carolina to this wilderness known as Tennessee. Jane and her children would have been happy to stay in North Carolina, but Samuel Polk claimed that the soil was giving out and it was time to sell while he could still get a good price for his land. Jane suspected the move had more to do with Samuel's father Ezekiel.

Ezekiel Polk was the anathema of Jane Polk. She was pious, prudent, cautious and gentle. He was irreverent, reckless and coarse. Samuel Polk feared no one and listened to no one except his father. And Ezekiel had sent word to his son that Tennessee was bursting with opportunities. Jane knew there was no use protesting when Samuel announced that the Polks were headed west. Jane rarely had her way anyway, but never where Ezekiel was in the opposing camp. Samuel could live with her disappointment but not his father's.

So, Jane struggled through the five-hundred-mile journey often fainting only to wake up that night in the back of the wagon with her children asleep all around her. The whole trip would have been so much easier if she were just carrying a girl. But try as she may, she silently admitted to herself more than once that she was glad it would be a boy because she was partial to her sons. She loved her daughters but she adored her boys.

Unlike her daughters, her boys were completely different. Frank was unruly but warm-hearted and was always the first to realize when his mother was not well. And young Marshall was already showing signs of being slyly mischievous in a quiet way. But like many mothers, Jane Polk was most intrigued and protective of her eldest son, James.

As she rested and fought off the nausea she gazed at James dutifully carrying her cooking pots from the wagon to her new kitchen, at least until Samuel could get around to getting a few slaves. Perhaps she favored James because Samuel did not. Samuel certainly loved James but he had never really understood his son. While Samuel was cunning and gregarious, James was the essence of his mother, quiet and industrious, but frail. Jane shuddered at the number of times James' various illnesses had almost taken him from her.

The worst of his ailments was rarely known to his parents because James was usually too embarrassed to tell them of his suffering. It was only when the pain became excruciating that he would approach them, weeping and looking at the ground. When that happened, Samuel and Jane knew that their son could take no more. Samuel would take his son outside into the woods and lower his breeches over his engorged organ, swollen to the point of being grotesque. Samuel would gently massage as tears streamed from James' eyes from pain and humiliation. Gradually Samuel would find the source of the blockage and guide it from the center of James' organ. The urine that James had been unable to pass would finally begin to flow in volumes that his father couldn't fathom even from a full-grown man.

For weeks thereafter, James would relieve himself twenty and thirty times a day. It would not be long however before he was once again quiet. Samuel and Jane learned to let him come to them; it seemed to help maintain some semblance of dignity. Sometimes though they couldn't wait. They would find James passed out in the yard or in a back room and would revive him so that Samuel could carry him into the woods and assist him.

As James put the last of the cookware in its place, he stopped and stared vacantly out the window. Jane could just see him through the open doorway and frowned. James was not a malingerer or daydreamer. If he stared into the distance and did nothing it meant that something was troubling him. Jane saw him do this several times during the journey from Mecklenburg County but, with the rest of the family about them, was not able to find out the problem. Now though, she could speak to him alone.

James turned from the window to look at his mother before she even said anything--he had always been very close and open with her. Jane nodded toward the woods out the window that had held James' gaze.

"It is a pretty place isn't it James?"

James nodded and smiled briefly but insincerely. Jane had lectured James about his smile. He rarely smiled with any depth of feeling but when he did there was no denying that his was an extraordinarily alluring smile that instantly transformed him from weak and somber to a warm and enchanting child. She knew he was not in the mood for small talk. At eleven years old, James preferred to get down to business.

"What's on your mind?"

"Marie Willis said that we had to move because God has not accepted me," James responded without emotion.

Jane Polk winced. Marie was a schoolmate of James' and the Reverend's daughter in North Carolina. Jane and Samuel took their first child to be baptized as an infant to the Reverend Willis but the ceremony was never completed. Early on the clergyman asked the parents for a profession of their faith which Jane easily and unreservedly gave. Samuel, however, made a joke which the Reverend did not find amusing. This sparked a lecture on Samuel's gambling forays followed by a colossal eruption by James' father that was still legendary gossip in the community ten years later. After lambasting the would-be baptizer Samuel swept up his son and led his weeping young bride from the sanctuary. Thereafter, Jane took each of her babies quietly to the church for their baptisms but James never received the blessing.

For a devoted worshiper like Mrs. Polk, James' situation

was truly vexing. Although she harbored grave doubts about her son's status with the Lord, she tried to assuage his anxiety.

She smiled her most maternal smile and stroked the fine black hair on the side of his head. "God has accepted you James because he accepts everyone and everything. Not being baptized does not mean that God loves you any less than anyone else."

James' reply was direct as always. "Then why are people baptized?"

Jane wrestled with this briefly but did the best she could, "Because it shows God that he is accepted by you."

"How can a baby know if it accepts God or not?"

Jane started to give her reason but realized that this was the type of point that would do more to soothe her son's cares than dogma. So, she shrugged and laughed, "I don't know, maybe it's a way to make sure that the baby has no choice. But since you have accepted God, that is all that matters. And we came here because the soil is better, not because James Knox Polk has never been baptized. Now you finish helping unload." She squeezed his arm and smacked his derriere playfully as he turned to go back outside.

As James Knox Polk went out the door of his new home, he felt a little better because he knew that he was probably not the reason his family packed up and left the only home he ever knew with his pregnant mother in tow. But he felt a little worse because his pregnant mother assumed that he had accepted God.

* * *

That same day, not a hundred miles north of the contemplative Master Polk, Andrew Jackson stood just across the border in Kentucky and paced off eight steps to the east while Charles Dickinson paced off eight steps to the west. The last week was eventful for Jackson, the new major general of the Tennessee militia.

Two months prior Jackson was swept off his feet by the former Vice President Burr. Burr stopped in route to the Mississippi River to enlist Jackson's aid in securing horses, men and weapons for an anticipated southern invasion by the Spanish.

Jackson gave Burr all he desired and promised to send further support as well as leading troops personally. Burr's wish was Jackson's command. Burr smiled his most paternal smile and assured Jackson that he would call upon the major general to help defend his country.

Aaron Burr called for Jackson close to two months later. But his message arrived a day after Jackson received a warrant witnessed by none other than Thomas Jefferson himself ordering the arrest of anyone aiding Aaron Burr in his

> ". . .quest for dictatorship and dominance
> over the West and the sovereign nation of
> Mexico. Anyone having contact with Mr. Burr
> shall ensure his return to the authorities
> to stand trial for treason."

As much as Andrew Jackson admired Aaron Burr's gusto and courage, he knew that Thomas Jefferson would win any battle with the wayward adventurer. Being on Mr. Burr's side would not be a particularly shrewd move for one as ambitious as Jackson. So, the Tennessee officer quietly sent orders for the troops he loaned Aaron Burr to return home immediately...and to bring Colonel Burr with them if possible.

After extricating himself from association with Aaron Burr, Jackson hurried off to William Coffey's field for an afternoon of long awaited horse racing and wagering. Upon arrival Jackson shared a bottle of rye with two friends and proceeded to yell for the start of the races. At that point the race organizer (the aforementioned Charles Dickinson) informed him that the races were canceled because of the residual wetness of the field from the prior week's rains. Major General Jackson accused Dickinson of cowardice, dishonesty and of fixing races as he bellowed that Mr. Dickinson was only canceling because Dickinson's horses could clearly not compete with those of the Jackson farm. At the end of his diatribe Jackson called Dickinson "a lying bastard" and turned to stumble away.

Jackson sobered quickly though when Dickinson said, "At least I am not married to an adulterous whore."

Jackson stopped and turned slowly back to Dickinson. This was the one insult that could cause Jackson to be blind with fury and Dickinson knew it. All who knew Andrew Jackson knew that his sore spot was any aspersion on the character of Rachel and her and Jackson's inadvertently premature marriage. Through gritted teeth Jackson demanded satisfaction.

As Jackson neared his eighth step he knew that he was as good as dead. Charles Dickinson was the most renowned shot in Tennessee. This was Dickinson's tenth duel without so much as a nick; it was Jackson's first. Jackson challenged John Sevier to a duel a few years before but both men proved inept at properly preparing their pistols and ended up laughing about their inability to fire their weapons rather than killing one another. But this time he knew his opponent would know all about how to fire his gun...

As Jackson whirled his worst fears were realized. Dickinson had already raised his pistol and taken aim. The explosion in Jackson's chest was in concert with the explosion of Dickinson's gun. But as Dickinson blinked while the smoke from his pistol cleared, his eyes widened in amazement. At first there was merely a puff of dust from Jackson's coat but a few seconds later the blood began to stream down Jackson's chest. When Dickinson saw the blood he breathed a sigh of relief. Jackson would soon fall dead. He began to turn away and walk to his horse for the ride back to Nashville.

He stopped when he heard the click. As Dickinson turned he saw Jackson holding his pistol aloft. He had pulled the trigger. But the gun had failed to fire.

Dickinson regained his composure and smiled. "Adieu Mr. Jackson."

Jackson remained in his spot and growled at his second who promptly commanded, "Mr. Dickinson, return to your mark. This man is shot. Surely you wouldn't deny him satisfaction in such a state?"

Dickinson shrugged and returned to his mark winking at his second and smiling at the voluptuous young girl who came out to watch him teach Andrew Jackson a lesson and whom Dickinson hoped to teach a lesson tonight. Dickinson was pondering such thoughts until he once again looked at Andrew Jackson. With a pool of blood forming at his feet Jackson patiently re-cocked his pistol and, without any sign of wavering, took aim at Dickinson. Jackson slowly released the hammer. The explosion this time had very little effect on Andrew Jackson. He missed his preferred target but he was not worried about marksmanship, only the effect on Mr. Dickinson.

The effect was profound. As he heard and saw the explosion Dickinson clutched at his chest. But the shot detonated instead in his abdomen. Charles Dickinson lived only long enough to feel the shot and the waste from his bowels exit through the hole that burst in his back. Andrew Jackson turned and solemnly handed his pistol to his second, took four steps toward his horse and fainted.

* * *

London: December 1806

On this, the last day of 1806, James Monroe did what he did whenever he was nervous, he rested his thumb in the cavernous dimple that punctuated his chin and gnawed at the side of his right index finger. Taken alone, Monroe's ears, nose, chin, forehead and narrow, ruddy face were distinctly unattractive. But his eyes somehow compensated. They were a dull blue, almost gray that radiated warmth and earthiness. One was so quickly drawn to the eyes that there was little opportunity to dwell on the absurdly long nose and protruding ears.

Monroe's eyes were not a ruse either. He was warm and earthy. Not a glad-hander, he was incapable of insincerity. His voice was soft and endearing while his manner was confident yet self-effacing. In short, Monroe was ideally suited to diplomacy which was precisely why he was in Europe.

Thomas Jefferson sent his long-time friend to negotiate with the French for navigation rights on the Mississippi River. But much to Monroe's surprise, he was greeted in Paris by the news that the United States had already hastily concluded the Louisiana Purchase. Jefferson then directed Monroe to Madrid to see if the Spaniards would sell Florida. In Spain Monroe was met with a flat refusal bordering on derision. Jefferson and his Secretary of State Madison then instructed Monroe to go to Great Britain to investigate the potential for a treaty ending British abductions of U.S. sailors on the high seas. So, Monroe spent the last year in London negotiating the treaty that he was now attempting to explain through correspondence to Jefferson and Madison.

Unfortunately, Monroe's eyes and magnetic demeanor could not overcome the fact that he did not drive a very hard bargain. After crossing the Delaware on Christmas Eve as an officer under General Washington during the Revolution and receiving a musket ball in his shoulder, Monroe was sent to France as the United States minister when the General became the first President. But by then Monroe had already bound his close ties to Thomas Jefferson who had recently resigned as Washington's Secretary of State. As a result of Jefferson's influence, Monroe adopted an affinity for everything French.

When Monroe arrived in Paris he delivered a laudatory speech gushing over the esteem that he and his fellow Americans had for the French and their Revolution. The French were enraptured with the new minister but Washington and his new Secretary of State Edmund Randolph were not. A severely worded reprimand was dispatched across the ocean reminding Monroe that the U.S. considered itself neutral in the ongoing feud between Great Britain and France and that glowing speeches praising the French were not likely to help maintain at least tolerable relations with the British.

But Monroe's real mistake was to help secure the release of the Revolution maker, Thomas Paine. After fanning the flames that led to the American revolt against the British, Paine traveled to France to join in the rebellion sweeping that country. His fondness for alcohol which inevitably spurred his fondness for hearing his own voice which inevitably spurred his fondness for criticizing the intelligence of his fellow men (usually the fellow men that were within the sound of his aforementioned preferred voice) soon landed Paine in a French jail where he languished for almost a year. This status suited George Washington just fine since he could not tolerate the arrogant Paine. But Monroe, whether it was because of Paine's efforts at freeing the Colonies from British rule or because he saw it as his duty as minister to see that American subjects were not held against their will or because Monroe enjoyed drinking almost as much as Paine, convinced the French to set him free.

Paine immediately took up residence with Monroe where he was nursed back to health from the illnesses contracted in prison. Once healthy, Paine wrote a scathing letter to Washington for leaving him to rot in prison. Washington said nothing publicly and did not respond to Paine's attack but he never forgave Monroe for his role in freeing that "miserable dipsomaniac." The next year Washington recalled Monroe after Monroe denounced a treaty that the Administration endorsed with the British. Washington had had enough of a minister that was more French than American. Three years after his recall Washington, already suffering with a mild case of the flu, contracted pneumonia and died after refusing to change into dry clothes when he came in from a cold December rain. He was too upset and angry to tend to his own well-being after hearing that Monroe was elected Governor of Virginia...

It was testimony to Monroe's charisma that he could endure and prosper even after a feud with the greatest hero of his time. But now as he sealed his letter to the President and enclosed the treaty, he wondered just how bright his future was. He knew that the treaty failed to address impressment of American sailors by the British which was the one point that Jefferson and Madison wanted addressed. But Monroe found out that he liked the British too and failed to stand firm on the impressment issue. Besides, he consoled himself, he did not really have any leverage to exert. The British were not as desperate for American trade as Americans were for British trade.

Monroe was not sure he *cared* whether he pleased Jefferson and Madison. He began to suspect (fueled by letters from his supporters in the States) that his mission was not one of diplomacy but of politics. During the last election, with Jefferson's popularity soaring, it was assumed that one of Jefferson's closest compatriots, Madison or Monroe, would succeed Jefferson in office. Not long thereafter, Monroe was sent on his foreign mission.

But his mission amounted to nothing more than a wild goose chase. He arrived in Paris only to find that Jefferson and Madison had already concluded a greater coup than Monroe could ever hope for, that is, not just the right to ship on the Mississippi, but complete ownership of the River. Then the President and Secretary of State asked him to negotiate a purchase of Florida with Spain that they knew would be rejected by Spain and a treaty with the British that they knew would be rejected by the President and Secretary of State.

Monroe doggedly refused to believe reports from the States that Jefferson and Madison were intentionally keeping Monroe out of the country to pave the way for Madison's Presidential aspirations--until William Pinckney arrived in London. Pinckney was a Federalist with Republican sympathies that Jefferson sent to assist Monroe in his negotiations. Jefferson and Madison assured him that Pinckney was a political necessity for any treaty that resulted from the negotiations to stand a chance of passage. For a time, Monroe was pacified and worked comfortably with Pinckney until more and more warnings poured in from various stateside confidants that Pinckney was nothing more than insurance against the unlikely occurrence that Monroe concluded an acceptable agreement alone and returned home a triumphant statesman riding a storm of popularity into the President's mansion. Now at least, the credit for any treaty would have to be shared.

Monroe was proud of the treaty he was sending to Jefferson and Madison. He knew he did the best he could with the British. But as he rose to go join Pinckney and his British counterparts to celebrate and to toast the New Year, he worried. He knew the storm was rising toward the type of confrontation he never relished. He survived his battle with the Father of his Country, but could he survive another with the author of the Declaration of Independence and the Father of the Constitution?

* * *

Pennsylvania: May 1808

"Jim. Wake up."
No response.
"C'mon Jim...you gotta wake up."
Nothing.
"Dammit Jim! WAKE UP!"
One eye opened long enough to identify the tormentor.
"What's the matter Jasper?" Jim responded with a yawn, crossing his arms and keeps his eyes closed.
"Davidson is headed this way," Jasper answered and awaited Jim's flurry of panic.
Jim didn't panic.
"So?"
"So?!? This place smells like a goddamned still blew in the middle of my Uncle's tobacco plantation."
"Is Millicent gone?"
"Yeah. She was a little easier to rouse than you."
"Good." Jim closed one eye again. He figured Davidson would have the good sense not to make a scene over a few cigars and some whiskey. But he wasn't so sure Davidson could overlook a state senator's daughter. Jim giggled as he thought about Millicent stumbling about drunk with him and his friends in their evening of debauchery at the end of this session. He hadn't even ended up making love to her last night.

He skipped his usual foray into Millicent Mackay's undergarments to allow his friends a shot at having their way with the adventuresome belle of Carlisle. For last night was nothing more than another installment in what was a rollicking year of drinking and intercourse for the handsome and cocky Jim Buchanan. His friends, for the most part, failed to fully exploit the various "opportunities" available at Dickinson College. So, he magnanimously stuck to cigars and whiskey and watched his friends try to woo the Lady Millicent with flattery, chivalry and booze.

Much to their chagrin this morning, his friends realized they had all passed out before the Lady Millicent who ultimately curled up on Jim's bed, bored and unsatiated. Jim finally passed out too but not before chuckling at his friends' naive efforts to seduce the Lady Millicent. They all proceeded cautiously laboring under the impression that Lady Millicent somehow cherished her virtue. Jim long ago learned that flattery and prudence were lost on Millicent--she liked a good crude joke and a warm bed and placed little value on the standard pretensions of well-bred college boys.

Jasper shook his head and slipped out the back door to watch the scene when Professor Davidson arrived. As much as Jasper liked his friend, he knew Jim was on thinner ice than Jim realized. Jim was brilliant, of that no one disagreed, including Jim. He was first in his class and he achieved this standing with minimal effort. While Jasper and his other friends studied day and night to get by, Jim glanced at his books in the day and terrorized the town of Carlisle at night while scoring top marks. He treated his professors with a haughty contempt as though they were unworthy of his genius.

Davidson knocked at the door but entered before receiving a reply. Jim pulled himself up and sloppily kicked the cigar butts and one whiskey bottle he saw under his bed. But it did little to disguise the fact that Jim Buchanan had found a whole band of merry men to join him this time.

"Jim, I have a letter for you to deliver to your father when you get back to Lancaster. See that he gets this promptly."

Buchanan took the letter with a shrug. "Sure," he responded in his most nonchalant tone. Davidson took a quick look at the room and gave Jim the most disappointed expression he could muster before shaking his head as he left.

Jasper reentered from his perch just out of sight through the window. "What's the letter say Jim?"

"Jasper, how in the hell would I know? It's sealed." Jim was often exasperated with his roommate. Jim was not about to open the letter. There was one man that he respected more than himself and that he also feared--his father. With James Buchanan Sr. there was no chicanery, only obedience.

He gave Jasper his most confident air. "Probably something to do with studying abroad after next year or something. Davidson is real big on that sort of thing." Jasper nodded. Jim was probably right, as usual.

Buchanan arrived in Lancaster, Pennsylvania a few days later ready for a summer of light work and recuperation from his "studies." Jim had forgotten about the letter after he gave it to his father until the elder Buchanan threw it on his lap with a look of rage that made the usually unflappable son swallow with anxiety. The senior James Buchanan hovered over the junior James Buchanan while he read:

My Esteemed Mr. Buchanan:

The faculty of Dickinson College has decided against extending an invitation to your son to return to Dickinson in the Fall. While Master Buchanan has excelled scholastically, he has consistently failed to adhere to established standards of conduct. The faculty urges you to prevail upon your son to rectify his behavior and set himself upon a more virtuous course.

Regretfully Yours,

Dr. Robert Davidson

* * *

Washington: January 1809

When he became the third President of the United States, Thomas Jefferson was embarrassed and disturbed by the immense grandeur of the Presidential mansion. He quickly took steps to make the house more functional and open, much like his own Monticello. Jefferson believed that a palatial residence for the President of the alleged home of liberty and equality was inappropriate.

But now, almost eight years later Jefferson was subconsciously thankful that he was safely ensconced in his office above the main floor of the house. He had had his successes. The Federalists were virtually dead. Jefferson and Madison managed to build the Republicans from a group that dominated Virginia to the country's only truly cohesive party. There was no doubt that a Republican would be the next President and, until mid-1808, there was no doubt that that Republican would be Madison. But Jefferson's other long-time compatriot James Monroe returned from England in the spring of 1808 with a chip on his shoulder.

First Monroe suspected that Madison and Jefferson were intentionally keeping him out of the country with a variety of fatuous foreign assignments. When Monroe forwarded the treaty that he concluded with the British to Jefferson and Madison, Jefferson rejected it out of hand because it failed to address impressment of American sailors by British trade ships. Jefferson refused to even submit the treaty to the Senate even though it contained significant trade concessions.

The failure to submit the treaty convinced Monroe that his two allies had turned on him. He arrived back in the States intent on grabbing the party's nomination for President. True to form Monroe failed to discuss his dismay with Jefferson and Madison. When Jefferson learned of Monroe's actions he summoned him to the Capital and queried why he was attempting to divide the party.

With tears in his eyes Monroe told Jefferson of his consternation at his treatment by his old friends and how he had no choice but to accept the invitations of those Republicans that opposed Madison. Jefferson responded with tears of his own and, after many hours and many glasses of wine, persuaded Monroe that his diplomatic missions were not intended to keep him out of the way. The President was dissatisfied with the English treaty but he knew that the problems with the Brits would not be solved with paper--that much was now apparent. He encouraged Monroe to be patient as he was younger than Madison and in better health. In order for the Republicans to carry out their program of creating a Union of highly autonomous states that recognized that they exerted more power collectively than apart, Republican control had to be solidified and enduring. Monroe was assured that his time was soon. In the meantime, Jefferson offered Monroe the governorship of the Louisiana Territory.

Monroe declined Jefferson's offer but apologized for

doubting his mentor's motives. He did not quash the drive to nominate him for President but he assumed a much lower profile. As a result, Jefferson was able to swing the necessary support to Madison.

After the election, however, when it was clear that Madison would eventually be declared the winner against a weak Federalist opponent, Madison sent word to Monroe again offering the Louisiana post. Monroe was incensed--he fully expected to be Secretary of State and Madison was once again attempting to send him to some remote outpost where he would be forgotten! Monroe sent a terse refusal and had not communicated with Madison since.

Jefferson somberly reflected on the demise of the friendship between his best friends like so many broken friendships he suffered in the last eight years. Jefferson wanted to be President, but now he rued the day of his election. From a professional ideologue, he degenerated into a professional politician. But he was never as good a politician as he was an ideologue.

Of the many friends he had lost, Aaron Burr disturbed him the most. He became consumed with revenge for Burr's failure to step aside in 1800. He stewed for days when Burr was acquitted of killing Hamilton but he became delirious when his constant nemesis John Marshall acquitted Burr of treason after Jefferson paid a handsome sum for Burr's capture. When the news of the acquittal arrived, the President flew into a rage of epic proportions.

Jefferson's lofty goals and ideals lost the battle with his desire for reprisals against "enemies." His detractors claimed victory because Jefferson became the incarnation of paranoia and its attendant paralysis. Ironically, his conduct was the same as that of another former friend, John Adams. And Jefferson skillfully capitalized upon the second President's phobias to get himself insinuated into the Presidency. He could almost hear Adams' sardonic voice scolding him for his naiveté.

Now, in calm reflection, Jefferson understood what happened. Just keeping himself and people who supported him in power became all that mattered. He accomplished that much because he was a competent, though not gifted, politician. And he knew with war looming with the British and a treasury mired in debt, the next President would have to be a gifted politician to have any hope of success.

Jefferson stood and walked to the window. As he watched the frozen streets of Washington start to bustle with the entourages of returning Congressmen the queasy feeling in his stomach returned. Again, he dwelt on the fact that he delivered the Presidency to a friend for whom he had boundless respect and probably doomed the precious Republican coalition in the process. For irrespective of his admiration for the man, Jefferson knew that James Madison was barely a competent politician, much less gifted.

Chapter 2:
James Madison

Virginia: May 1809

Even though he was mildly light-headed from the ale of which he now took another short sip, John Tyler was fully cognizant of his situation. Nineteen years old, he was the newest member of the Virginia State Bar. In celebration, his father took him to supper at the opulent Lafayette House where Tyler now sat with his three dining companions basking in the glow of his future.

To any onlooker the glow had less to do with young Mr. Tyler's future than with the notoriety of the men sitting with him. Next to him sat his father, John Tyler Sr., the governor of Virginia. A wealthy planter and landowner that was one of the founding fathers of the country, Governor Tyler was even more popular in Virginia than Jefferson, Madison and other famous patriots from that state--primarily because he stayed home and did not seek national prominence like the others.

Caddie-corner from the elder Tyler sat Jefferson himself. The recently retired President came to Richmond to talk with his old friend the Governor about designing and constructing a University at Charlottesville near Monticello, Jefferson's home. Governor Tyler invited Jefferson to join him in toasting the advent of his son's law career. Both men did not anticipate that John Tyler would remain long toiling as an attorney. Indeed, it was fully expected that his political career would commence before he was 21.

The third member of John Tyler Jr.'s distinguished veneration gathering was the most intriguing to the other guests

55

in the dining room. Edmund Randolph was nominally a Federalist who served as the country's first Attorney General under George Washington. He also served in the same administration as Secretary of State for a brief period until a British minister with a grudge fabricated correspondence implicating Randolph in the solicitation of bribes. Although the charges were false, Washington, ever cautious about his image, agreed to accept Randolph's resignation when it was tentatively offered.

Randolph's political history was not the reason why Richmond's elite were fascinated by his presence in the Lafayette House. Despite his Federalist inclinations, neither Jefferson nor the Governor were ever threatened by Randolph's potency among the Virginia voters. While serving in Washington's Cabinet Jefferson was often glad for Randolph's influence with the President on close questions since, despite being ostensively in Alexander Hamilton's camp, Randolph more often agreed with Jefferson. This tended to leave the impression with Washington that many Federalists would support his decision, even if Thomas Jefferson propounded the original idea.

What made Randolph's attendance at this meal of interest was his ability as a lawyer, not as a politician. After Aaron Burr's grand scheme to conquer Mexico and declare himself emperor of South America crumbled, Jefferson savored the inevitable public humiliation that the treason charges leveled at his former Vice President portended.

Despite his questionable motives, Aaron Burr did not come dangerously close to various reins of power throughout his career because he was lucky. He knew that results were accomplished by having the right people in the right place at the right time. On a small scale, Burr was the master of alliances that melded together and operated as efficiently as the finest of England's developing factories. It was only on a large scale that he seemed to invariably overplay his hand.

When he was brought to Washington to stand trial, Burr did what he did best. He put in place an almost unbeatable alliance. He hired Edmund Randolph, the second best legal mind in the country and the second most prominent Federalist in Virginia to try his case before John Marshall--the best legal mind in the country and the most prominent Federalist in Virginia.

Jefferson's team of government prosecutors were simply no match for Randolph. And it did not hurt that the Chief Justice not only admired Randolph, but had no strong desire to see Thomas Jefferson vindicated on any score. Burr was set free and fled to Europe to begin scheming anew. It was common knowledge that the acquittal left Jefferson embittered and beaten.

Since the Burr trial Jefferson and Randolph had not met so there was a palpable tension in the air when John Tyler, Jr. appeared with Randolph to dine with the Governor and the third President. Neither the Governor nor his son knew that the other had taken the liberty of inviting their respective guests. The younger Tyler had good reason for inviting Randolph. He served his final apprenticeship under the famous lawyer and Randolph saw to it that Tyler was accepted into the Bar despite the latter's youth.

Although the Governor always got along with Randolph, he stiffened when he saw his son enter the restaurant with his mentor. Jefferson saw this but did not turn. It was not until Randolph was abreast of the former President that he realized who was seated with the Governor. The two Tylers immediately lowered their eyes awaiting the frosty reception that was sure to follow. But it did not follow.

Randolph was not uncomfortable. He had tried far too many cases to allow his job to control his social outings. And he expected others to understand that being the country's premier litigator had nothing to do with his personal sympathies. He hesitated to greet Jefferson not for fear of being rebuffed but because he had not seen him since early in his Presidency. He was stunned by his contemporary's hoary appearance.

The mane of red hair that Jefferson had worn to demonstrate his disdain for the powdered wigs of the Revolutionary era may as well have been...a powdered wig. Flecks of red remained but not enough to keep the white hair from making his always ruddy complexion look ablaze in crimson. The delicate face that had once radiated intelligence now emanated fatigue and years of worry. The relaxed, lanky frame was now hunched and stilted.

While Randolph was silently evaluating Jefferson's physical decline, the remaining patrons of the Lafayette House were shifting uncomfortably anticipating the necessary effort of one man or the other to beg off on a meal with so obvious a nemesis. Jefferson, however, knew that no such thought was going through Randolph's mind nor was it particularly compelling in his own consciousness. With a flash of the elan that had typified his youth and that was the only familiar mark that Randolph could grasp, Jefferson smiled and slid into the empty chair to his right beckoning to Randolph to sit next to him.

"Counselor! Come let us toast your child prodigy and tell us how you made your most famous silk purse from my favorite swine, Mr. Burr."

"Mr. President, you do me great homage but ill-deserved. I provided only the fabric. John Marshall is the gifted seamstress."

Jefferson laughed and responded, "If only the Chief Justice could find a pattern that I found attractive."

Randolph eased into the proffered chair and clapped Jefferson on the back. "My dear man, the Chief Justice swears that he has tried but that you simply have no eye for fashion! You want everything scant and simple while he insists that all material be used!"

As the irreverent byplay continued, the crowd and the John Tylers breathed a collective sigh of relief. The guest of honor eased in next to his father and tried to look like he was at least 40 or 50 years old. Men like Jefferson and Randolph were frequent visitors to his parents' home when he was growing up and Tyler never gave them a second thought. But it suddenly struck the new attorney that being seen in the presence of Virginia's elite citizenry surely made him the envy of everyone in the Lafayette House, in Richmond, in Virginia and probably most of the country.

As he adopted his most debonair facade, Tyler again silently cursed his long Roman nose with its pronounced hook right at the middle of his face. Even among this stellar cast John Tyler stood out not for his fame or wealth, but because of his nose. He was not unattractive, even he knew this since he was currently courting Letitia Christian, the beautiful daughter of a wealthy planter that could quite clearly have her choice of any of Virginia's up and coming aristocracy. Nonetheless, his long, lanky frame was a particularly cruel accent to his long, lanky nose.

His nose also saddled his voice with a cruel accent. Although he had the melodious drawl of his fellow Virginians, Tyler's angular proboscis caused him to sound stuffy; literally and figuratively. As a result, especially in gatherings such as this, he tended to try and speak in as low a voice as possible. By and large this strategy was effective, but his boyish enthusiasm would seep through at times giving visible alarm to his audience at his sudden transformation from mature young man to spoiled young patrician.

This latter perception of Tyler was unfortunate, for while some of his siblings filled the bill, Tyler did not. He took an active interest in his father's political activities for as long as the Governor could remember, often sitting quietly just outside of his father's parlor while the most formidable men of the day drank, spit tobacco and discussed the progress of the young country that most of them were instrumental in forming.

Despite the penchant for a more powerful federal government that was sweeping his own generation, Tyler was already an avowed defender of States rights. Tyler silently attributed his differing view to the fact that none of his peers had been a student of politics and government for as long as he had. Given time, he was sure they would see the sense of his position which was so closely allied with the men that had frequented his father's parlor.

The leader, if not the creator, of the States rights cause sat across from both Tylers now holding forth on the virtues of his plan for the University of Virginia. Both Tylers had heard this particular speech many times over the years, but not Randolph. The Tylers listened politely fully aware that Jefferson was speaking not to them (who had long ago been sold on the University) but to the wealthy and influential Randolph. For whatever notoriety Jefferson achieved otherwise, he had never achieved the affluence necessary to finance the type of educational institution of which he dreamed.

Jefferson was gesturing toward the younger John Tyler and explaining to Randolph how aspiring attorneys could attend the school before serving their apprenticeship thus receiving some grounding in the law prior to working on real cases. Randolph was visibly intrigued but he could not resist another jibe at Jefferson.

"And would these young men be instructed that the Supreme Court of Virginia or the United States is supreme?"

Jefferson took no offense. The University was more important to him now than any political ideology. "They will be taught whatever the consciences of the professors of the Edmund Randolph School of Law dictate!"

With that and the ensuing guffaws, Jefferson had one more backer for his school. As John Tyler joined in the guffaws, he marveled at how quickly and easily alliances shifted in the ranks of the elite.

* * *

Russia: February 1810

Among the many things Peter the Great hated, Moscow headed the list. But one of the advantages of being the emperor (as opposed to President) is that you can have your capital city wherever you want. So, late in the seventeenth century Peter ordered peasants and serfs from all over his vast country to build him a city on the soggy banks of the Neva River so that he could both rule and indulge in his passion: ships. The Russian nobility was forced to take up residence in the Tsar's new capital to stay in his good graces, but they were not happy.

St. Petersburg was a swamp in the spring and summer; it was constantly cold, windy and dark in the winter. For a brief period in the fall it was bearable. John Quincy Adams arrived in St. Petersburg in the fall. So, he concluded that the dire accounts he received about the Russian capital were embellished. But now, with each passing day of relentless gales off the Baltic Sea that pelted his face with snow and ice, he concluded that the tales of desolation were woefully understated.

The Russian ministry was certainly a challenge but it was not glamorous. Adams belonged in Great Britain or back in Prussia where he had served so well, but he accepted the Russian post with equanimity. Madison probably did the best he could under the circumstances. Even though Adams consistently backed Jefferson's policies as a senator, he continued to criticize Jefferson's leadership. As a result, no one was quite sure what Adams really thought about anything. The few remaining Federalists believed Adams defected while the Republicans saw an Adams and therefore, a man not to be trusted.

But Jefferson and Madison knew that Adams was a talented diplomat that would not waiver in pursuing the best course for the United States abroad. They blamed his apparent vacillation as a senator on the fact that he lived in foreign countries most of his life--he simply had no comprehension of domestic issues.

While Madison did not say as much, Adams was sure that he would spend a short time in St. Petersburg and then would be quietly reassigned to one of the more romantic countries. In the meantime, he was making the best of the situation.

Czar Alexander I was ten years younger than Adams and, although neither was a formidable player on the world stage, they forged a solid relationship built on mutual trust and respect. The Czar admired Adams' calm demeanor and clarity of thought. The emperor was surprised that an unsophisticated country like the United States sent him a minister that was not only polished but intelligent, as demonstrated by his quick assimilation of the Russian language.

On the other hand, Adams was intrigued by the Czar's efforts to reorganize his arcane government while managing to hold off the advances and threats of Napoleon who was otherwise having his way with the rest of Europe. Alexander's accomplishments were even more stunning to Adams since they were achieved with a populace that Adams found singularly unimpressive. He found the Russians to be warm and generous, but John Quincy Adams had little use for warm and generous. He placed value on industry and intelligence, two qualities that he found in short supply in Alexander's Russia. He was immediately struck by the copious quantities of alcohol consumed by the citizenry. A temperate drinker, Adams discovered quickly that the inebriated revelry that permeated Washington and reviled him during his tenure as senator was nothing more than a quiet evening of sampling fine madeira compared to the nightly Russian bacchanals.

Aside from their inebriated persona (or perhaps because of it) Adams found the Russians to be remarkably apathetic. He saw how easily Peter the Great could have ordered these people to travel thousands of miles leaving their families and homes to build this city on a marsh. They were backwards, fearing only God and the Czar. In a way, this attitude made for an uncomplicated existence that seemed to suit Alexander's subjects. When called on to work or fight, they would. If they were not called, they drank.

However uninspired the Russians were with respect to their own way of life, they met threats to the mother country with a determination and alacrity that was astounding. While building his capital city Peter also rallied the serfs and peasants to ward off the Swedes to the west and the Turks to the south. But now as Napoleon manhandled the Prussians and other formidable foes with an eye cast toward Russia, Adams was certain that Napoleon's fall would come when he made his inevitable thrust at this frozen land. The Russians would outnumber the French troops and would readily sacrifice as many of those lives as necessary to protect their squalor and depravity. So even if Adams could not be in France or England negotiating an end to those two countries' dispute, he was at least in the one place that offered the best hope for foiling Napoleon's imperialistic ambitions.

Not that Adams would have been in much of a position to negotiate even if he was stationed elsewhere. Much to his disappointment Madison had done little to improve the United States' lot since becoming President. The British and the French both continued to abuse American shipping rights by attacking vessels that were bound for other's ports. The British compounded this insult by taking American sailors hostage and forcing them into demeaning servitude aboard British vessels.

Both sides justified their actions by claiming that they were entitled to thwart any country that aided their foe.

Jefferson's response to the situation was to impose the Non-Intercourse Act prohibiting trade with either country. Madison did not do much better in substituting Macon's Bill No. 2 which offered to suspend trade with the enemy of any country that would accept American neutrality. The treacherous Napoleon quickly accepted, prompting the British to unleash a reign of terror on the high seas with more American seamen than ever disappearing because the United States was not neutral anymore. It was clearly favoring France.

Adams knew that Jefferson and Madison had no other alternatives and did not fault them for that. What he did fault them for was that throughout the two-sided and then one-sided embargoes the Presidents did nothing to create other alternatives. Both men considered a standing army a threat to civilian rule and allowed the country's ability to fight to deteriorate to all but impotent levels. While the embargoes had negligible effect on France and Britain since neither country needed American goods, they were devastating to businesses at home. The U.S. was being treated like a little brother, not big or brave enough to have its way, but worth cuffing around just often enough to keep things that way.

Macon's Bill had the unintended effect of causing Americans to unite in their hatred of Great Britain and to clamor for war. Madison, who a year before was handed a country wanting justice but to still trade, now had a country wanting justice, trade and a war with the most powerful nation on earth. And Adams knew that justice and trade could never happen without war. And without war, Adams would have little to negotiate about even if he was in England. It would be akin, as Adams' father had often put it, to a eunuch shopping in a whorehouse.

Adams shook his head at the thought of his father and Jefferson and Madison. So talented at conceiving a country, these same men were proving to be less competent at raising their offspring. Their utopian view of a free nation isolated by vast oceans fell victim to the one variable common to all dreams:

economic reality. Yet, for once, it was the progeny teaching the parents the value of a dollar.

* * *

Indiana Territory: November 1811

The Wabash River swallowed Tippecanoe Creek some twenty yards from where William Harrison lay attempting to get comfortable on the cold inhospitable earth that was also his bed. As he lay prone, he noted that yet another member of his troop, the red-headed McGrew boy, had tossed off his blanket, rose and walked into the woods to relieve himself. The tumbling waterways were proving to be omnipotent catalysts to bladders throughout the camp.

At 3:30 in the morning Harrison was beginning to despair that he would get any sleep this night. Later that morning, he would cross the river and meet one of the leaders of the united tribes, Tecumseh's brother, an Indian that called himself the Prophet.

Governor Harrison spent the last five years "negotiating" with the Indians of the Northwest and, in the process, obtaining millions of acres for the United States. His greatest acquisition came at the expense of the Miami tribe just over two years before. He obtained the Treaty of Fort Wayne from the Miamis by offering a little gold, a lot of whiskey and judiciously tendered but thinly veiled threats of violent reprisals. President Madison was pleased.

In 1810, however, the two Shawnee brothers began circulating among the tribes exorcising them to repudiate all treaties entered with the white man and to take back their land. Harrison met briefly with Tecumseh a year before but to no avail. Tecumseh had only contempt for the territorial governor and threatened to slaughter any white man that dared to enter "Indian territory."

Tecumseh and the Prophet disturbed Harrison. Unlike their fellow braves, the brothers did not drink. And more and more, they were convincing the tribesmen uniting behind them that alcohol was the evil means by which the white man wreaked his terrible havoc. Harrison never felt any particular animosity toward the Indians because they were so easy to subdue. Indeed, Harrison considered himself something of a protector to these backward natives.

But Tecumseh and the Prophet were changing Harrison's comfortable guardianship of the tribes. Across the river, the brothers were establishing a rapidly growing settlement which was being called Prophetstown where the brothers counseled on the nefarious deeds of the white man and his unconscionable treaties while exalting their own collective culture. And they strictly prohibited indulgence in alcohol within their group.

Indians were flooding to Prophetstown and moving back onto lands previously ceded under Harrison's drunken pacts, often killing the white settlers that developed the land in the interim. Harrison's tried and true strategy of threats, alcohol and benevolence was now generating little success. He was not sure what changed but he did know that whatever these Shawnee savages were telling the united tribes, they were becoming audacious to a point that Harrison could not countenance.

After two years of pleading with the President, Madison finally relented and allowed Harrison to gather a small force to "visit" the Indians. Madison made it very plain, however, that Harrison was not to instigate any sort of confrontation. So, the Governor led his troops west, pausing in August to have them build a fort which was, not surprisingly, dubbed Fort Harrison. After that he learned that Tecumseh left Prophetstown and would be gone for at least two months. The time had come to march to the spot where the waters crossed.

Harrison was tempted to simply attack Prophetstown upon arrival--an approach whole-heartedly endorsed by his troops. But Madison's instructions were stern and Harrison knew that his standing was not sufficient to defy the President. Yet.

Harrison chose to send a messenger across the river asking permission to enter the settlement the following day to meet with the Prophet. The messenger returned, which, in and of itself, was a good sign. He said that the Prophet would meet with the Governor.

With his back aching and the pulsating fatigue of sleep deprivation, Harrison wondered what he would say to the Indian leader. He led his troops here with the hope that he could do battle, not negotiate. But his hands were tied. Then he detected the break in Tippecanoe Creek's current.

The steady flow had been inciting his own bladder all night. Twice already he had made the short jaunt in the crisp evening air, the second time with negligible results. Nonetheless he was about to make his third journey when the urge subsided. At first the palliation was welcomed. But then Harrison realized that his urine had not ebbed, the creek had. And McGrew had not returned.

The Governor rolled quietly and slowly a few feet to the south and awakened his lieutenant by whispering calmly but sternly, "The Indians have crossed the river. Get ready to fight."

But the order was too late. Harrison's men were fighting to untangle themselves from their blankets when the first wave of Indians swarmed into the camp in a venomous cacophony of screams of rage, terror and fear. Harrison scrambled up to his horse as the Indians scrambled down from theirs--beating, stabbing and killing the hapless soldiers struggling to gain their bearings.

Harrison tried to stay calm. He wanted to surreptitiously mount his horse and somehow slip into the middle of the fray. He would inspire courage by his brave presence in the heart of the battle. His plan went awry in a flurry of horse hooves, nausea and panic.

As he swung himself into his saddle, he saw the young Shawnee warrior on a dirty gray mare running straight toward Harrison's own black stallion. But the Indian had no weapon. His right hand dripped blood as he windmilled his arm and caterwauled hideous and terrifying curses at Harrison. At the last instant, the mare swerved and the rider deposited his grisly package in Harrison's saddle, nestled against his crotch. Bound together with hair from the tail of the gray mare, McGrew's unmistakable red scalp and mutilated genitalia caused Harrison to gag as he swiped the crude gauntlet from the saddle. With a light head and inflamed heart, the Governor plunged into combat.

At the Battle of Fallen Timbers, Harrison was a foot soldier following the orders of General Anthony Wayne. He fought bravely but he remembered his fear, praying continuously that the battle would be short--either by virtue of a swift victory or by his own quick death. But General Wayne inspired him to the point that he never considered the third alternative of fleeing with his life intact.

Now, with bile rising in his throat Harrison tried to concentrate on what Wayne did to keep his men fighting. Everywhere he turned he saw white men trying to escape savages that were dripping with the blood of those that had not escaped. The Governor drew his sword from its sheath and dispatched an unmounted Indian trying to drag Harrison from his horse. In one motion, he dislodged most of the upper half of the Indian's head. At the same time, he realized that he had to ride to the rear of his troops away from the confluence of the river and the creek.

His powerful stallion leaped bodies, campfires and disoriented, scared men to head off most of the hundreds of men who avoided the Indians' initial thrust and were running for their lives. As Harrison wheeled his horse about to face his terrified troops and behind them their inspired adversaries, a soldier came too close to the stallion. As he turned his head to check on the progress of the Indians, the soldier never saw Harrison's boot come out of the stirrup and kick the fleeing boy in the front of his neck. As the private lay gasping for air Harrison held his sword aloft and roared, "Avenge your brothers or I will have your scalps myself! WE HAVE MUSKETS!"

With that Harrison dropped to the ground and retrieved the musket of the boy who now was blue. Calmly, Harrison loaded the musket and waited for the next Indian to appear. A muscular warrior soon came through the woods at the head of a contingent of whooping red men. Harrison reached down and thrust his hand down the throat of the choking boy and pulled his tongue back into his mouth. He jerked the boy to his feet by his hair to stand alongside him and raised the musket. With a thundering report the muscular warrior fell from his horse, a musket ball lodged in his throat.

Harrison acted on pure audacity and instinct but his men

appeared shamed into halting their retreat. They slowed momentarily expecting to watch Harrison be butchered under a flurry of knives and tomahawks. But even Harrison did not expect the Indians to stop too.

Most of the Indians' horses were still moving forward but the Indians ceased their bloodthirsty screams and watched their fallen leader writhing on the ground, blood gushing from the hole in his windpipe. Harrison seized the moment, swinging himself into his saddle and bellowing "Prepare to fire!" As his men scrambled for their guns, Harrison saw that the Indians had become tentative and approached with caution. The first musket shot from the troops fell another approaching brave and the tide turned.

The Indians disappeared back into the woods almost as quickly as they had come, scattering in all directions. The few that headed directly back through the white men's camp were shot. Harrison's men regained their composure and started to pursue in a random chaotic fashion until Harrison ordered them into formation. "Cross the creek." His men knew what the Governor intended and gladly fell into line.

With their muskets held high, for they now knew that the Indians did not fear the soldiers but only their weapons, Harrison's men splashed across Tippecanoe Creek and clambered through the brush on the other side.

When they finally reached the crest overlooking Prophetstown, the sun was up. With hope and anticipation, Harrison's troops awaited his command. The Governor saw little activity in the settlement below and knew from the absence of horses that most of the inhabitants had fled. In a tone that admitted more resignation than exultation, Harrison proclaimed, "Burn it."

Two hours later, Prophetstown was beyond salvation. But as Harrison watched his men vent their rage over their fallen comrades amidst the flames of the inferno, he knew that Prophetstown was the ephemeral symbol of a problem that would endure.

As Harrison turned to re-cross Tippecanoe Creek to help bury the two hundred bodies lying in his camp, Tecumseh, the

Prophet and Black Hawk watched the smoke rise a mile away from the fires of Prophetstown. And, more than ever, they burned with hatred.

* * *

July 1812

Captain Zachary Taylor took the dispatch from the lieutenant and stuffed it in his shirt pocket. Taylor was holding two queens and two nines. Like any good poker player, he pretended to be distracted by the young lieutenant's entrance but surreptitiously studied the other three players' faces.

He arched a stream of tobacco juice three feet to his right into a spittoon. Again, like any good poker player he never drank enough to cloud his judgment. But he maintained the trust of his fellow players with his remarkably accurate spitting ability. He told the lieutenant to wait outside at the same time he requested only one card. The one card was a queen.

Fortunately, Colonel Rogers was not as careful about his drinking as Captain Taylor. With a flourish, he also took one card and immediately bet the limit. Of course, he drove Peters out but it was never hard to get Peters to fold. Taylor raised Rogers' bet slightly and Halstein met Taylor's bet. Predictably Rogers raised Taylor's and bet the limit. Taylor raised Rogers slightly again and Halstein folded. Rogers raised Taylor the limit again. Taylor raised Halstein the limit. Rogers called.

Taylor laid down his full house. Rogers took his straight and placed it gingerly at the bottom of the deck and murmured something about the "luckiest sonuvabitch" he'd ever met.

Zachary Taylor *was* lucky in a lot of ways. He was married to the beautiful Peggy Mackall who was with their baby daughter back in Kentucky. As a soldier he had seen more of the west than just about any man alive and, even more remarkably, he was still alive. He fought and traveled in the heart of Indian country and was unscathed. Two years earlier he reorganized Fort Knox and gained the admiration and friendship of Governor William Henry Harrison. And now that friend and admirer was not only the Governor but a national hero who made the frontier safe for settlers at the Battle of Tippecanoe. And Zachary Taylor was 27 years old.

As the poker game came to an end, Taylor rose and stepped outside. As he surveyed the valley below from the bluff that Fort Harrison was perched upon, Taylor wondered when the Indian attack would come. No matter what the eastern newspapers were telling people about Governor Harrison's exploits, this was still not a safe place for settlers. Unlike President Madison, Taylor was no Indian hater and unlike Governor Harrison, he did his level best to carry out his orders but to also play fair with the Indians.

Despite his assignment to protect the frontier, Taylor had a measure of respect for the Indians. As a farmer and rancher, Taylor learned by studying the Indians' methods of crop rotation and their fastidious use of the game they killed. The settlers he was being paid to protect, on the other hand, wasted land and often killed the abundant wildlife for nothing other than sport. To his mind, Taylor knew he was white and that he had to protect his own but that did not mean that he couldn't be as parsimonious in eradicating the Indian threat as the Indians were with nature.

Taylor heard the young lieutenant clear his throat and cursed himself for forgetting the dispatch in his pocket. He still was not completely used to junior officers waiting for him to give them orders. He unfolded the dispatch and instantly recognized Governor Harrison's uneven scrawl:

Captain Taylor,

> *With this message I am notifying you that the United States has declared war upon Great Britain. You are directed to take all necessary steps to defendFort Harrison from attack by our enemies. I also inform you of my appointment as major general of the Kentucky militia and thus, of my resignation as territorial governor. God speed to you in the coming months.*

> *W.H. Harrison*

Taylor turned his face toward the valley again. He did not want his men to see him smile. He would have to tell them that they were now at war and he did not want to make light of that fact. But Taylor knew that war with England was inevitable and that a soldier had no business fearing a war. Taylor did smile at the lush green valley though as he dwelled once again on his luck. The man who had taken so much of a liking to Taylor was now not only a national hero but was head of the Kentucky militia. It could only be a matter of time before Harrison put out the call for his young Captain. An ebullient Zachary Taylor savored the thought of his first taste of a real war and getting to see Peggy and his little girl all at the same time.

* * *

Washington: August 1814

The last crate of documents was unloaded from a wagon and hauled into an abandoned cabin tucked away in the woods a few miles west of the Potomac River. James Monroe watched as it was deposited next to the crate which held the Declaration of Independence.

"McGregor, no one comes in this room."

McGregor, a large farm boy from Monroe's home county in Virginia nodded and latched the door of the cabin behind them as they walked out. All the men who moved the piles of documents to this hideaway stood momentarily wiping their brows before heading back to Washington. The humidity was suffocating in the sweltering August heat that the men labored in for the last twenty-four hours.

Monroe mounted his horse and rode back to a secluded lookout on the west bank of the Potomac. There was little activity in Washington down below. Monroe and President Madison mended their relationship in 1811 when Madison decided that hostilities with Great Britain had degraded to the point that he could no longer jeopardize the country's welfare by maintaining his first head of the State department, Robert Smith. Smith was appointed to appease the mild opposition Madison faced in his election to the Presidency. But Smith quickly proved to not only be a less than skilled or diplomatic statesman, he was disloyal. Madison long contemplated his replacement but finally acted when Albert Gallatin, the brilliant Secretary of Treasury that both Jefferson and Madison relied upon heavily, threatened to resign if Smith was not replaced.

Madison knew that Monroe was enraged by Madison's failure to appoint Monroe in the first instance and refused to heed Madison's feeble apologies. But Madison went to Richmond to see Monroe three months after Monroe became Governor of Virginia. In Richmond, Madison supplicated to Monroe to let bygones be bygones. The country was faced with a crisis and the President needed someone he could trust.

Monroe was never one to hold a grudge, especially when one played to his delicate ego. He resigned as Governor and dove headlong into his duties as Secretary of State. There was little to be done about the British as he learned while Minister in London. But he overhauled the wreckage in which Smith left the Department. And that enabled him to swiftly order and perform the removal of every State document from the Capital to the woods across the Potomac.

Between the incompetence of Smith as Secretary of State and the two men who served Madison as Secretary of War, William Eustis and now John Armstrong, "Mr. Madison's War", as pundits and plowboys alike were calling it, was not going well. Less than twenty hours before Monroe was forced to send messengers through the city crying to "clear out". The British were marching toward Washington.

Advance scouts made it clear that the undisciplined pack of volunteers charged with defending Washington would be no match for the monolithic British troops. Even more humiliating for Monroe, the Revolutionary War hero, was the fact that the British were not hurrying to the Capital. They were almost sauntering to the city. Rather than using the extra time to fortify the city or gather extra troops, the Secretary of War left the city and advised the soldiers to do the same if they wanted to survive. A few brave men remained but, by and large, the men accepted Armstrong's suggestion as an order and departed.

As Monroe took the last batch of documents out of Washington he was dismayed by the scene he left behind. The only humanity that would greet the enemy soldiers would be a handful of brave but doomed American militia men and a fair number of stupid but greedy whores that saw any congregation of men from out of town as an opportunity for overflow business. Monroe decided against telling them that it was unlikely that the British would be interested in paying fair compensation for their services.

The streets were eerily silent for hours when Monroe led the last procession out. The smell of garbage and human excrement was overwhelming as usual with only the pigs that roamed the streets of the Capital seeming to not mind the stench. The heat of the summer made the odor more unbearable as Monroe shielded his face with a handkerchief.

But even more revolting to Monroe was the thought that the city would be relinquished with no tangible resistance. He reflected on the late General Washington who died not on the glorious battlefields of his life, but because of his enmity for Monroe. The Secretary of State watched the British soldiers begin marching into the city named for the man that Monroe wished was alive once again to engage the Crown in war, no matter how steep the odds.

***

Three days later the President and Dolley Madison returned to the Capital. With tears in her eyes Dolley stared at the smoldering remains of a town that had just started to become a city. Slowly, people started to trickle back into Washington. All were stunned by the carnage wrought by the British.

The Madisons quickly became the focal point for blame. As their carriage crawled past the empty shells of government buildings, a crowd began to gather and follow them. A bruised and angry prostitute ran alongside the carriage, "Jemmy Madison! You're nothing but a goddamn coward! Those bastards raped me and where in the hell were you and all your goddamned soldiers then?!!!"

"Where are ya when the fighting starts Jemmy?!!!"

"You're fightin' a hell of a war Jemmy!"

"Mrs. Madison, your husband is a coward!"

"THEY RAPED ME!"

"My damn store is gone because you thought WE could fight the British! Well WE can't and obviously neither can YOU!"

"COWARD!"

"THEY RAAAAAPED MEEEEEE!"

"Will we be having the usual tea TODAY Mrs. Madison?!?!?!"

"General Washington never would have left you coward!"

The Madisons' driver finally saw an opening and drove the horses out of the throng. Madison bowed his head and held Dolley's hand firmly.

"Jemmy, don't let them bother you. You tried to get back."

"I know Dolley but they're right. I left you here when I knew the British were advancing. It was foolish. And I let the city go without a fight."

Silence enveloped the carriage. The charred carcasses of pigs dotted the road to the White House as flies and birds picked at their remains. Dolley wretched as they came upon the body of one of the few soldiers that had tried to defend the Capital. His head lolled to the side hanging by the vein and the skin that the British had not severed. His pants were gone and a pig's head rested on the soldier's crotch. The British not only burned the Capital, they made sport of it.

This war was a disaster. Madison knew that it was pure folly to try and battle the British but he swayed under pressure from the young "War Hawk" Congressmen, Henry Clay of Kentucky and John Calhoun of South Carolina. There was no escaping the fact that the burning of Washington was his fault though. First, he declared war even though he was the same man who allowed the country's militia to dwindle and fall into disarray because of his fear of a standing army. Then he made political appointments that appeased his opponents but all but doomed the war effort.

As Madison now surveyed the scorched hulk of the city

that he helped found, he saw with crystal clarity that government had no function if it was not to protect its citizens and that there was no time for politics during a war. While the War Hawks screamed for war to "teach the British a lesson", they refused to pass the necessary appropriations to support a war effort. They demanded that certain men be appointed officers and those same men turned out to be disloyal to the point of treachery.

Madison almost smiled when he thought of the odd way the war had progressed. American troops whipped the British at every turn in Canada but were thoroughly beaten on American soil. At the outset of the war General William Hull gave up Detroit without firing a shot and Madison dismissed Hull and ordered him court-martialed. Since then the Americans routed the British and their Indian allies north of the border numerous times. After Hull's debacle Madison appointed William Henry Harrison Commander of the Northwest. Harrison proceeded to regain Detroit and marched into Canada. At the Battle of Thames, Harrison not only gained more territory but the cause of so many Indian troubles, Tecumseh, was killed. Madison recalled his feelings of jubilation as he read of Harrison's victories over the British and the removal of the Indian threat that long hampered his and Jefferson's dream of westward expansion.

After the Battle of Thames though, American troops continued onto the provincial capital of York and burned the city to the ground. Five months later when Madison heard that the British had landed at Chesapeake Bay, he knew that Washington was in danger.

But Madison's Secretary of War John Armstrong refused to act. Pleading a lack of manpower and funds, Armstrong all but conceded Washington to the enemy. Two days before the British arrived in Washington, Madison went to a Navy shipyard to check its preparedness for the upcoming battle. The British were clearly watching the President's moves because they almost instantly cut him off from returning to Washington.

A messenger managed to sneak through the lines to tell Dolley to leave the Capital as quickly as possible. Dolley also understood that after what the Americans had done to York, there was no hope that Washington would be spared. She gathered the

Madisons' silver service, cut a picture of George Washington from its frame and left in a carriage for Virginia. That night she took refuge in a farmer's house for a few hours until the farmer's wife realized who she was and decided that having the first lady in her house would not be particularly safe when the British arrived. With cursory apologies, Dolley was asked to leave. She found a plantation late that night and set out early the next morning to find the President. From Virginia, they waited until a messenger arrived to inform them that it was safe to return to Washington.

Madison seethed but he could not blame the people for accusing him of cowardice. When the enemy came, their "leader" was gone. Trying to tell them now that he was prevented from getting back would only compound the problem by layering an excuse over his absence.

As the President's carriage arrived in front of the mansion, the Madisons' melancholy reached new depths. The British soldiers went to great pains to make sure that this building be rendered useless. What remained of the edifice was no longer resilient white, but at its best spots was a sooty gray and, at its worst, was pitch black.

An old black slave walked slowly from the portico to the Madisons' carriage. "Ain't no use in yo goin' in dere Mr. President. Ain't nuthin' left. Ain't nuthin' at all."

Dolley turned her head away and silently nodded her agreement with the slave.

"Dat French fellow said yo and Mrs. Madison could stay in the Octagon."

"Thank you Mr. Hastings. Are you and your family taken care of?"

"I'll be O.K. Mr. President. The family is all gone with the Brits."

Madison sat up. "What?"

"He's right Mr. President." James Monroe rode up alongside the carriage. "The British took all the slaves that they could find and that could make the trip and put them on a boat bound for Canada. One of our traders said the boat makes a usual run to Halifax."

Madison smiled. "Well then maybe some good came from all of this." Despite owning several slaves himself, Madison was embarrassed by the institution in the supposed home of liberty. He asked, "How are you James?"

"I'm as well as can be expected. I trust that you both came through this unharmed?"

Madison nodded. "James, we have to get out of this war. The country just can't fight yet."

The soldier in Monroe would not allow him to agree. So, he queried instead, "On what terms do you propose?"

"The best that John Quincy Adams can get."

"And what if Mr. Clay objects?"

"He won't. He will be right there `negotiating' too."

"And what makes you think he will go?"

Madison nodded at the burned shell of the house behind him. "Because he wants to live there one day and he knows now that we won't beat the British. The only way he can get around the fact that he got us into this war is to help get us out. And he's smart enough to know that John Quincy Adams is the only man that can get us out short of surrender. It won't hurt Henry Clay one bit to take some of that credit."

Monroe grimaced as he thought of his own ill-fated diplomatic efforts. But the President was right, Adams was the only American who understood Europe sufficiently to negotiate his way out of an ill-advised war.

"It will take time to get word to Adams and to arrange a meeting. What if the British ravage the rest of the country in the meantime?"

Madison looked Monroe directly in the eye. "That is how you will get into this house," he said thrusting his thumb over his shoulder.

Monroe shook his head. "I don't understand my friend."

Madison leaned back in the carriage and looked away from Monroe as he said, "Because as Secretary of State you will instruct Adams as to the terms to end the war. As my new Secretary of War, you will see to it that we are able to walk away from the British on agreed terms--not theirs."

Monroe sputtered, "But Mr. President..."

Madison looked at Monroe again. "James, for too long I have made political mistakes. Mistakes that almost cost me your friendship. I need you now. If we are successful, you will be President. If we are not, no one will be President."

As the President and Mrs. Madison pulled away, James Monroe turned his horse first one way and then shifted and headed for what was left of the War department, both literally and figuratively.

* * *

Baltimore: September 1814

James Buchanan thought the little jaunt to Maryland worked out splendidly as he made his way behind the thirty or so "confiscated" horses that he and other members of the "Lancaster County Dragoons" were driving through the outskirts of Baltimore. While many of his fellow soldiers groused about their lack of combat duty, Buchanan was silently relieved at the task assigned to him. Things were going too well to be killed.

Buchanan was readmitted to Dickinson College in 1809 after his father's intercession. Unfortunately, the specter of expulsion did little to inculcate the younger Buchanan with a sense of humility. He tempered his behavior slightly by being a little less overt, but he continued to disdain his professors and by no means stiffened his work habits.

From 1809 until 1812 Buchanan studied law with slightly more diligence but still never lacking for amusement. He opened his law practice and struggled the first two years but things were looking up. He was recently nominated and elected state Assemblyman for Lancaster County. He was nominated as a Federalist, a party that was dead nationally but still the power elite in Lancaster County.

While he was exulting in his election, word came of the burning of Washington. With the aid of a few glasses of port and his own cocky confidence at his election, Buchanan mounted the town stump and called upon the men of the county to join him and ride to Baltimore where the Redcoats were said to be marching to vindicate the "heinous" crimes of the British. Swiftly, the Lancaster County Dragoons were formed and the next day a sober Jim Buchanan was wondering why he opened his mouth.

By the time the Dragoons reached Baltimore Buchanan gathered his courage and was ready to do battle. When Major Ridgely called for ten volunteers for a secret mission, Buchanan boldly threw his own name out first. Assuming he would be asked to scout and detain the British while Baltimore's defenses were readied, Buchanan almost burst into laughter when the Major asked him and his fellow volunteers to go to nearby Ellicot's Mills and gather as many horses for the main troops as possible.

Buchanan donned the closest assemblage of clothes resembling an officer's uniform that he could find and rode off to steal horses. While his compatriots grumbled about the distasteful duty, Buchanan silently rejoiced at his good fortune of avoiding being in the thick of the battle just when his political ambitions were sprouting wings. And, true to form, Jim Buchanan turned out to be an excellent horse thief who also had a good time in the process.

He played Robin Hood more than once in the "mission", taking horses from a wealthy planter and delivering one or two of them to some poor damsel in need of transportation. As a result, while his fellow volunteers slept outside and kept watch over their equine loot, Jim slept in a warm bed in the arms of some grateful beneficiary.

As he rode through the streets with drunken revelers taunting him and his fellow volunteers, Buchanan did not mind. During his absence the remaining Lancaster County Dragoons and the regular militia defended Baltimore and Fort McHenry bravely and the uninspired British troops withdrew. The British soldiers were tired of fighting this inconsequential war by now and began to dissipate. Their goal was to capture the American Capital and this was accomplished.

In the jubilation over the "defeat" of the enemy, the secret mission Dragoons blended quickly with the regulars and basked in the adulation of Baltimore. Jim Buchanan glowed as he reflected on his prospects. As he made his way into and up the stairs of Gadsby's Hotel and past the huge mirror at the head of those stairs, he saw a 23-year-old man on his way to the state assembly as a war hero, neither of which would harm his fledgling law practice. And he saw the voluptuous blond maiden on his arm that he met his first night in Baltimore who was clearly relishing another evening of port, tall tales and other dalliances with Robin Hood a la Pennsylvania.

* * *

Ghent: December 1814

John Quincy Adams gazed out the window at the snow falling. It was Christmas Eve in this city of artists and canals. He was told that Ghent was a smaller version of Venice and from what he could remember of his boyhood travels, he decided that this was true.

The usually passionless Adams was melancholy. He left St. Petersburg immediately upon receiving President Madison's dispatch and spent the last month negotiating an end to the war with the British. He left his wife Louisa in Russia thinking he would return there after the negotiations. But word came from Washington that Madison had appointed him as Minister to England. Earlier this same evening the British signed an agreement to end the hostilities. But Adams was not jubilant.

He was about to arrive as minister to a country that he always felt was the only appropriate challenge for his abilities. Yet his appointment came fast on the heels of a peace treaty that demonstrated just how poorly the United States performed in the war.

Further, Adams' wife was ill and homesick--they had not seen their two oldest boys, John and George, in five years. They were eleven and thirteen now. Louisa had not forgiven Adams for his decision to leave them in the States when he was appointed Russian minister in 1809. And now Louisa was going to have to sell their home in Russia and bring their belongings to London with their remaining son, eight-year-old Charles, in tow.

John Quincy and Louisa never had a warm relationship. Louisa could match Adams' caustic personality when she was not ill, which, fortunately or unfortunately, was not very often. Generally, Adams was not troubled by his strained home life because of his devotion to his work. Through total immersion he could avoid confronting the very real fact that his wife was miserable and blamed him.

Initially, Adams was thrilled to receive Madison's telegram asking him to head the delegation to end the war. Madison bestowed broad powers on Adams. Finally, Adams felt that his talents prevailed over politics. He was asked to extract his country from a war it could never win. But then he received a second telegram from Secretary of State James Monroe.

Adams knew immediately that politics was still present in its most cumbersome form--a bipartisan negotiating committee. Adams' hopes for tough bargaining with a meaningful peace were dashed as quickly as they were raised as he surveyed the roster of his fellow delegates that Monroe sent to him.

Albert Gallatin was a welcome addition with his brilliance for finance and ability to translate any proposal into its economic impact. And Gallatin knew his abilities well enough to not intrude by taking the lead in the negotiations. Senator Bayard and Minister Russell were minor annoyances.

But Henry Clay was another matter. Tall and vulgar, it did not take long to discern that Clay was as diametrically the opposite of Adams as a human could be. Adams shuddered as he heard activity begin to build in the room next to his as another of Clay's poker parties gained momentum. Night after night throughout the negotiations Adams struggled to maintain his usual routine of early to bed, early to rise while Clay and his companions drank, gambled and cussed and their European harlots giggled in the room next door.

Clay's stamina amazed Adams. Clay could cavort all night and still dominate the peace discussions all day. Clay was dogmatic with the British. More than once Adams had to coax the Brits back to the table after Clay offended them with either a direct insult or crude story or joke.

On the one hand James Madison's instructions were clear.

Adams was to end the war at any cost. On the other hand, Madison could not have made Adams' task more difficult than by saddling him with the roguish Clay who detested the British. Clay was the new American. Devoid of any connection to the Revolution, Clay and his fellow westerners were a contrary lot. They saw England as a country of effete snobs that refused to treat the United States with due respect. Since the west had little trade with Europe, it had little sympathy for the eastern states' dependence on British trade. So, Clay was not particularly concerned whether he angered the British negotiators or not.

But Adams knew that his own political career would be at an end if he did not accomplish the President's goal of ending the war. Thus, he persevered and finally forged the treaty to end the war--and nothing more. None of the issues which started the war were resolved. Not even the impressment of American sailors by the British was addressed, the very problem that Clay used to foment the war for a militarily impotent America. But even Clay knew that continued fighting could only have disastrous consequences for his country. In the end, Clay reluctantly signed the agreement.

With the treaty signed Adams would begin preparations the following day to leave for England. Tonight he had no negotiations to prepare for and no ministerial duties to attend to. It was one of those rare occasions that John Quincy Adams could not escape into the solitude of his work.

He crossed the room and found his writing materials. Sitting before a warm fire, he was startled momentarily by the sound of glass shattering in Senator Clay's room. Regaining his composure, he penned a lengthy letter to his mother. John Quincy was always acutely aware of his mother's keen intellect and valued her input. Unfortunately, Louisa did not share her husband's affection for his parents, particularly the former President. John Quincy had to concede that his family was harsh at times but the Adams' were not noted for their gentle nature.

But now, without the press of state business, Adams did think about his wife and the hard journey she would have to make. He was determined that her fragile constitution would be buoyed by hope for improvement in their equally fragile marriage.

Louisa would be thrilled to leave St. Petersburg for London. Louisa was British and always preferred her own country to the United States, not to mention the miserable environs of Russia. But John Quincy Adams knew that he was incapable of giving his wife happiness alone. So, Adams did not allow time to pass idly. The letter to his mother contained the only formula that he knew would give Louisa joy. If his mother could execute his instructions quickly, when Louisa and Charles arrived in London, George and John would be there to greet their brother and their rapturous mother.

* * *

New Orleans: January 1815

Two weeks later, on the other side of the world, no one in New Orleans knew about the treaty that John Quincy Adams signed with the British. Andrew Jackson smiled as he sat astride a grand white stallion he confiscated two weeks earlier from a farmer. Through the dissipating fog British troops were stumbling over the stubble of the burned cane fields where Jackson's motley collection of regular troops, freed slaves, creoles and mercenaries just completed a stunning rout of the British. Aside from stumps of cane, the British soldiers were also floundering over the bodies of their comrades in arms. Thousands of redcoats lay dead across the field. The most recent count indicated that Jackson lost fifteen men.

Andrew Jackson was born fatherless. Andrew Jackson Sr. lifted a log two weeks before Andrew Jr.'s birth and felt a tear in his abdomen. Minutes later, he was dead. His two older brothers and Andrew Jr. did their best to protect their mother but they also did their best to be men as quickly as possible which, of course, did little for Elizabeth Jackson's peace of mind. They gambled, smoked, drank and brawled early and often.

Then the Revolution came. A war for the Jackson boys was like a bone for a dog. Only the eldest, Hugh, was old enough to volunteer as an official soldier but that did not keep Robert and Andrew from hanging around the army camps and sneaking into an occasional battle.

Andrew Jackson's bitter hatred for the redcoats and anything British had its genesis in the Revolution. But it became an obsession when the news came that Hugh was wounded and left to die in the heat by the British. More and more after that, Andrew deviated from his assigned duties as a messenger to join in the fighting wherever and whenever possible. And at thirteen years old he became known as something of a nemesis to the British.

He and Robert, who was sixteen, were drinking at a cousin's home one day when redcoats burst into the home and took the Jackson boys prisoner. Two days later a British officer arrived at the British camp and spied the two boys lolling about the prisoners' quarters. He walked over and cuffed Andrew.

"My boots are in need of shining, child. I'm sure that you know how to shine boots, don't you?"

Robert looked on and knew what was coming. The officer never should have referred to Andrew as a "child" thought Robert. As he figured, Andrew lofted a stream of tobacco that creased the officer's nose perfectly.

The boys were not prepared for what came next though.

The officer slowly withdrew a lace handkerchief and wiped the spittle from his face as Robert giggled and Andrew looked away. The officer smiled showing a row of yellow jagged teeth. He sighed and chuckled at the same time. Nodding to an aide he observed, "These Americans are a daring lot, eh?"

The aide grinned as the yellow toothed officer turned to walk away, for he knew what was next. With lightning speed the officer's sword was out of its scabbard and two swift blows landed on the reeling thirteen-year-old. The first blow missed its mark and sliced Andrew's hand cleanly but not deeply. The second blow was right on target though.

With teeming ferocity the officer's sword smashed into Andrew's face shattering his jaw and leaving a cavernous gash. As he looked with horror at the exposed bone and cartilage of his brother's face, Robert never saw the officer's sword sweep toward his own face. Robert's wound was not as deep as Andrew's, just a clean long thin line that took form briefly before it was covered in the red that washed over Robert's ear, neck and streamed into his mouth.

For three more days the boys remained as prisoners without any attention to their infected wounds. Robert became delirious. Andrew knew that his brother had contracted smallpox. Elizabeth Jackson arrived and convinced the British to allow her sons to leave, promising that they would not participate in the war any further.

She was able to keep her promise with respect to Robert when he dropped dead two days later as the decimated family marched home. Andrew buried his brother quaking with the fever that now racked his own smallpox infested body. When they reached an acquaintance's home Elizabeth left her only remaining child to recuperate while she set out to find a new home. Her own was destroyed by rampaging British soldiers.

A week later Andrew Jackson recovered sufficiently to leave his bed and help find a home for he and his mother. Borrowing a horse, he set out to find Elizabeth Jackson. As he neared Charleston he paused at a cemetery to watch a group of men throwing the last piles of earth onto what appeared to be an enormous grave. One of the men he recognized as his uncle, a shopkeeper in Charleston who Elizabeth said she was going to visit about assistance for her and her son.

Andrew's uncle was startled to see his nephew. "Andrew, what are you doing here? Your mother said you were gravely ill and unable to travel!" Andrew responded that he was fine and inquired after his mother. His uncle paused and then his eyes filled with tears as he told the boy that had never known his father and who had lost both of his brothers in the last year, "Andrew, your Ma is dead. She got the plague. We been burying them in these big graves for weeks--just ain't time for a decent burial for all of them."

Now, as he ran his finger along the scar that the yellow toothed officer had given him thirty-four years before, Andrew Jackson watched the British soldiers deposit their weapons in front of him and turn to be taken prisoner. He resisted the impulse to horsewhip every one of them.

If Jackson gave in to that impulse he would only confirm

what the people of New Orleans believed he was-- a tyrant. For the latter part of 1814 Jackson ruled New Orleans through the imposition of martial law. A curfew was instituted and restrictions placed on movement among the citizenry. Anywhere else these orders would have been met with resentment but resignation. In New Orleans, however, the Creoles not only resented Jackson's edicts but rebelled. The curfew was routinely flaunted by the high-living locals and Jackson just as routinely ordered them jailed and, in more severe cases, flogged.

The situation reached a head when the British arrived at the mouth of the Mississippi and distracted the civilians away from the dictatorial General Jackson. General Jackson, in turn, immediately eased his mandate and opened the doors of the overflowing prisons subject to prompt enlistment in his army. He organized his rag-tag militia and prepared the defense of New Orleans so masterfully that when the British launched their "surprise" attack on the Bayou, they ran head-on into a withering onslaught of artillery fire.

So instead of the despised autocrat of two days prior, Andrew Jackson was now the beloved bellwether of courage. Already a ball in his honor was being organized for this same evening.

A gangly creole rode up with a British decoration and a sword and presented it to Jackson. Through an interpreter, the General was informed that the items belonged to Sir Edward Packenham, the British commander. Packenham was killed during the battle. Jackson signaled to a lieutenant and told him to bring back a British captain that had just presented his musket to Jackson.

The British captain stood resolutely before Jackson and the white stallion. The American General winced as he climbed down and confronted the captain. The pistol ball that Charles Dickinson put in his chest almost nine years earlier was still in place. Sudden movements like getting off his horse too quickly caused him great pain.

Standing before the British officer Jackson said through clinched teeth, "For thirty-five years I have dreamed of this day. The day that I show the so-called British gentlemen how a true gentleman conducts himself. I give you your commander's sword and your troops. And I give you your freedom. Now get the hell out of my country."

* * *

New York: October 1816

Fall was resplendent in Albany. The colors surrounding the capitol building were never more brilliant. Dazzling crimson, orange and yellow seared the landscape in the crisp autumn morning as Martin Van Buren and his political team caucused across the road from the capitol.

In 1812 Van Buren took his seat as the state senator from his home district of Kinderhook. Quickly, he gained a reputation as a true party man adept at forging alliances. In recognition of his considerable skills as an attorney, Governor Tompkins appointed him as the Attorney General of New York in 1815.

Senator and Attorney General Van Buren listened thoughtfully to the chatter of his companions while surveying the autumn splendor. His gaze was directed over the right shoulder of William Marcy, the editor of the *Northern Budget*, a Republican newspaper from the blossoming village of Troy. Looking over Marcy's shoulder was no easy task, especially for the diminutive Van Buren. Well over six feet tall, Marcy seemed even broader than tall. Van Buren took an instant liking to Marcy not only because of the editor's charming manner, but because he was a shrewd political planner that was an invaluable resource for both strategy and execution.

To Marcy's right stood Henry Seymour. In his second term in the state senate, Seymour was proving to be a solid, if unspectacular, ally. Prunish and slight, Seymour was alert and perceptive. While Van Buren doubted that Seymour ever charmed anyone in his life, his reputation for passionless logic gained him respect, if not many friends.

The final member of the quadripartite was Roger Skinner, a senator from the northern frontier, an area that was growing by leaps and bounds as emigrants from Vermont spilled in to farm upstate New York to take advantage of the trade that was sure to follow the opening of the Erie Canal. While Skinner shared Marcy's size and charming countenance, he did not share his ability for calm reflection. Senator Skinner was contentious and impulsive in the extreme, much like the roughhewn constituency he represented.

Whatever political differences the four men shared, they shared one overriding aversion. In less than one month, their collective political enemy, DeWitt Clinton would be elected Governor of New York.

DeWitt Clinton was probably the only Federalist left in the country capable of being elected to an office of any substance. But even then, his popularity ended at the boundaries of New York as his failed Presidential bid of 1812 demonstrated. Even though the Federalists' political star was waning, in 1812 they were still a viable force both nationally and locally.

In 1815 though, the Federalists came crashing down. Martin Van Buren realized for the first time just how important well-timed publicity was in garnering votes. The cause of the Federalists' downfall was their strident opposition to the War of 1812. After Andrew Jackson's rout of the British at the Battle of New Orleans, a patriotic fervor swept the country and the Federalists were denounced and derided as cowards and infidels for opposing the war.

Van Buren was pleased to see the Federalists' fall from grace but was bemused by the cause. The Battle of New Orleans was meaningless. The Treaty of Ghent was already signed ending the war on terms that made the whole three years of fighting moot. But the general population appeared to reject this fact.

After Jackson's victory, President Madison went from being a beleaguered bungler to an inspiring leader. Andrew Jackson went from reckless frontier adventurer and quasi-despot to chivalrous hero. And John Quincy Adams' treaty of surrender was washed away in the adulation. Van Buren watched the events with great interest and realized immediately how important his friendship with William Marcy was. For it was Van Buren's intention to rely heavily on Marcy in bringing about the collapse of future governor Clinton.

Clinton avoided extinction amidst the demise of the Federalists by stewarding through the approval of the Erie Canal. Through sheer personal charisma and popular appeal, Clinton steered the Canal to fruition bereft of a party. But Van Buren was convinced that a politician could never survive without a party.

Skinner was smacking his left palm with the fist of his right hand. "We have to bring down Clinton now. Once he's governor New York will be the bastard son of the country. Monroe will never deal with the only state still harboring the Federalists. We've got the evidence--let's use it!"

Van Buren said nothing as Seymour tried to reason with Skinner. Just as it was a given that Clinton would be elected governor in a few weeks, it was an even surer bet that James Monroe would be elected President at the same time. The Federalists nominated Rufus King, also from New York, to oppose Monroe but James Madison designated Monroe for succession and right now that meant more than issues or ability. Monroe could claim successful conduct of the war effort as Secretary of War and Secretary of State even if the war was not a success.

Van Buren supported Monroe but not because of any abiding respect for his talents. Monroe was the perfect symbol of the real pride of the Revolution and the illusory pride of the War of 1812 to preside over the country while Van Buren positioned himself for a jump to the national scene where he would expand his party organization to impact broader issues than just New York. Then Van Buren would be the kingmaker, not Madison or Monroe or any other Revolutionary era figure. After Monroe, a new dawn would break when politicians would need a party. Simply being a leader of the Revolution would not suffice-- Monroe was the last man left who could make that claim. All the rest were dead or dying.

As Van Buren turned his attention back to the conversation he was alarmed to hear Seymour wavering. "Maybe you're right Roger, maybe we better start now. If the public finds out now that Clinton has already made promises to his friends for the Erie Canal work and Cabinet positions, we might keep him out of office. Matty, maybe we should rethink this."

Van Buren remained composed and slipped his arm through Seymour's affectionately. Speaking in his quick, clicking voice Van Buren said, "Henry, we must stick to the plan. Roger is right of course. New York will not be popular with the administration for electing Clinton. But we must be realistic--our man does not have a chance against Clinton.

"If we publish what we know to be the case now, it will be viewed as a tawdry election stunt. But if we wait for Clinton to follow through with his promises once he is governor and then reveal that he gave assurances prior to being elected, think of all the laborers that will never vote for a Federalist again, Clinton or otherwise, when they realize that they never had a chance to work on the Canal.

"And with Governor Tompkins as Vice President, we will have a voice keeping the President informed of developments here in New York. So, the administration may be dismayed at first, but will ultimately be the proud bearer of the claim that it presided over the death of the Federalists. No gentlemen, it is not always a bad thing to not have your man elected."

Van Buren paused and then added, "We must wait and then," gesturing at Marcy, "allow our friend to print both what is true and what is, shall we say, just." With a wink, Van Buren turned and headed for the door of the capitol confident that his team was of one mind.

Skinner, always fodder for the wily charm of Matty Van Buren shrugged and capitulated. Seymour smiled and commented, "As usual, he's right" and followed Van Buren.

Left standing alone, Marcy laughed and headed away from the capitol muttering, "The Little Magician strikes again."

Chapter 3:
James Monroe

The headline of the Boston Columbian Centinel proclaimed

PRESIDENT MONROE, ERA OF GOOD FEELINGS ARRIVE

Elizabeth Monroe said in her subdued tone, "My, Mr. Russell has outdone himself this time."

James Monroe paused in adjusting his cravat at the sound of his wife's voice. Elizabeth did not speak often but, when she did, it still never failed to arouse him. After thirty years of marriage, Monroe was becoming more and more embarrassed by his lewd reaction.

Elizabeth was still a remarkably beautiful woman. In her youth, she was breathtaking. But James Monroe was considered quite a catch himself, so exposure to breathtaking women was not unusual. Monroe was almost chagrined to find himself lusting not after her finely sculpted face with her large, dreamy brown eyes or her comely figure, but after her husky, yet lilting voice.

She was ready for their evening. In a French gown of white silk with delicately brocaded gold trim and a simple but elegant string of pearls, Monroe touched her lightly on the shoulder from behind and gazed at the swell of her still shapely breasts from above. She reached up and touched his hand lightly. As happened all too often anymore, they would have to defer making love while they met another social obligation and then returned to their hotel room, seeking only sleep.

91

Tonight, they would be the city of Boston's honored guests for its Fourth of July celebration. Unlike his fellow Virginians before him though, Monroe was truly welcome in this, the home of the Federalist party. Jefferson and Madison never dared the type of goodwill tour that Monroe was currently engaged in. But the Battle of New Orleans and the false pride General Jackson's heroics instilled in the country made it possible for even a living symbol of Republicanism and southern Revolutionary gentility like James Monroe to be vaunted.

Monroe pointed at the headline of the Boston paper his wife just read to him. "I wonder how long Mr. Russell's sentiments will hold true," he stated more than asked.

Elizabeth never had the gift for politics that Dolley Madison exhibited and merely shrugged, declining to be drawn into her husband's desire to pontificate. He tended to be a pessimist when it came to his political future. But the way she saw it, what was there left to be pessimistic about once one was elected President?

The President waited for a moment but knew that she would respond no further. Unconsciously, he frowned. Often he watched with mild envy when Jemmy Madison and Dolley discussed political affairs in earnest with their mutual respect in full bloom and wished that he and Elizabeth might engage in such weighty dialogue. But Monroe had two problems. First, Elizabeth found politics mundane. Second, the President was incapable of raising politics above the mundane.

Thomas Jefferson was innovative and charismatic. James Madison made up for his lack of charm and vivacity with a studiousness and industry that were unparalleled. But Monroe had no extraordinary qualifications for the Presidency. He was a brave soldier and an able, if unspectacular, public servant. He had the good fortune to be the Secretary of State at a time when the mood of the public was positive and therefore, irrationally perhaps, the logical successor to the Presidency.

Yet despite all his honors, Monroe remained perplexed by his inability to entice his own wife into even the mildest political repartee. Elizabeth, on the other hand, understood fully her husband's frustration but decided that he would only be more deflated when she was forced to feign interest in his time-worn musings on national affairs. She loved her husband dearly and knew that he was a genuinely popular man...but the country was expanding and changing more rapidly than he could ever comprehend. He was not a visionary like his two Virginian friends before him. He was merely a symbol of what went before while the United States wrestled with what would come after.

* * *

Forty-five minutes later the President and Mrs. Monroe stood in the entrance of the Governor's residence and were introduced to scores of people that they never saw before and would never see again. As Monroe smiled politely and Elizabeth accepted compliments on her appearance graciously, the President kept peering through the hallway into the sitting room where John and Abigail Adams sat and watched the throng being herded past the Chief Executive and First Lady.

Monroe was haunted by John Adams' appearance. Thomas Jefferson and Adams mended their tattered friendship a few years earlier and since that time Jefferson repeatedly raved about Adams' erudite and warm correspondence. "Never has Mr. Adams been freer with his intellect and wit" Jefferson claimed. But Jefferson had not seen Adams since just before the second President stole away from Washington before dawn on the day of Jefferson's inauguration. Adams quaked from acute palsy and his once merely ashen face was now ghostly pale. His now outdated wig was askew and carelessly powdered. He sat with his prodigious belly blocking him from moving. Even the always radiant Abigail looked tired and neglected.

But all to whom he spoke said that Adams' mind was as sharp and his sarcasm as biting as ever. Monroe did not know Adams well but inadvertently developed a dislike for him through his association with Madison and a respect for him through his association with Jefferson. He now wished to break free of the obligatory greeting of guests so he could talk to Adams and report back to his Virginian friends on Adams' condition.

Monroe was jolted from his focus on the decrepit former President by a comment from the matronly Bostonian that he was currently bowing to unconsciously.

"You and Mr. Madison cannot absolve the stain of your sin by shipping Negroes off to Liberia. If they are to be free there, why can't they be free here?"

Monroe flushed. "My dear woman, they can be free here, but can they live?"

The line behind her simultaneously stalling and shifting nervously, the brash matron pressed on, "I'm sure the British said the same about us and we seem to be doing fine."

Monroe mocked surprise. "Ma'am, we don't live with the British."

She ignored the President's retort. "So we should herd them on ships and hope they survive so they can return to the savagery from which they came?"

Monroe began to become annoyed with this corpulent nemesis. He and Jemmy Madison both actively supported the drive to abolish slavery in the South, not through the simple but naive step of abolition but by deportation to Africa on a systematic and gradual basis. He read some of the pamphlets being circulated by these "abolitionists" but this was his first face to face encounter. And he had already grown weary of it.

Monroe toyed with making light of the situation but thought twice--after all, this was still Massachusetts no matter how friendly he was treated up to now. He frowned and gave the woman a sympathetic gaze before replying. "I must do what I think best. Regardless of your feelings, I know the black man better than I believe you do."

Her eyes widened. "True, I only know free Negroes."

The President winced. He knew he was vulnerable and wished for the quick wit and charm of Jefferson at this moment. He struggled and said the right thing although his delivery was rushed and awkward. "I do not believe you and I disagree on goals, only methods."

Much to his relief, while she did not appear satisfied, she felt victorious and after giving him a short but disdainful glare she moved on. Two guests later, an inebriated merchant nodded at the woman who had made her way to the interior of the room and whispered in Monroe's nose, "Pay no mind to Mrs. Barker. This year she's got a thing for the niggers. Next year it'll be something else." Monroe smiled weakly, unsure who bothered him more, Mrs. Barker or the drunken merchant.

The Governor heard of the embarrassing confrontation with "Mrs. Barker" and rescued the President by escorting him and Elizabeth into the room where John and Abigail Adams watched the proceedings. Monroe started to bow and assume an unintentional but nonetheless condescending manner when, to his dismay, the Adams started to laugh. Abigail's was a hearty, twinkling laugh; John's was controlled, almost derisive.

The former President said to the current President, "Ah, my good Virginian, our Massachusetts matrons bringing you to task for your, shall we say, unique view of equality."

Elizabeth could feel her husband bristling as he responded, "I take it she is not atypical of your 'Massachusetts matrons'."

Abigail, subdued from guffaw to titter to smile, replied, "I'm afraid you're correct Mr. President. What is worse is that, while I try not to be as belligerent as Mrs. Barker, I agree wholeheartedly with her views. With all due respect, I'm afraid the gentlemen of Virginia have no defense when it comes to the question of slavery. The southern states can hardly claim to be "the land of the free" as Mr. Key's song says as long as the black man remains in bondage."

"But Mrs. Adams, it has not been that long since slavery was not just a southern institution."

Mrs. Adams sighed. "That much is true. But we saw fit to give the black man the same freedom that we enjoy." Monroe started to speak but Abigail silenced him with a raised finger. "I know, I know. If you and Mr. Madison have your way, you will give the Negro his freedom by shipping him off to Africa to be with his people. So instead of having the opportunity to make his way in this new land with thousands of miles of unexplored and unsettled land, you'll condemn him to return to the savagery of a place that he has never really known."

Monroe paused and proceeded delicately. As he spoke he wondered how he became embroiled in this debate with the women of New England. "Well, Mrs. Adams, I'm not sure we can safely conclude that the American frontier is less savage or any less known to the Negro than Africa. But more importantly, what kind of opportunity can be offered to the Negro in a country where he was once a slave? While I hope that I am benevolent, I'm afraid we must acknowledge that most of my fellow slaveholders will not be kindly disposed toward treating their former servants as equals. You will have two separate societies-- the white and the black. And believe me, the black one will not be allowed to prevail or prosper. And if the government tries to make them equal, it will be faced with open revolt." When the Adams and the highly conspicuous eavesdroppers surrounding the conversation looked skeptical, Monroe added. "I think you need look no farther than this enchanting party that my friend the Governor has thrown for the celebration of our country. I note that here, where the Negroes are free, the only Negroes in attendance tonight are the servants."

There was a low murmur as the crowd passed on the President's words. While Monroe relaxed, confident that he had handled the situation with the right mix of deference and aplomb, his wife set to work to change the topic. Elizabeth knew that any further discussion would be hazardous not only because of the volatile nature of the subject but because Monroe's whole argument was a repetition of the speech that Jemmy Madison delivered at several parties, but usually among his fellow southerners, not in the bosom of abolitionism. In short, her husband would soon be in over his head if the debate continued.

John Adams welcomed Elizabeth's charming intercession for he alone among the northerners knew that Monroe verbally plagiarized Madison's old argument. Adams was tired of politics; he and Abigail lost a dozen years together while he sacrificed for his country only to suffer ignominy at the hands of "politics". Abigail was not well and John did not want her wasting energy on matters of the day that she could not change, irrespective of how correct John thought she was. At the most she had a year to live and he did not want her dissipating their valuable remaining time on something as imbecilic and unrewarding as "politics".

* * *

New York: August 1817

If one could have heard John Quincy's and Louisa Adams' thoughts as they stepped off the gangplank, the contrast would have been alarming. After eight years in Europe John Quincy felt a chill despite the muggy evening. He swallowed a moment of emotion and drank in the biggest city of the country for which he sailed across the ocean to become Secretary of State.

Louisa, on the other hand, despite running a high fever and battling the gout, dwelled instead on her loathing for this barbaric land. She knew that the chances of ever seeing England again were remote. She and the men in her life, her husband and three sons, would move to that wretched city of Washington where John Quincy would assume his new post and work himself to the bone to show these "Americans" how wrong they were to delay in calling upon his considerable diplomacy skills. And then, like Madison and Monroe before him, he would become President. Everyone knew that the State department had come to be the training ground for the Presidency. And once that happened, her last hope of seeing England again would be dashed.

That John Quincy Adams had his eye on the Presidency could not be doubted. But the desire to serve or wield power were minor reasons for his goal. Revenge was the major reason. Revenge for the shabby treatment his father received from his fellow revolutionaries and the citizenry who owed him so much during his Presidency. Revenge for the years in dreary international posts like St. Petersburg while lesser intellects received the premier posts. Revenge for being forced to negotiate with the preeminent power in the world with an obnoxious political appointee like Henry Clay hamstringing his efforts. Revenge for every stupid mistake that his predecessors in office had and would make. John Quincy Adams had no illusions about his charm or wit, but he was damn sure of his intelligence and other men's lack thereof.

The years in England were happy ones for John and Louisa. Their eldest boys George and John joined their parents and their brother Charles. While their father immersed himself in his political duties as usual, their mother immersed them in the culture and grandeur of her native land. Louisa knew that eventually she would have to return to the United States, but she was going to do all she could to inculcate her boys with a taste for the superiority of Britain while she could. She knew she failed to accomplish this with George and John but held hope that her efforts were not wasted on Charles.

At any rate, for the first time in years, Louisa and John Quincy Adams had a reasonably tranquil marriage. Never a volatile couple, they tended to simply not speak for days or even weeks and did not share the same bed during their lowest periods. But in England Louisa knew that her happiness was due in part to John Quincy's efforts to obtain the post and to have her sons join her. For this, she developed a certain grudging respect that ultimately began to resemble affection.

* * *

North Carolina: June 1818

The sweltering humidity of Chapel Hill was a minor annoyance to the proud parents of the University of North Carolina graduating class of 1818. Jane Polk, in particular, thought nothing of the heat. She was sure it was probably hotter back in Tennessee, her ostensive home. But for the first time in twelve years she was back in her real home state.

She listened to the young man delivering the commencement address in melodious but, to her, incomprehensible Latin. She didn't care that she could not understand. She sat transfixed with a mother's pride. The young man was James Knox Polk, her oldest son. The quiet boy that always mystified his father returned to his birthplace and now was being lauded for his scholastic achievements. In three short years James mastered Greek, Latin, literature and would receive his degree in mathematics, with honors.

Jane Polk did not have the vaguest notion what James learned or what his various new titles meant, just that he would be a different man than his father. Certainly, he would be a leader like his father and, hopefully, successful like his father. But Jane wanted James' father, Samuel, to see that a man could be as successful and popular as he without being aggressive, coarse and, sometimes, mean. Samuel was happy to see his son get a degree and was proud but he did not attend the graduation. As much as he loved James, he was convinced that James simply did not have the temperament to amount to much.

Although Samuel never said as much, Jane knew that her rugged husband found their son's many childhood ailments an annoyance which lessened James' as a man in his eyes. The countless trips into the woods to help his son relieve himself had sickened Samuel and burned images into his mind that he was never able to shake. When James was seventeen Samuel solved his son's poor health.

Samuel and James rode 230 miles into Kentucky to see a Dr. McDowell about James' frequent inability to pass urine. The stone in James' organ had become larger and more troublesome with each passing year. But the Polks heard that Dr. McDowell had healed others suffering from stones. While James had long since taken over the chore of moving the stone to relieve himself, the process was still painful and he often delayed until he could stand it no longer, thus making the pain that much more acute.

In Dr. McDowell's office James removed his trousers and sat on the edge of the Doctor's operating table. His arms were tied securely to his side and he was strapped around the waste to the table itself. His father did not watch as two huge men that Samuel paid two dollars apiece held James' legs apart. Dr. McDowell handed James a tumbler of brandy and advised him to drink it quickly which the patient did. With that, the Doctor sliced open the young man who, to his surprise, let out a small groan but nothing more. In a blood drenched-hand the Doctor held the stone aloft. One leg holder fainted. The other threw up.

Despite James' recovery and remarkable improvement in his health in general, the episode was too much for Samuel Polk to assimilate. He spoke with affection for his eldest son but was nonetheless more distant from him than ever.

What was odd was that Jane was far more disturbed by

Samuel's attitude than James. James always seemed to accept the fact that he and his father were different. Jane saw Samuel's lack of confidence in James as a direct reflection on her, however, since she and James were so much alike. While she never dared to confront Samuel about his attitude toward their oldest child, it was a constant source of irritation to her.

As the ceremonies closed Jane made her way down to her son. He stood away from his classmates who were already engaging in the kind of bawdy revelry that, for some reason, typified these events. James politely accepted compliments on his speech from people that Jane was quite sure had no more idea of what he had said than she, and again she shivered with pride.

As she grew near she paused. James was gaunt and pale. She had not seen him since she first arrived the morning before. He had to work on his speech so she spent the time shopping for her other children and visiting a few cousins that lived in Chapel Hill. James looked tired when she arrived but now she saw with alarm that he was not just tired, he was sick. Though he tried to look as hearty as possible, his mother could see that he was not well.

She reached James and they embraced. As they did this she whispered, "James you must rest. All of this education will be no good if you are not healthy."

He winced and so, of course, did she. She tried to make her point lightly but James was much too serious for well-intentioned levity. She knew immediately that her request would go unheeded. Her son was driven like no man she ever knew and could not be bothered by mundane matters like his health.

For his part, James recovered and smiled affectionately at his mother. He pulled her to his side and continued to greet well-wishers. Jane could feel him sway occasionally but willed himself to remain in place. He was cordial but not exuberant.

His demeanor changed when a handsome couple of obvious means approached with a plain but meticulously clothed young girl. James became almost animated allowing his seldom used smile to be lavished upon these well-bred strangers. After brief congratulations and salutations James introduced Jane.

"Mother, I would like to introduce Mr. and Mrs. Childress

and their daughter Sarah. Sarah and I were classmates in Murfreesboro. The Childresses treated me as family during my stay there."

Jane recalled receiving letters from James about this kind-hearted and, apparently, powerful family. "It is a pleasure to meet you. James has written me many letters about your kindnesses."

Mr. Childress spoke. "James is a fine young man. My compliments to Mr. Polk and yourself."

Intrigued, Jane turned to Sarah. "So you and James were classmates at Mr. Black's school in Murfreesboro?"

Without waiting for an answer, Jane made, for her, a bold statement. "I think that is wonderful that your parents are willing to allow a girl the opportunity to learn." Samuel would never allow his daughters such a luxury.

Sarah smiled but answered instead, "Wasn't James' speech magnificent?"

Jane beamed. "Why yes, it was...although I'm afraid my Latin leaves a lot to be desired." She laughed but Sarah did not. Again, she only smiled serenely and replied,

"I knew when James left Mr. Black's that he would give the Latin address. He was superior to even our instructors at Mr. Black's!"

James interceded, "Sarah you exaggerate so!"

Sarah pressed on, "But I don't. You know that by the time you left Mr. Abbott had nothing more to teach you." She turned to Jane. "There are elements of Sanskrit that even Mr. Abbott did not know but that James mastered."

Jane only laughed. This bright infatuated girl who could not have been more than fifteen years old was too much for her.

The Childresses invited Jane and her son to join them for dinner that evening at their hotel. Uncharacteristically, James seized the invitation and said that he and his mother would be "delighted', again a word that James never used.

Mr. Childress bowed to Jane and said, "Splendid, we will look forward to this evening."

Sarah chimed in, "It is so nice to meet you Mrs. Polk. I will see you tonight James."

James grinned nervously and responded somewhat out of

context, "Thank you Sarah."

As Sarah walked off with her parents Jane speculated as to whether James was equally smitten with Sarah. She shook herself realizing that Sarah would have only been twelve years old when James was in Murfreesboro. Preposterous!

Jane was startled out of her thoughts when she heard her son, beaming and spirited moments before, collapse in a chair beside her. He smiled weakly at her and sighed. "Perhaps you're right. I could use a little rest." Three months later (after James recovered), as she and her son left for Nashville, Jane could still vividly see her exhausted, feverish son sitting in a heap on his graduation day after playing Apollo to a fifteen-year old girl.

* * *

Pennsylvania: June 1819

It was not romantically executed, but it was a romantic setting. On the moonlit promenade of her father's resplendent estate Anne Coleman looked into James Buchanan's eyes (which unfortunately were not looking back) and said, "With my father's approval, I would be honored to marry you Mr. Buchanan."

Jim Buchanan was a little troubled by the caveat concerning her father, but hopefully that could be overcome. At 28 years old Jim knew that his political career would require a respectable wife before he got any older. And Anne Coleman filled the bill perfectly. She was shy but attractive. More importantly, she was the daughter of the wealthiest man in Lancaster County, Robert Coleman. While Jim Buchanan had matured sufficiently to realize that money alone was no basis for a marriage, he did recognize the substantial benefits that could accrue from such a union.

At this moment, the logical next step after receiving an affirmative reply to a proposal of marriage would have been to kiss his fiance which is what Jim Buchanan wished to do and what Anne Coleman wanted him to do. But he didn't. For all his wit and charm with other men and with ladies that he had known on a less formal basis, on those few occasions where Jim felt any stirring of emotion, his suave facade dissolved. So, Jim met the news of his imminent marriage with a passionless, "Well, good. I, of course, am very pleased."

Anne smiled. She heard many stories over the years about Jim Buchanan's potential and concurrent notoriety, but found him most attractive in these awkward interludes between the height of sentiment and the return to the depth of superficial banter. She asked in an almost apologetic tone, "Would you like to talk to Father?"

Jim replied, "Yes. That would be good." He winced. Stilted and cold. Christ! He just asked this girl to marry him and he was utterly incapable of displaying any sense of love or even comfort. He knew that he did not have enough experience with real love to know whether he was in love with Anne yet or not. He did know that he was very fond of her. He also knew that he would come to love Anne because he felt it would be improper to try and bed her prior to marriage. And that sense of propriety was never a major stumbling block for him up to now.

He managed to shake off his mawkish performance and focus on the task at hand. Jim was not the first suitor to ask for Anne's hand. By all rights she should have been married years before, but her father either flatly prohibited earlier proposals or frightened the young men to the point of paralysis and ultimately, withdrawal. He was cool to Jim up to this time and Jim was sure that part of Mr. Coleman's behavior could be traced to the rumor that he believed that any man courting his daughter was really courting his money. Jim knew that a young lawyer with political aspirations would have a hard time ducking these accusations.

Anne led Jim through the entry to her father's mansion and into his study where he sat, as one would expect, smoking a pipe and reading the evening paper. The study was as austere as Mr. Coleman. Rich dark grains characterized the long wooden panels that dominated the room. The one window was long and thin, slightly opened, but all one could see was the thicket of trees and bramble--even during the day this was meant to be a dark, intimidating chamber. The rows of books were not designed to connote a diverse soul. Rather they were uniform in their theme; money. The only one that Jim was familiar with was Adam

Smith's *An Inquiry into the Nature and Causes of the Wealth of Nations.*

Mr. Coleman did not look up at Anne or Jim but only nodded when Anne asked, "Father, Jim would like to speak with you." With that, Anne withdrew. Anne never really talked about her father with Jim. On the one hand, she seemed devoted to Robert Coleman, but, on the other, she almost appeared to quake on the rare instances where she and Jim were in Mr. Coleman's presence together.

Jim hesitated but was not surprised when Mr. Coleman beat him to the punch. "You are wanting to marry Caroline?" Mr. Coleman was the only one to refer to his daughter by her middle name.

Jim felt himself relax. He saw in this man the Professor Davidsons of his life. Men who could keep him from his goals brought out a cockiness in him that he never understood. With Anne and his own parents he was stolid and withdrawn--he knew that they would accept him irrespective of his demeanor. But a figure of authority presented a challenge to Jim and the consequences of overt irreverence never seemed to work its way into his thinking. So to Mr. Coleman's query Jim laughed lightly and crossed the room with his back to Anne/Caroline's father and peered at the shelves of capitalist literature before responding. "Actually, Mr. Coleman I've kind of had my eye on this house. I don't suppose this could be included in the dowry?"

When Mr. Coleman failed to even smile, Jim was emboldened. He turned toward his potential father-in-law who was mildly taken aback but nonetheless acetic. Jim crossed the room again to the window and let the evening breeze cool him momentarily. He would pace this room all night if necessary. But he would not sit down. He would not put himself in a position where Coleman could lecture him. Jim was already at a disadvantage by virtue of age, wealth and relationship to Anne; he would not let Coleman have complete control.

Again, Jim spoke. "Yes Mr. Coleman, I want to marry Anne (ah yes, show him that you know his daughter on a different basis!). I want to marry her for many reasons. She is lovely and makes excellent company. She is kind-hearted and not demanding. These attributes make her the ideal wife for a young man that wishes to dedicate his life to the public service." Jim paused momentarily to allow Coleman a chance to try and hurl his first barb. Coleman tried and Jim took the words from his mouth.

"Of course, dedicating one's life to public service means getting elected which takes money and the social connections that are necessary to gain access to money. So, in this last regard, again, your daughter is ideal."

Coleman exploded out of his chair at which point Jim knew that he would wed Anne Coleman. Coleman pointed a finger in the air exclaiming, "Ah ha! So, you are after her money!"

Jim smiled as nonchalantly as possible. "Of course I am. What good does it do for Anne to have money if all it does is buy her things? With her grace and money and my aptitude for politics and people, she will be able to buy far more than mere things. She will serve her country and gain prominence. She will leave behind not only money, but a mark. So yes Mr. Coleman, I want your daughter's money. But not for the reasons you think."

It was now Robert Coleman's turn to cross the room. He stood by the window and now let the breeze cool him briefly. He then turned and looked Jim directly in the eye about a foot away. He said, in a quiet but firm growl, "Buchanan, I have known about you for years. Your father is a good man. Unfortunately, I have doubts about you. First, you are full of yourself. Second, any man who chooses politics as his life's ambition is either naive or a crook. But Caroline is in love with you and it is time she married.

"But let me warn you. You better be naive, because if I find out that you are a crook or that you harm my girl in any way, you will never hold office again in your short life. Do I make myself clear?"

Jim extended his hand. "Abundantly sir. I will take care of her."

Anne's father did not take his hand but again turned his attention to the breeze and the window. To Jim, whose hand was still hanging aloft at the end of his outstretched arm, he said, "We'll see."

Jim, having been dismissed more summarily and by people who disliked him more than Mr. Coleman and, considering the circumstances, left to tell Anne/Caroline the happy news in his own joyless way.

* * *

Washington: June 1819

The Capital city was almost empty as politicians and their entourages tried to escape the heat, mosquitoes and stench that infiltrated Washington in July. President Monroe sat in the small garden just outside the south portico of the White House (as it was now referred to). Monroe marveled at how quickly and meticulously the House was restored after the British devastation in 1814. Within three years the House was better than new which was remarkable since it took ten years to construct originally. The south portico as a backdrop for pronouncements of state and for informal meetings was Monroe's contribution to the ongoing ornamentation of the President's mansion.

The euphoria that followed the War of 1812 and that greeted James Monroe upon taking office in 1817 had begun to subside. The economy finally started to slow after the inevitable rebuilding and reopening of trade boom after the war. And politicians were beginning to stir and find ways to criticize one another in a way that was not fashionable for the last few years. Of course, as the criticism began to gather force it converged on the President as it always had before and as it always would. Monroe was still very popular but not as immune to political slights as before.

Monroe's greatest political liability thus far in his administration was presently sitting to his left finishing off the last of a cherry tart that Monroe's chef prepared for this breakfast meeting. General Andrew Jackson's fondness for confectionery delights preceded him. Since Monroe both wished to chastise the hero of the Battle of New Orleans and to seek a favor from him, he hoped to get the General in a propitious frame of mind.

Seated to Monroe's right was Lieutenant Colonel Zachary

Taylor. Monroe was meeting the quiet but unkempt Taylor for the first time. While he was not particularly impressed by Taylor's appearance, he was advised that the young military man was both courageous and level-headed.

The President knew time was growing short. He was due to start receiving the daily horde of office seekers in a half hour. He got to the point.

"General, you understand I presume, that John Calhoun and others wish for me to subject you to the most severe public censure for your actions in Florida?"

Andrew Jackson flashed but replied calmly, "I hope Mr. President that you will not be swayed by those who see me as a threat to their Presidential hopes and so seek to punish a man for merely serving his country."

Monroe smiled and remarked. "Should you run for President you should have no problem securing the Georgia vote."

Jackson laughed a little too heartily. Monroe listened to the reports dozens of times. Seminole Indians and escaped slaves crossed from Spanish-owned Florida into Georgia on a constant basis since the War, staying only long enough to loot, rape and burn before returning to the sanctuary of Spain's dominion. Monroe called upon Jackson to investigate the disturbances and report back to him. He specifically told Jackson not to enter Florida.

Jackson not only entered Florida, he drove deep into the territory, and conducted his own program of looting and burning before returning to the safety of the United States. But before he left Florida, Jackson held a dramatic, yet completely staged, trial of two British expatriates named Alexander Arbuthnot and Robert Ambrister whom he accused of inciting the Seminoles to attack American property. After predictably finding the Englishmen guilty, Jackson ordered Arbuthnot hanged and Ambrister shot. His troops dutifully carried out his orders.

While the grateful people of Georgia had very little trouble with invading Indians or slaves since that time, within a week of Jackson's exploits, both the Spanish and English ministers were demanding satisfaction. And Presidential aspirants like Henry

Clay and Monroe's own Secretary of War John Calhoun saw an opportunity to knock Jackson from his steed that was galloping toward the White House. After apologizing to the foreign ministers, Monroe declined to punish Jackson.

Monroe did not particularly care for the General, but he knew that he would not be President now if it was not for Old Hickory's (as Jackson's soldiers called him) actions in New Orleans. Faced with the fact that the United States tried to stand up for its rights against England and failed miserably, Jackson fought a seemingly meaningless battle in the swamps of Louisiana and transformed Monroe from a beleaguered Secretary of War to the clear choice to succeed James Madison as President. But for Andy Jackson, James Monroe would now be back in Virginia trying to revive a law practice that was never really viable in the first place. So, despite his personal feelings of disdain he knew he was as indebted to Jackson in a moral sense as he was to his many creditors in Virginia in a monetary sense. And he also knew that the General was still far too popular to be at odds with.

Monroe leaned forward. "General I have no intention of humiliating one who has so decisively sacrificed for his country but I must caution you to not exceed orders in the future."

Jackson did not commit. "And what does the future hold?"

Monroe smiled again. "Oh, I think you have your own ideas about what the future will ultimately hold, but I would like to give you an opportunity to try your hand at governing to see if you really would like it here." Monroe waived in the general direction of the White House.

Jackson remonstrated, "Mr. President, I will only come to this house if called to serve. I have no such ambitions."

Monroe winked at Lieutenant Taylor who looked alarmed. Monroe continued. "As you know General, aside from his claims of indignation, the Spanish minister de Onis has also understood that your adventures demonstrated that Spain is utterly incapable of defending its American possessions. So, for the last week Secretary Adams has been meeting with the Mr. de Onis and they have concluded an agreement for the acquisition of Florida. I would like you to serve as Florida's first Governor."

Both Jackson and Taylor shot forward simultaneously exclaiming "What?"

Monroe continued, "Of course it will take time for Congressional approval and I will delay a little longer so that your recent excesses may recede a little further but I do believe that the Seminoles will not have forgotten you. General, you are the one man that I can appoint with little or no fear that the citizenry will defy. I think you have shown how you react to defiance. Lieutenant Taylor will supervise construction of suitable quarters for you in the meantime before returning to Louisiana."

Jackson replied, "Mr. President, I would be honored to serve if you feel it will not be too, uh, risky for you sir."

Again, Monroe grinned. "I assure you it is too politically risky which is why your appointment will not be announced until after the election next year. But that should not preclude you and Lieutenant Taylor from getting ready."

"No sir," answered Andrew Jackson with a smile.

"No sir," echoed Zachary Taylor with a frown.

* * *

Zachary Taylor followed General Jackson from the White House and waited while Old Hickory mounted his white stallion. From his mount Jackson said, "Lieutenant, I will forward instructions for Mrs. Jackson's requirements for quarters within the week so that you may begin your work."

Taylor gave the General the most formal salute he could muster and replied "Yessir." The more ritualistic aspects of military life were always a problem for Taylor but he had too sharp a sense of strategy and organization to allow a propensity for slovenly attire and demeanor to be a hindrance. Indeed, it was futile for the Lieutenant to look anything other than slovenly as God saddled him with a slovenly body. He was in excellent condition primarily from his willingness to join his men in the labor that was required of them, a habit that his men found admirable.

But no matter how hard Taylor worked, he still had

extremely bowed short legs that supported a long but thick torso with ape-like arms that were completely out of proportion to the rest of his frame. Atop this odd anatomy sat an even odder head. Although it was narrow with a sharply pointed nose, it was huge. Increasingly farsighted, Taylor compounded his comic appearance by continually squinting rather than giving in to the necessity of spectacles.

But what Zachary Taylor could not see with his eyes, he could see as plain as day with his mind. Taylor clambered aboard his horse (his peculiar configuration also made this a difficult task) and ruminated about the meeting he just had with the President of the United States and the greatest hero the country had seen since George Washington. Taylor was not in awe, however. The President was clearly an old man to be revered for his past deeds but he appeared to have no comprehension of the changing face of his country from southern gentry and northern merchants to northern industrial visionaries, southerners nervously watching their way of life being chipped away by the changing north and by the exodus of people to the west where a generation of frontier adventurers and explorers had taken root.

Andrew Jackson, on the other hand, understood the make-up of the nation all too clearly. Despite his protests to the contrary, Taylor knew that Jackson had designs on the White House. To a young, idealistic (if unconventional) military man like Taylor, a soldier had no business using his successes in battle to gain public office.

Even more basic to Taylor though was the fact that he did not like Jackson. While Jackson was met with acclaim in the rest of the country, Taylor spent his last few years in Louisiana which he decided to make his home. The cajuns and other inhabitants of the bayou country were happy to see the hero of New Orleans move on. Taylor listened to countless stories of Jackson's tyrannical rule with sufficient repetition that he had little trouble accepting their veracity. After the Battle that made Jackson famous, the General overtly facilitated every opportunity for public adulation and a populace that came to view the man from Tennessee as synonymous with martial law was not inclined to resist.

Then Jackson went to Florida and set back the United States' strides toward being accepted by Europe as more than a backward nation of exiles' grandchildren by stupidly executing Arbuthnot and Ambrister. While justifying the slayings by arguing that the Englishmen aided the enemy, it was beyond doubt to all who were the least bit acquainted with Jackson that the killings were nothing more than another act of retribution for the death of Jackson's brothers and for the scar down his cheek that constantly reminded Jackson and all who knew him how much he detested the British.

Taylor stopped his horse and gazed back toward the White House. He knew it was probably inevitable that Andrew Jackson would one day live there unless he seriously erred again in Florida. Taylor knew enough of Jackson that that was not likely. While the popular notion was that Jackson was a swashbuckling eccentric that threw caution to the wind, Taylor saw Jackson's calculation and cunning too often to buy into such a theory. Jackson was shrewd and unquestionably intelligent, but he preferred to be identified with the rough-hewn frontiersmen that sang songs of his heroism and bravery and did not blanch at his occasional savagery.

Taylor closed his eyes and tried to think about Peggy. This was far more pleasant than dwelling on the President's decision to hand General Jackson his own fiefdom and the instrumental role that Zachary Taylor would play in conceiving the new kingdom. But Taylor would not thwart the President's order regardless of his own aversion to the would-be ruler. He was a soldier that knew how to take orders.

* * *

July 1819

Henry Clay had his long legs propped on the edge of his desk. He turned and spit.

General William Henry Harrison sat in a stiff, undersized chair across from Clay. The Senator from Kentucky's office was remarkably spare saving the immense chair and desk upon which the resident was currently perched. Harrison, having just concluded an unremarkable term in Congress, waited for Clay's arms to rise to place the Senator's hands behind his head. When the first movement occurred, Harrison began the dialogue.

"Henry, I hope you will keep an eye on the appropriation. Since I will be heading back to Ohio tomorrow, I will need your assistance."

"Ah hell, General, don't worry about a thing. We'll get that money for you. I'll make sure of it."

Harrison bowed his head. "Thank you."

Clay laughed and swung his feet down and slapped the desk with his palm. Harrison knew that meant Clay's end of the deal was about to come.

"So you're gonna go try and run around with those scoundrels up in Columbus."

Harrison thought this was a weak introduction since there were no notoriously roguish politicos in Ohio's capital city. But he played along.

"I reckon, for better or worse. Anna's havin' a hard go with nine children and a husband who's home just long enough to get her in an expectin' way again."

Clay laughed again. "Well General, a man's gotta look after his own, that's for sure." He became serious. "Look General, I'll be blunt. We're makin' sure that you get that Senate seat and, in return, I'm gonna need your help."

Harrison nodded earnestly while Clay continued.

"As you know, the President is going to be reelected next year. But it is not too early to start getting ready for '24. And Ohio is going to be a key state."

Harrison had to agree. Recent convention dictated that the Secretary of State would be the front-runner for succession but John Quincy Adams did not have the charisma or political alliances that made James Madison's and James Monroe's elections inevitable. So, many ambitious politicians were licking their lips over the Presidential election of 1824 with varying degrees of voracity. And Henry Clay's appetite was clearly the most whetted of them all.

Clay was also correct about the importance of Ohio. As a

large western state still reveling in its frontier infancy, the stubborn and stodgy Adams would not appeal. It would be crucial for Clay to coalesce support from the states surrounding his own Kentucky where he would build from his devoted supporters. In the last year it became common knowledge the Andrew Jackson coveted the Presidency as well, thus making it even more important for Clay to get an early start at garnering as much western backing as possible since Jackson was certain to appeal to the frontier voters.

Finally, Clay was correct in calling upon Harrison to bring Ohio into the fold. Harrison's fellow citizens in Ohio revered the General as the hero of Tippecanoe. Outside of his home state the General came to be viewed as a pitiful soul constantly beseeching anyone who would listen that he and his soldiers were entitled to substantial back pay for their service in the Indian and British conflicts. Bereft of documentation for his claims, Harrison looked like a beggar scavenging for some means of supporting his extraordinary brood in Ohio. And there was some measure of truth in the perception.

But, in Ohio, the General was celebrated at every turn. His influence would carry the day for virtually any Presidential hopeful. The two men sitting in Henry Clay's office knew this. Harrison clarified the terms of the deal.

"Henry, you look after that appropriation and I'll look after Ohio."

* * *

Pennsylvania: December 1819

Frank Cartwright was an intimidating looking man so it was not hard to believe that the charge of assault leveled against him had some basis in fact. Frank was not violent but was known to flare stupendously when he had enough to drink and when a capable antagonist was present. Donald Ekhart, better known as "Mole" Ekhart, was a highly capable antagonist. Mole was both furtive and obnoxious; he made his living endearing himself to those with money and illegal goals who could not risk actual pursuit of their goals themselves but who were willing to pay Mole to facilitate their ends.

Frank was a full head taller than Mole, but was slow. His broad shoulders and huge hands could have snapped Mole into several small parts had he delivered on the threat that he was accused of issuing. Frank was a laborer. Most often he worked for the livery stables but he toiled for most of the merchants of Lancaster at one point or another. He was well-liked. Mole wasn't.

Frank's troubles started when Mole taunted him in the presence of Frank's sister. Mole tormented Frank since they were children when Frank was a poor student for reasons beyond his control and Mole was a poor student because he wanted to be. Frank's sister never married, making good on her promise to their dead parents to look after Frank. But she could have married at any time. Cara Cartwright was beautiful and well-mannered. But she adored her brother and marriage held no interest for her as long as she had Frank to take care of.

The brother and sister sat at Mrs. Dorchester's dining hall two weeks before when Mole passed by at the conclusion of his meal. As he did so many times before, Mole stopped to irritate Frank before continuing on his way. Leaning down and whispering so that Cara could not hear, Mole had told Frank, "Moron, I could sure use a taste of that sister of yours for dessert."

Although Frank certainly intended to kill Mole, when he leapt to his feet and withdrew his knife, he dumped the table over onto Cara. By the time he tended to his sister, and returned his attention to Mole, Frank forgot about killing him and only declared his intent to kill Mole. Mole sat slumped in the chair where he collapsed laughing when Cara's supper desecrated her only nice dress. His puckered face and squinted eyes all expanded to capacity though when Frank grabbed Mole's chair with Mole in place and discarded the furniture and occupant through Mrs. Dorchester's door with the warning that he would kill Mole if he ever looked at Cara.

While the crowd at Mrs. Dorchester's cheered Frank's disposal of Mole, Mole went to the sheriff and asked for charges against Frank. While the sheriff had no desire to sanctify Mole, he had no choice but to arrest Frank for threatening the life of a man when Frank could not remember what Mole whispered to him. And, a dozen witnesses confirmed that Frank, indeed, threw Mole into the street, promising to kill him.

Jim Buchanan knew that Frank was probably fully justified in assaulting Mole. He merely did what so many of the citizens of Lancaster would like to do to Mole. But Frank's feeble mind was incapable of recalling what brought on his fury. Jim was also confident that Judge Burnworth did not want to convict Frank, but the evidence was one-sided unless Frank could remember what Mole said. And Frank couldn't.

Cara Cartwright came to Buchanan to represent Frank because she heard he was the best attorney in town. And she was right. He was so good in fact that he did not need, nor did he have time, for Frank's case. Jim's practice was thriving to the point that he had failed to visit his fiancé Anne in almost two months. When he returned from Harrisburg earlier in the month, he paid a social call on the wife of his close friend and client William Jenkins. Mrs. Jenkins' sister, Grace, was visiting the Jenkins' and Jim was both charmed and charming. Although he stayed longer than he intended, Jim left with only fanciful thoughts of infidelity.

Anne Coleman soon heard that not only did Jim fail to visit her upon his return to Lancaster, he instead spent the afternoon flirting with the (by the time the story reached her) "beguiling" Grace. When Jim did call upon Anne she was packing to visit her sister in Philadelphia. Alternating between fury and tears, she announced that she would not be taken for granted, that it was clear that her father and friends were right, Jim was after the Coleman fortune and that their engagement was off.

Jim was so stunned by the tirade of the normally submissive Anne that he left simply and quietly, feeling that protesting would serve no purpose. He was confident that after Anne's return from Philadelphia he would be able to reason with her. The scene troubled him though. He had grown fond of Anne but was lame in his attempts at romance. While he relished marriage, he had very little experience or skill at formal courting.

Short term flirting, yes. Courting, no.

It was a few days after Anne's departure that Cara Cartwright appeared in his second-floor office overlooking East King Street. Cara's visit coincided with Jim's renewed confidence in his ability to win back Anne's hand. With his self-assurance restored, Jim was once again able to work diligently and recognize a beautiful woman when he saw one.

Cara's story about her mentally deficient brother and his wormy nemesis had very little effect on Buchanan because he knew it wouldn't pay well and because he was doing less and less criminal law as more lucrative pursuits flooded his door. But Cara's earnest pleas coupled with her pouty lips and tear-filled ocean blue eyes made Jim accept the case.

Now, as Jim glanced at his forlorn client, the prosecutor was finishing his questioning of the thespian, Mole. Mole vividly described Frank's "unprovoked" actions and the humiliation he suffered. The prosecutor sat down across from Jim and nodded. Jim turned to Cara seated in the row behind the defense table and said quietly but in the tone of cockiness that long ago became his hallmark, "Get ready to take your brother home."

While Cara looked at him quizzically, he addressed Judge Burnworth.

"Your honor, I have just a few questions for the victim concerning his charge of assault based on the so-called threat that my client made on Mr. Ekhart's life."

Jim turned to Mole and strolled casually toward the witness box asking, "Mr. Ekhart, let us suppose for a minute that you were a man of courage, a man who does not scare easily. If that were the case, would you have taken my client's threat seriously?"

Mole's slitted eyes narrowed even more as he hissed, "Sir, I am as courageous as any man."

Buchanan feigned surprise. "Are you saying that even at the time of this assault you were and are a brave man."

"I defy you to find a man as brave as me."

"Well then I stand before you, a man braver than you because I am not afraid of Frank Cartwright."

Mole bellowed. "I am not afraid of Frank Cartwright."

Jim sighed dramatically, "Well you are not now afraid of Frank Cartwright. But certainly, in the past, you were afraid of my client."

Mole pounded his fist on the rail and said in slow measured words, "I am not and never have been afraid of your client. Your client is a moron."

Jim smiled at Mole and replied, "A moron he may be, but your brilliance has set him free." Jim turned to Judge Burnworth. "Your honor, since Mr. Ekhart is not afraid of and never has been afraid of my client, the requisite fear of bodily harm does not exist and an assault cannot have occurred. I move the charges be dismissed."

The prosecutor half-heartedly objected as Judge Burnworth slammed his gavel down and ordered the case dismissed. Jim winked at Cara as he shook Frank's hand. Jim was about to inquire into Frank's and particularly his sister's dinner plans when his law clerk burst into the courtroom and rushed between them. Jim frowned at his young apprentice when he tugged at Jim's sleeve and beseeched him to follow him outside.

Jim whispered and yelled at the same time, "Baxter, can't this wait?"

The young man shook his head. "I'm afraid not, sir. Mr. Coleman's man left a message for you and told me to tell you that it was urgent."

Jim followed lost in thought. What would be so urgent that Anne's father would send a special message to his future son-in-law for whom he still had no great fondness? He felt a little chagrined at his mild infatuation with Cara Cartwright while his fiancé had fled Lancaster over his lack of affection. Perhaps Mr. Coleman decided to intercede on his daughter's behalf.

As he trudged up the outside steps to the second floor and his office, he paused and looked at the street below. He saw Daphne Hartlinger standing in the soggy street below staring at him with a pensive gaze. Daphne was one of Anne's closest friends. But when Jim tipped his hat, Daphne shook her head and walked aimlessly away. Jim wondered and then smiled as he walked in the door that Baxter left open.

Baxter presented Jim with the message. Jim knew that

Baxter already knew the contents of the message. It was not that long since Jim was a clerk sharing the secrets of his master with the servants of others who were equally inclined to divulge the information they were bound to hold confidential. Mr. Coleman's messenger undoubtedly relayed the contents of the envelope to Baxter. Otherwise there was little reason for Baxter to take the unusual and unprecedented step of retrieving Jim from court.

Jim leaned back in his chair and tore open the small envelope. He withdrew a small piece of expensive stationery that had two sentences in handwriting that Jim did not recognize. He sat bolt upright as he read over and over again:

> *My sister Caroline died here at my home after*
> *a brief illness.*
> *I thought it proper that you be notified.*

Jim's mind swirled as he read Anne's sister's note without comprehending. As he avoided the possibility that Anne was dead, he instead focused on the question of why the note was delivered by Mr. Coleman's messenger. How had the note from Philadelphia gone first to him? When he asked this question aloud, Baxter, who did know the contents of the note, knew that his mentor was somewhere between hysteria and shock.

Three days later Jim held his unopened letter to Robert Coleman requesting permission to attend Anne's funeral. Coleman refused to even receive the letter much less Jim in person.

Anne Coleman killed herself.

Jim threw the letter into the grate that warmed his office and pulled on his coat.

She had, in typical demure fashion, quietly swallowed poison and went to bed in her sister's guestroom. The next day she died of poisoning. And a broken heart.

Now, four days after she died, James Buchanan began anew. For the first time in three days he emerged from his office. Unshaven and uncharacteristically unkempt, Jim climbed into a wagon bound for Mercersburg and his own family. He was subdued. His brashness and cavalier spirit nearly got him expelled from Dickinson. The same traits left his family embarrassed that one of their own spent the War of 1812 as a horse thief. Now he would return home to announce that his egotism caused his fiancé to commit suicide.

As the coach rocked and swayed and carried him from the town that he knew Robert Coleman would never allow him to succeed in, he knew that his ever-present confidence would be his only hope of survival, just as it had always been his downfall. He was determined to appear confident to family, clients and friends. But he would also be genuinely contrite. For if he could be confident, he could never again be cocky. For the first time in his life, he learned from a mistake.

* * *

New York: March 1822

There are not many places colder than Buffalo, New York with the wind blowing in from the Great Lakes of Erie and Ontario. In early March with Spring in the offing it seems even more biting. The young couple strolling along the bank of the more southern of the lakes winced with each blast of frigid air.

Buffalo was a collection of merchants serving a small port for Lake Erie. It was smaller than it was in 1814 after suffering the same fate as the nation's Capital in the War of 1812--the British sacked Buffalo and set most of it ablaze. The burning converted western New York from a population mildly opposed to the War to ardent patriots devoted to revenge against England. Fortunately, or unfortunately, John Quincy Adams concluded the Treaty of Ghent before the ragged western New York militia could engage the Brits.

So, the small population set to work rebuilding its village. The "small population" included a pretty, strong-willed school teacher named Abigail Powers and her former pupil and current fiancé, Millard Fillmore. Bundled against the cold as they were, one could not readily see what a striking pair they made.

Abigail's silky brunette hair was gathered beneath a

magnificently layered collection of shawls and scarves that she wrapped about her head and shoulders. With her delicate cheeks and pug-nose covered to avoid the chill, one could only see her dark eyes peering up at her tall, powerfully built beaux's ice blue eyes. The attraction was complete when Millard smiled. With a smile, Fillmore went from appearing simply intelligent and handsome to appearing intelligent, handsome and magnetically warm.

Millard Fillmore's attraction to Abigail began shortly after enrolling in her class as a seventeen-year old that spent his youth working his father's farm and doing very little reading. Abigail recognized Fillmore's hunger for education within his first week and a few months later presented him with his first dictionary. Rather than using the book for reference, however, Fillmore read the dictionary. And as his vocabulary grew to almost absurd bounds, his infatuation with his instructor blossomed into love. When it became clear that Fillmore had no intention of spending his life as a farmer, Abigail was no longer able to deny her fondness for him. For three years they courted, the last year engaged to be married at some unspecified future date.

Abigail consented to this more hearty than romantic stroll after Millard arrived at her boarding house unusually distracted. When it became clear that the evening would be a total loss until he unwound, she suggested a walk. He readily acceded. Together they ventured into the arctic air.

Their walk was silent for close to a mile as Abigail went from concerned to cold and irritated. Just as she was ready to insist on turning around, Fillmore stopped and peered out from the northern tip of Lake Erie. He sighed and then said, "Wood had me give notice on Cary Norwood today."

Abigail slipped her hand into Millard's pocket, found his gloved palm and squeezed. For the last year Fillmore had clerked for a nearby county judge named Walter Wood. While Wood was kind to Fillmore, he was one of the largest property owners and wealthiest men in the area. As a result, Fillmore's duties had less to do with the law than with overseeing Judge Wood's properties, collecting rents and evicting those who did not pay up. The judge compensated Fillmore well for his "clerking" but the young clerk had greater aspirations than being a highly compensated rent collector.

In five years Millard Fillmore went from a semi-literate son of a farmer to a well-read and almost ambitious man. He knew that his handling of Judge Wood's errands earned him begrudging respect for his civility and compassion in difficult situations, but his compassion was limited by what the judge would let him get away with. Soon he would be admitted to the New York Bar and a new lawyer would have a hard time building a practice when his only claim to notoriety was as the landlord's henchman.

Abigail knew that Millard was torn between his indebtedness to Judge Wood and his desire to make his own name--a good and positive name. For the last few months she saw it building in him like the waters of the Niagara when they began to gnaw away at the ice holding them captive in this, the dead of winter.

She spoke almost in a murmur. "Millard, at some point the servant satisfies his obligation and the master starts to slide into arrears."

Fillmore looked down at her. "But I'm not sure that I won't lose all the value I have accumulated while I've been satisfying my 'obligation' to the judge, as you put it."

Abigail freed herself of his arm and hand, "That is the chance you will have to take. The risks are the same now as they will be tomorrow or the next day or the next!"

Fillmore bit his lip and walked a few steps. He knew she was right but it still made him uncomfortable. He grew up in a home where his father made all the decisions with no input from his mother. Yet here he was engaged to a woman with far more education and, indeed, wisdom, than himself. Abigail's intelligence was the catalyst to their attraction but her perceptiveness still disconcerted him.

He turned back toward her and changed the subject after tossing off a resigned but noncommittal smile. He waved his hand at Lake Erie, "Abigail, in a few years the canal will stretch from this point up to Albany and across the state. Buffalo is going to be a city with boundless opportunities when that happens."

Abigail let her scarves drop slightly. Of course, she was the one who convinced Millard that Governor Clinton's plan to build the Erie Canal would lead to a boom in western New York. The gubernatorial election of 1817 centered on one issue and one issue only--whether to elect Clinton, the Canal's primary proponent or Peter Porter who opposed the Canal. Clinton, perhaps the last electable Federalist, claimed an overwhelming victory and work on the waterway that would connect the Atlantic Ocean and Lake Erie began almost immediately. Since one end of the Canal was targeted for Buffalo, it was inevitable that Buffalo would see a massive influx of merchants, traders and workers from all directions. Construction of additional port facilities was already proceeding at a furious pace. And Buffalo's few lawyers were inundated with work. The future Fillmores knew that the time was ripe to start a practice before the Canal passed them by, both literally and figuratively.

Abigail slipped her arms around Millard and looked up at him, "Then I guess its time to tell Judge Wood that your ship is coming in and you can't miss it."

Fillmore smiled and looked at her face that was now fully exposed to the icy wind to the point of making her cimmerian eyes water. She looked more vulnerable and less determined. Fillmore didn't hesitate. He cradled her head softly in his arm and kissed her slowly and passionately. As they pressed together they accomplished what six layers of clothes could not. They were, at last, warm.

* * *

Maine: April 1823

The Kennebec River lapped over its banks as spring descended on the new state of Maine. Four years earlier Massachusetts decided to grant its troublesome northern neighbor its independence rather than committing any further resources to maintaining order in this distant, untamed land. A year later, the potent abolitionist population of Massachusetts was delighted when Henry Clay engineered the passage of the Missouri

Compromise which brought both Missouri and Maine into the Union. The "compromise" was that the admission of Missouri did not create an advantage in Congress for the slave states because any leverage was offset by the admission of another small northern, non-slave state that would get two senators as well. Whatever disincentives existed for keeping Maine as part of Massachusetts were compensated for in the Compromise.

Nathaniel Hawthorne was cynical about the concept of Maine as a state. Certainly, it had a small, stable population and a few industries of note, but mostly it was a bleak, motionless icebox in the winter and a foraging ground for hunters and fishermen in the summer. Maine would never be the center of things, just an intriguing detour.

Hawthorne threw down his satchel and lowered himself to the ground, ultimately reclining against the soggy base of one of the thousands of trees that lined the Kennebec. While Maine's fall foliage was the stuff of romance and poetry, Hawthorne preferred the spring. The autumn tended to depress him as the constant precursor to an interminable winter of cold and study. The spring, on the other hand, bode warmth and the freedom of summer.

As a sophomore at Bowdoin College, Hawthorne came north from Salem, Massachusetts seeking solitude to hone his skills as a writer. So far he had done very little honing and instead made the subconscious decision to focus on another necessary attribute for a writer--life experiences. And so today he would enact his usual ritual of reaching into his bag and withdrawing his current (and only) novel which had reached the grand total of thirteen pages, and a flask.

Hawthorne's book had a working title of *Fanshawe*. Hawthorne was surprised by the dark tale he outlined for *Fanshawe*. Despite his difficulty with writing in bright images, he personally did not feel disconsolate. On the contrary, today was typical of the many contented days he spent in the last year with Frank Pierce.

Franklin Pierce was the same age as his friend Nat but was a year ahead of Hawthorne at Bowdoin. The year before Pierce took the aspiring freshman author under his wing and showed him how to just get by in his classes, chase girls and drink. He was not able to interest Hawthorne in his first love though--trout fishing.

Hawthorne loved to go fishing with Pierce. He just never fished. He preferred to watch from the banks sipping from a flask and pretending to write while Pierce stealthily pursued his prey. Usually he worked in a nap while his "mentor" toiled on the river.

Today was Frank's first day on the Kennebec in 1823. Hawthorne spent all morning trying to keep up as Pierce hastened to squeeze every minute of angling out of the day. Neither student bothered to bring any textbooks in their satchels; only the barely conceived *Fanshawe* and Izaak Walton's one hundred seventy-year old *The Compleat Angler* made the trip.

As anxious as Pierce was to get to the river, Hawthorne marveled at his patience once there. Frank waded out to a small island in the middle of the river that would be covered in another month by the raging torrent the Kennebec would become. With his breeches rolled up above his knees and his bare feet dangling lightly in the current, Frank sat with his back to Hawthorne. He reclined ever so slightly to be as inconspicuous as possible while he studied the pool on the far side where even his non-fishing friend could see a trout's snout breaking the surface on a regular, almost rhythmic, basis.

Finally, Pierce gathered in the end of his line and plucked an artificial fly that he tied from his small wooden box that always accompanied Frank and *The Compleat Angler* on their fishing outings. The first time Frank showed Hawthorne his box of flies, Hawthorne laughed and sneeringly asked, "A fish is to believe these to be flies?"

Pierce responded primarily with sarcasm and secondarily with irritation as he closed the box on his hooks wrapped in thread and frayed yarns, "It is so fortunate that I am trying to outwit the fish rather than you Nat for you are far too clever. Luckily, the trout are not so discerning, not having your vast intellect. They only care that their food is approximately the same color and size, not whether it has two eyes, a handsome nose and a sunny disposition!" With that Hawthorne gave up ridiculing Pierce's peculiar infatuation with entomology.

Methodically Pierce tied his first proposed fly of the day

and flicked it into the water guiding it to drift over the pool. He repeated this precisely twenty times before again gathering his line and changing to another fly. Twenty more casts and no fish later Pierce again retrieved the failed fake insect. He then reached into his fly box and held a large green and yellow ball aloft and gazed at it in the hazy sunshine briefly, just long enough for Hawthorne to see that the fly was tinctured like the bugs that he had already been swatting off *Fanshawe* for the last hour.

Hawthorne sat up and watched Pierce cast his third offering into the pool. The fly floated just to the right of the spot where the trout were bumping the surface and retreating. The next cast again was too far right. Pierce compensated on the next cast but too far to the left.

Again, too far right.

Too far left.

To the left.

Too far right.

Too far left.

Right down the middle.

In an explosion of water, fisherman and fish both leaped up, fish pirouetting and descending gracefully back into the water before emerging again with a sloppier but fiercer dive as it took the line that raced through Pierce's offering hand.

Hawthorne turned his attention to the fisherman. With his thin lips curled into his almost mischievous grin and brown eyes alight with excitement, Hawthorne saw again why Pierce was so popular with their peers, both male and female. Frank's stunning good looks were augmented by a charismatic personality and warmth that made him all but irresistible. Nat Hawthorne would never admit it to Frank, but he relished every moment with his friend.

The fish having taken all the line that was allowed to it, Pierce now began the process of bringing line in, letting line out, bringing more line in, letting less line out until the brook trout at the end of his line glided into his hand resting in the water next to his right foot.

Frank detached the fly and flung the seventeen-inch ex-resident of the Kennebec River across the water where it landed at Nat's feet twitching and staring vacantly. Nat said quietly, "Next time be more discerning. Look for eyes, a handsome nose and a sunny disposition in your food. And friends."

* * *

Virginia: May 1823

Monticello was Thomas Jefferson's pride and joy. More of a laboratory than a home, James Madison enjoyed spending time at Monticello with its owner more than just about anything else he could think of. It was here that Jefferson was at his philosophical and vigorous best.

The third and fourth presidents sat under one of the many shade trees that Jefferson cultivated on his property. Madison's nephew's children played nearby beneath fruit trees of every variety. Jefferson spent his long career away from Monticello gathering flowers, trees, shrubs, vines and other horticultural fodder for his home. His efforts blossomed into almost four hundred fruit trees, more shade trees and countless strains of flowers. After pouring every dollar that he had and many, many more that he didn't have into Monticello, he was finally spending his last few years at home.

Jefferson's financial woes seemed to waft away in the floral scents of spring that inundated Monticello. In every other place, save one, Jefferson was myopic about his lack of funds. Madison, on the other hand, was equally in debt but always assumed that his frail physical condition could not withstand prolonged trepidation over his myriad liabilities.

The one other locale where Jefferson seemed to be able to disregard his monetary problems was the budding campus of the University of Virginia. With Jefferson's quiet but determined support the state legislature passed the charter for the University in 1819 and since that time Jefferson devoted himself to building the premier educational institution of the South. Every positive ounce of energy he had left was reserved for two things, Monticello and the University.

A slave, more enfeebled than even his master, set juice

between the two former chief executives. This refreshment was undoubtedly the product of Jefferson's juicer that he modified and, perhaps, perfected. While Monticello's gardens were grand, the interior of the dwelling was equally wondrous. Monticello both benefited and suffered from the lack of any tempering female influence. As a result, Jefferson's assorted inventions, gadgets and devices abounded in the house. It was fascinating to the visitor to marvel at all the contrivances that Jefferson crafted to make life more convenient, but Madison had to agree with Dolley's evaluation that Jefferson's home was not really a home at all, but a museum of not yet historic bric-a-brac.

As the slave shuffled back to the house with its juicer and other appliances, Madison watched as his eighty-year old friend struggled to lift his glass. Eight or nine months earlier Jefferson fell from the terrace while descending from the main house, badly breaking his left arm. He only recently had the sling removed but it was clear that the arm did not heal well and probably never would. With his right arm riddled with rheumatism, Jefferson was obviously fading fast physically.

Mentally, however, Madison marveled at Jefferson's alacrity. The courters of power in Washington still tried to curry Jefferson's favor on a daily basis, knowing that a word of confidence from the former President still was the surest path to popularity. And while Jefferson at least professed a desire to play no role in politics again, he understood his role as the most popular living figure from the Revolution.

Jefferson did not dole out platitudes freely or incautiously, however. On the contrary, he was still fully informed on every issue about which he spoke. He spoke now of President James Monroe.

"Jemmy, our friend has been something of a disappointment to me. He has refused my advice on appointments and seems determined to not exercise any influence toward the future President."

Madison nodded with a benign smile. He had been listening to Jefferson's "disappointment" with Monroe for a few years. The latest disillusionment resulted from Monroe's failure to appoint two overt friends of Jefferson's to prominent posts. "Tom, James must be President in his own right to exert any control. If he appointed Peyton and Duane he would have given credence to every cynic that trumpets that Monticello is the Capital rather than Washington. While I was content to rely heavily on your sound judgment and still able to remain secure, we've always known that James is not as, well, comfortable when he suspects that the people may not feel him to be his own man."

Jefferson grunted acknowledgment. "Yes, I know James' heart is right, but his judgment always has limited his effectiveness. How odd, no man has caused me as much anxiety as James has through the years, yet there has never been a truer friend." Jefferson paused to laboriously sip from his beverage. With a heavy series of breaths he continued. "It troubles me that James doesn't take a more active role in selecting a successor. I think he owes it to the party to exert some influence."

Madison's eyebrows arched in surprise. With age Jefferson had become embarrassingly candid, even to the point of exalting the interests of his Republican party. "Tom, on whose behalf would you have him exert influence?"

Jefferson shook his head, "I guess I'm not sure. But he appears to be content to let John Quincy Adams run the country now and I have heard that he considers him acceptable to lead the country next."

Madison knew the answer but allowed Jefferson the opportunity to vent his fears when he asked, "And what scares you about your prodigy?"

Jefferson gave Madison a look of feigned irritation. "I know, I'm probably as much to blame as any for John Quincy's prosperity. He's a fine man, but Jemmy, he's still a Federalist and consolidationist first and foremost. He'll take power from the states and make Washington omnipotent."

Madison chuckled, "I'm afraid you're overstating the case. After all there is only so much damage a President can do as you and I have demonstrated."

At this, Jefferson laughed but was undeterred. "Nonetheless, John Quincy is his father's son. He'll not compromise where he can bully nor will he listen when he doesn't have to."

Madison had to agree. There was little doubt that the two Adams were cut from the same stubborn cloth. He declined to be drawn into a dialogue about Massachusetts' most famous and most traduced family. "So, again, what are our friend the President's alternatives? General Jackson?"

Jefferson shrugged. "I think not. As much as I am pleased to see a man of such common origins be considered, he is mercurial. I'm not sure the office can withstand a man with his thirst for power. A military man with a temper hardly seems appropriate to lead the country."

Madison nodded assent. "Mr. Calhoun?"

Jefferson was vehement. "That is a man that will never be President. This Missouri Compromise foolishness should demonstrate that. The northerners will never allow someone with Mr. Calhoun's zeal for slavery to be President."

Madison bated his friend. "Ah then, certainly the architect of the Compromise, Mr. Clay, will be acceptable to the north."

"Jemmy, you know that that Compromise was nothing of the sort. It simply defines a battle line that will eventually threaten the Union. The abolitionists will cling to their idealistic notions of freedom for the Negroes while our southern brethren cling to slavery, not because it makes any economic sense but because their pride won't let them capitulate to the north. Good Lord, no one has understood the problem better than you. Slavery is not right in a free society, but neither is casting the Negro adrift when he is inferior intellectually and unwanted socially."

Madison listened to his own words which it seemed only Thomas Jefferson ever heeded. They were unique as large slaveholders in that they were also committed to emancipation. But, unlike the abolitionists, Jefferson and Madison favored deportation so that Negroes could reside with other men of color. Both were firmly convinced that the black man could not survive in the South where he would always be seen as subordinate, nor in the North where the abolitionists' tune would change when jobs began to go to Negroes willing to work for lower wages. Despite their assuredness that blacks were inferior to whites, that did not lead them to conclude that bondage was defensible. It was, to them, a matter of how to free the slaves, not if.

Madison stayed silent. Jefferson backed away from the Compromise which he knew he had already perorated to Madison about too many times. Waving his hand slowly he said, "Clay may suffer from the same delusions as General Jackson. He tries to be the friend to all but I think he would just as soon be King given half a chance. But, of the three, he may be best. At least he would walk a middle road on the slavery issue."

"But can the country afford a middle road? Sooner or later the matter must be resolved."

Jefferson nodded. "Oh, you know I agree and it will be resolved if it is allowed to take its course. I am afraid that people will not allow that to happen, however."

There was a long silence as the two figures who had grown to epic proportions reflected. Finally, Jefferson reached out and clutched Madison's arm. His large hand almost encircled the fourth President's tiny limb. They helped one another to their feet. "As you say Jemmy, 'tis not our problem, right? We'll stay out of it as old men should do. Come. Let me show you the saplings that the Latin American minister brought last week."

Madison followed gladly. The purpose of his visit was to see Thomas Jefferson the gardener and scientist, not the President. He came as James Madison, the friend and confidant, not the President.

* * *

Washington: January 1824

Martin Van Buren could hardly believe that he was relishing this night. The senator from New York uncharacteristically found himself a corner to watch the proceedings for a while before he started mingling in a party that leant itself to more mingling and charming than even Senator Van Buren could achieve in one night.

What made this all implausible to Van Buren was the fact that the hosts of the party were Secretary of State John Quincy Adams and his wife Louisa. Van Buren almost feigned an excuse to avoid appearing at the Adams' house because he could not imagine a party hosted by the stubborn and dour Adams as anything other than tortured. But, clearly, this was Louisa's show, not her husband's. English born and bred, Louisa was making the statement that Americans had a lot to learn about throwing a good party.

What made the rapidly apparent success of the gathering even more remarkable was its purpose. The Adams' fete was in honor of that most American of individuals, General Andrew Jackson and his recent military exploits. While there was nothing extraordinary about celebrating a country's military heroes, the fact that the almost virulently anti-social Adams' were not only throwing what was already being referred to as the "party of the decade", they were pulling out all the stops to glorify the roughhewn Jackson--the very essence of the common man that the whole Adams family was notorious for holding in contempt.

The Adams' reputedly issued over 900 invitations to the party and it appeared that very few people declined. Virtually every member of Congress was present and Van Buren knew that President Monroe would appear in due course as well. But aside from the usual Washington coterie that Van Buren saw all too frequently, there was a cavalcade of Jackson cronies, admirers and hangers on from the west. Most of them stood in awe of the grand specter that Louisa Adams created but were gradually beginning to function again. Louisa's decorations, fare and, indeed, the very pace of the party were classic European. Louisa placed small ensembles in various rooms throughout the house that favored the guests with music from different countries across the Atlantic. And it was rumored that Louisa herself would do a short recital later in the evening on the harp.

To Van Buren, it was all wondrous. Although he was the most powerful man in New York politics, he spent very little time around true frontiersmen and had never been to Europe. He was amused by the westerners' fascination with their first taste of high society. Yet he was even more delighted at those that frequented high society on a steady basis. They were clearly stupefied by the novel fashion that Louisa chose to entertain them. The Adams' seemed to be saying that they were willing to socialize with their fellow citizens but only in a manner that the monarchy would find acceptable.

Van Buren grew melancholy briefly. He knew that he would enjoy this evening, but he would enjoy it alone. While the senator, like Louisa Adams, loved the finer things that life had to offer, his own wife was more like John Quincy Adams. While Jannetje was not disagreeable as Adams so often was, she had preferred to avoid social gatherings and was, at best, circumspect at parties. But Van Buren had loved her with that odd force of nature that makes opposites long for one another. When she died from tuberculosis in 1819 leaving him and their four sons alone, the ever-energetic and optimistic Van Buren sank to his lowest depths and contemplated shucking his political career altogether.

After several months of despair, Van Buren came to realize that, for him, politics was the end in itself. As he poured himself into his partisan activities with greater resolve and ingenuity than ever, he drew greater satisfaction from his victories and progressed in overcoming his loss. He still thought of his wife often, but more in terms of how proud she would be of him than how much he missed her.

To say that Van Buren prospered politically in the last five years was a gross understatement. First, he was the architect behind two distinct subsets of New York's Tammany political machine. The direct subset was the Albany Regency that Van Buren tuned to be an agile and devastating force for making the Democratic party's voice heard. The second level was more visible then the Regency, the Bucktail faction of the Democrats. The Bucktails took their name from a rather absurd fixture to many of their followers' hats worn at some of their early rallies. Governor DeWitt Clinton's fellow Federalists derisively referred to the hat ornaments as the hind portion of a deer much to the glee of the Democrats who adopted the name as another weapon to identify their party with the common man.

At the pinnacle of both organizations was Martin Van Buren. While he did not openly associate himself with the Bucktails, they clearly drew their orders from his sergeants in the Regency. Through solid party discipline and loyalty, constant attention to the cultivation of voters and judicious use of the press, the Regency killed off the Federalists in New York, the last place that the species was to be found in force. Alexander Hamilton's native state was now firmly grounded in Jeffersonian politics.

Van Buren understood that more voters would always come from the middle and lower classes. Obviously, he argued, there were more people looking to improve their lot than there were not. Because of that fact, more people who felt powerless would exercise their right to vote than those who did not feel powerless. So, the Democrats courted agricultural interests, passed laws protecting debtors from being imprisoned and pushed for local control versus support from Washington.

The Democrats were not all like-minded individuals. They often had very different agendas. But this was where Van Buren was the most magical. He instilled in all party members the sense that by working for the collective good, their personal goals would ultimately be met. While his troops were not always uniform in their passion for the issue at hand, if the party stood firm, so did they. Van Buren accomplished this allegiance not with threats or intimidation, but with a velvet glove that stroked and caressed until cooperation was not only a fact but a religion.

As much as his ability to sense what most of the population wanted to hear and to coax his colleagues into unifying behind that theme, Van Buren mastered use of the press as no politician before him, though many tried. In particular, he forged an impervious bond with William Marcy, the editor of the *Northern Budget*. Together they used the *Budget* as the trumpet of the Democrats.

More than anything else though, Marcy and Van Buren used the *Budget* to eliminate the last obstacle to total domination by the party in New York. Through carefully timed and subtle stories it was insinuated that those close to DeWitt Clinton accepted personal gratuities in exchange for patronage in doling out work on the Erie Canal. The Canal resulted almost single-handedly from Clinton's acts of parturition. As those that failed to receive contracts for Canal work and those whose work ended read between the lines, the Governor's invulnerable popularity began to erode. Eventually, in a move that was grotesquely political, Clinton appointed his arch-nemesis Van Buren as State

Attorney General. Rather than corralling the opposition leader, the appointment proved to be the final nail for Clinton. Van Buren performed his duties ably and without fanfare while continuing as a state senator. The veiled attacks in the press on Clinton subsided but the Governor made it clear that he regarded Van Buren as an equal in terms of political clout in New York.

By 1820, Van Buren awakened from his short political exile caused by Jannetje's death and surveyed his prospects. New York was firmly in the grip of the Albany Regency which was in turn being run by the likes of Ben Butler, Bill Marcy and others that were devoted to the "Little Magician" as Marcy liked to call Van Buren. Van Buren decided the time had come to stake his claim in Washington as the man who controlled the state with more votes than any other. In 1821 he came to Washington as New York's representative to the United States Senate.

Both Van Buren's power and uniqueness were instantly recognized in the Capital. As slavery and differing economies demarcated the manner in which the northern states would vote versus the southern states, it was clear that New York would become the key to national power. Without Van Buren's Albany Regency, New York might have been just another northern state voting in favor of industry and against anything that propped up southern slavery. But Van Buren knew that the north and south needed one another, however odious the institution of slavery was to him personally.

Unlike any other country in history, the United States had the ability to be self-sufficient. The abundance of raw materials from the south and rapidly growing west fed northern industry. Trade with foreign countries made U.S. merchants wealthier, but the country could survive without such trade. So, unlike other countries, Van Buren knew that the United States could wait out any trade embargo because it would survive. The nation's economy would suffer and merchants and farmers would bemoan their lack of fortune, but the nation *would* survive.

For this reason, Van Buren viewed the slavery issue with alarm. The Missouri Compromise demonstrated how divided the country was. Like so many of his contemporaries and especially the man whom he admired most, Thomas Jefferson, Van Buren felt the whole Compromise episode boded ill for the Union. Secession or insurrection was prevented, but it seemed only temporarily. When another western territory was prime for statehood, the issue would have to be faced again. The alternative of foregoing further westward expansion and the vast riches that those regions promised was simply not an option.

Van Buren found slavery repugnant. But he found the practices of the northern abolitionists almost as reprehensible. It had not been that long since the northern states accepted the institution of slavery. Indeed, Abraham Van Buren maintained a stable of Negroes in Kinderhook, New York during Martin's youth. But gradually the cost of feeding and housing slaves began to make slavery uneconomic. So, the northern slaves were set free to work for subsistence wages when they could find a job, then were often assaulted by the northern whites whose jobs they had taken or who simply refused to abide working alongside a "nigger." Finally, many a northern black went further north to Canada or even to the South where they were recruited forcibly into slavery, but at least they could eat and had a roof over their heads.

Thus, Van Buren found the abolitionist cries of immorality hard to stomach. He was convinced that history would eventually repeat in the South. As an economic proposition, slavery was not viable. It would die as black families propagated and cost more and more to house and feed and keep healthy--for, of course, what good was an unhealthy, hungry slave?

But southerners were proud. Many already recognized that slavery was probably costing them money. But they were not going to allow a crowd of northern zealots to preach to them about morality. There was also the very real problem of what to do with the freed slaves. Many a southern white feared for the safety of his family if his slaves' shackles were removed. Visions of slaughter and abolitionist-fueled retribution furrowed his brow. And the southern slave owners who did recognize the need to eliminate the institution also knew that the North would not want the blacks heading to northern cities (and taking jobs for lower wages) and their "moral" communities.

With his control over New York votes and his Jeffersonian

principles, Van Buren did not support sectional causes or candidates--he supported maintenance of the Union which in turn benefited New York. And benefiting New York was what mattered most to Van Buren. The mere fact that a politician or idea was southern in origin meant nothing to Van Buren. If the man or the cause would further the goal of natural extinction of slavery versus conflict, would strengthen the dependency of the North and South on one another and would not affect New York's status as the ultimate arbiter, Senator Van Buren could be counted on to insure success.

With a Presidential election looming at the close of the year, Van Buren's influence grew particularly important. But Van Buren knew that his influence would be negligible this one time. For close to a year he quietly built support for Monroe's Secretary of Treasury, William Crawford of Georgia. To Van Buren, Crawford was the perfect compromise candidate between north and south; Crawford would be acceptable to the South being a southerner but sufficiently opposed to slavery to appease the North.

In the last three months, however, Van Buren's plan unraveled as Crawford suffered a succession of strokes that all but removed him from the race. Crawford was adamant that he could still perform if elected and, although it was clear to Van Buren that he could not, Van Buren continued his support. To Van Buren there was no firmer political principle than loyalty.

So, Van Buren would steer the Regency to support Crawford while the remainder of the country voted otherwise. Four other candidates emerged and they were all at this, the party of the decade.

Van Buren saw Secretary of War John Calhoun standing beneath a wreath of pine and laurel talking with a group of fellow southerners. Calhoun was a menacing man that, like Van Buren, was a States rights man. But Calhoun believed that the States rights should prevail even at the cost of dissolution of the Union. Further, Calhoun was from South Carolina and not only owned slaves, he was one of the most ardent and outspoken supporters of the institution. Van Buren knew that Calhoun would never be President. At best, he would be a viable Vice Presidential option, bringing along the provincial support he commanded. No, thought Van Buren, Calhoun is a powerful man from a puny little southern state.

The next possibility was the guest of honor. It was said that despite public protests to the contrary, Andy Jackson wanted very much to be President. His detractors accused him of megalomania and cried that he was far too volatile for the office. But there was little doubt that the hero of New Orleans could garner votes if he chose to run. Van Buren only recently befriended the man after the Tennessee legislature selected Jackson to serve in the Senate. Van Buren was determined to get to know the General and his predilections better.

The last two candidates had slipped behind a small string quartet that was playing a crisp piece that Van Buren could barely discern. He was located about halfway between the string players and a harpsichord virtuoso. The musicians were strategically placed to allow no guest to be without musical accompaniment. It was only at a few odd spots in the Adams' home such as where Van Buren was ensconced that the music overlapped. Still, it was not displeasing to the ear. Especially to these untrained American ears that were mesmerized by these new, enchanting strains.

Van Buren watched Henry Clay and John Quincy Adams' discussion behind the string quartet with interest. It was well known that the Secretary of State and the Congressman from Kentucky had little use for one another. So, it struck Van Buren as odd that these two men would seclude themselves to reduce the chances of their conversation being for public consumption. Van Buren personally liked Clay but they disagreed on most issues. That was, Van Buren disagreed on those few issues where Clay took a clear stand. And therein lay the problem with the gregarious Kentuckian; he rarely took a substantive stand that one could trace back to him. Van Buren knew that high profile offices like Governor and President required one to take a stand, even if that stand changed after the election. No, Van Buren thought, Clay is a powerful man from a puny little western state.

John Quincy Adams was not a candidate because of his charm, his record or even his power. He was a candidate because he was Secretary of State. It was becoming tradition for the Secretary of State to accede to the Presidency. Not that Adams failed as head of the State Department. On the contrary, he elevated the United States to the level of a country to be reckoned with by obtaining Florida from the Spanish, arranging joint occupation of the Oregon territories with Great Britain and writing the manifesto for the President that was now called the Monroe Doctrine. The Doctrine gave notice that the U.S. was willing to go to war with any European power attempting to meddle in the Western Hemisphere.

But Adams was a bastard. He was dogmatic, mean-spirited and, worst of all, he grew up in the monarchal countries of Europe imbued with a sense that a central government was always preferable to a series of semi-autonomous localized bodies. Adams had his followers who would vote for him because he was the closest candidate to the Federalist principles that still resided in the hearts of many of the wealthy and influential. Even if it was now unfashionable to call such principles by name.

Van Buren wondered if this whole gathering was a "thank you" of sorts from Adams and Clay to Jackson for even making it possible for them to be considered for the Presidency. Because Jackson trounced the British in the swamps of Louisiana in a battle that was meaningless while Adams and Clay were concluding the treaty ending the war, very few people noted the fact that the treaty constituted surrender by the Americans. While the Americans reveled in the heroism of "Old Hickory" as Jackson was affectionately called, the British cared little about New Orleans. They had won the war. So, because of the fortuitous confluence of events, Adams and Clay never experienced the ignominy of negotiating the country's surrender to the despised Brits.

Van Buren reckoned that Clay would do well in Kentucky but not elsewhere. Adams would fare well in the populous north but definitely not in the South. Jackson would draw votes primarily in the South but was popular throughout the country. The success of his candidacy depended on his ability to overcome Van Buren's delivery of New York to the incapacitated Crawford and the handful of western and southern votes that Clay and Calhoun would keep from the General.

The election of 1824 would be close and Van Buren despaired that his pledge to William Crawford would keep him from playing a role in choosing Monroe's successor. But as he watched John Quincy Adams shake his head at the obvious beseeching of Henry Clay, the Little Magician decided that it was not too early to start studying the options for the election of 1828 when Van Buren would once again be able to throw the weight of New York behind his choice for President. He had not achieved control in Washington as completely as he had in New York. Yet.

He accepted a refill of his glass of madeira and eased himself out of the corner to allow the guests to pay homage to the key to New York. And so the key to New York could pay homage to the guest of honor.

PART II

THE CORRUPT BARGAIN AND OLD HICKORY

(1825-1837)

Chapter 1:
John Quincy Adams

He was rash. For twenty years John Quincy Adams methodically went about following in his father's footsteps, not hoping, but planning, to ascend to the Presidency. Now that he accomplished the goal, he knew that the prize was empty. Like the St. Petersburg winters, his administration was doomed to bone-chilling stagnation with little or no hope of light.

Adams sat in a small room a few blocks from his future home, the house that James Monroe would continue to occupy for a couple more weeks. Usually a prolific writer, Adams was unable to focus sufficiently to write a simple letter to his father. All he could think about was how much his own term already looked like that of John Adams'. He entered the Presidency as a man without any real party support and a constituency that could hardly be described as rabidly loyal. He was the worst of elected officials, chosen because the other candidates were deemed unacceptable. Even his father started his term with the benefit of a population that viewed him as a hero of the Revolutionary.

To make matters worse, John Quincy Adams was not even the popular choice. General Andrew Jackson received more popular and electoral votes than Adams. Adams did finish well ahead of William Crawford of Georgia who, in turn, finished slightly ahead of Henry Clay. But none of the candidates received a majority of the electoral votes. Under the twelfth amendment to the Constitution, the election was to be decided in the House of Representatives. At that point, Adams made the mistake that he already knew would cripple his Presidency.

Once the election went to the House, Henry Clay was no longer a candidate, having received the fewest votes in the general election. Thus, the Presidency would go to whomever Clay threw his support. Clay immediately approached Adams and reiterated the very subject that he raised prior to the election--what to do in the event of a tie. For several months, Clay warned Adams that a tie was inevitable but Adams ignored his admonitions. Adams served with Clay in negotiating the Treaty of Ghent and dealt with him on foreign policy issues for the last eight years as Secretary of State. Adams always expended as little energy as possible on Clay, shrugging him off as an uncouth westerner of little or no substance. What little interaction the men had was usually of the petty, demeaning nature.

But Adams overlooked Clay's greatest asset. Henry Clay was an extraordinary politician with the ability to assess outcomes far in advance of their occurrence. Clay accurately predicted the result of the election of 1824 before the first vote was ever cast.

When the lack of any majority was manifest, Clay was ready. He called on Adams and pointed out that he was correct in his assessment of the election. To this Adams begrudgingly acceded. Clay's next statement, however, caught Adams completely off-guard. He still recalled Clay jabbing his finger into his chest and saying, "Adams, you and I are all that stand in the way of that crazy man becoming President."

Adams frowned at Clay's characterization of Jackson but had to agree that Jackson was certainly volatile. Clay went on to say, "Give me your word that I will have a voice in your administration and I will see that you have an administration."

Adams had answered cautiously. "A diplomatic post would certainly be..."

Clay had snapped, "Dammit Adams! Don't talk to the man who is going to make you President about any damned foreign assignment where he'll stay conveniently out of your damn way! I'm talking about State."

Adams stared, incredulous. He thought about laughing but thought otherwise. "You recognize that I would rely on my own judgment and experience far more than any Cabinet member. I am qualified in that regard, I feel."

Clay resisted the temptation to chastise Adams for his arrogance. He simply replied, "All I ask is that you listen."

Adams nodded and thus became President. After a short period, he made his Cabinet announcement including Clay as Secretary of State. The outcry was deafening. A Jacksonian paper declared the deal a "corrupt bargain" and portrayed General Jackson as the poor westerner that once again fell prey to eastern conniving.

Adams deplored his decision. How many times since that conversation had it occurred to him that Clay had no choice but to support Adams? For Clay to support Jackson would have meant capitulation to Clay's only challenger for western leadership. And not even Clay's moral fungibility would allow him to support Crawford. Crawford's physical ailments eliminated him as a viable candidate. No, ultimately, state department or not, Clay would have come to Adams who Adams knew Clay detested as much as *he* detested Clay. And it was their well-known mutual disregard for one another that caused the public to shake its head in disbelief at the hypocrisy of its new President and Secretary of State.

In one short conversation, John Quincy Adams fell for Henry Clay's bluff and realized once again that it was dangerous to underestimate a talented politician. Adams thought about that one night in Ghent when he didn't work. He wished he had played poker with Henry Clay then, instead of now.

* * *

April 1825

The newest Congressman from Tennessee was all business. James Knox Polk was elected to come to Washington to represent his adopted home state with the assistance of none other than the hero of New Orleans himself, Andy Jackson. Jim developed a friendship with the General almost rivaling that of his own father's amity with Old Hickory. After Jim expressed an interest in politics there was very little in the way of campaigning left to be done once Andrew Jackson got wind of young Jim's ambitions.

Jim's ascension also pleased Samuel Polk. His father seemed to hold his eldest son in some esteem for the first time. Jim's serious demeanor would not cause him to progress rapidly in the back-stroking world of politics but Samuel knew that his son's determination would allow him to build a solid reputation for results and adherence to his promises. There were two paths to success in politics, charm or extremely hard work. James Knox Polk would never fare well on the former path but few could match him step for step on the latter path. His consumption with whatever current task was at hand bordered on maniacal.

Jim married his schoolmate Sarah Childress on January 1 of the year before. Just as his mother suspected at his graduation from the University of North Carolina, Jim was taken with the much younger Sarah. After graduation, they courted off and on for several years before Jim realized that he was, indeed, smitten. Their marriage was not grounded in romance, however, it was fused by an unusual intellectual respect. They were never happier than when they were debating a topic of current interest.

Jim and Sarah were now engaged in the act which they considered nothing more than a marital obligation. For over a year they tried to conceive a child with no success. Given their lack of success their love-making was more precautionary than anything else, just in case they could have children. Sarah was a devout Presbyterian who believed in sex only for procreation purposes. Their failure to procreate left Jim with little desire as he had for all things that thwarted him.

Their bodies were far more clothed than not as little regard was given to preliminary tenderness or sentiment. Neither felt the warmth of the other except for perfunctory kissing that accomplished the goal of arousal, to the extent necessary. With the same regimented focus that Jim might apply to reviewing a proposed bill or arguing with a colleague, he did his duty.

His work done, Jim gathered his sleeping garments again. Sarah closed her eyes momentarily and then did the same. She was twenty-one years old and the wife of a young man that was the prodigy of the country's most popular man. Her husband respected her intelligence and her ability to hold her own in any discussion. She had all this, so she rationalized: If God meant her to have children too, he was probably being too benevolent.

She expressed this sentiment to Jim before when he seemed to despair at their lack of offspring. Jim would nod and, like he did with his mother for so many years, not tell his wife of his doubts about the whims and caprice of a higher being. Likewise, he did not tell his wife that their lack of children probably had more to do with Dr. McDowell, a tumbler of brandy and the scar on his genitalia than the arbitrary judgment of a deity.

* * *

Virginia: October 1825

Thomas Jefferson, James Madison and James Monroe sat in chairs on the dais along with other members of the Board of Governors of the University of Virginia. They were old. Jefferson had been declining for years and, on this day, seemed to have reached the bottom. Madison was always frail and sickly looking and certainly was not getting any less so. But now even the dashing if somewhat gangly Monroe clearly lost the battle for eternal youth. His hair was gray and disheveled. His eyes were still warm but not bright.

Monroe watched his friend Jefferson with concern. They were listening to Chapman Johnson exhort the students before them to confess their sins. The night before a crowd of young scholars obviously violated the University's prohibition of alcohol on campus and made the mistake of taking their activities from a mildly disruptive frolic to a destructive and sordid riot. The students' antipathy for two British professors manifested itself in the way of drunks. They hurled rocks and their spent bottles through the windows of the educators' offices while further showering the cowering professors with the type of vile invective that the angriest of sober men could not fathom.

The student body was now assembled before the Board of Governors. Chapman Johnson was a large man with extraordinary oratory skills. One of Virginia's finest lawyers, he was now attempting to apply the same magic he exerted on many a jury to the young minds before him. And he was failing. Monroe gazed at the sea of smirking faces before him knowing that no revelations would be forthcoming soon.

Monroe watched Jefferson carefully. He knew that Madison was having the same thoughts. Here sat their friend whose many accomplishments were mere window dressing in his own mind compared to the building of this University. The school was Jefferson's dream for as long as either of them remembered. Monroe recalled he and Madison's surprise when Jefferson told them he had already written his own epitaph. Jefferson's tombstone would not mention that he was President, Vice President, Secretary of State or any of his other public offices. It would simply report that he had written the Declaration of Independence and was the father of the University of Virginia.

Jefferson fretted over the construction and funding of the University more than any of the countless other projects in his life. He sent emissaries around the world to recruit the finest scholars that could be secured to teach. He threw off the shackles of age and demonstrated the radiance of youth once again at the dedication of the new school.

The two professors who bore the brunt of the students' intoxicated hostility, George Long and Thomas Key, were perfect examples of Jefferson's zeal for this, the culmination and repository of his remarkable experiences and wisdom. These British scholars came to America not because the University could offer them the type of salary that makes one leave his home but because Jefferson's recruiters painted a visage of an institution devoid of the strictures and confining thought that marked typical University curriculum. Key, a mathematician and Long, a linguist, came to Charlottesville with high hopes of breaking new ground in education. As he did with a whole country, Jefferson's dream was a University focused not on the molding of young minds but on the exchange of ideas. Jefferson fervently believed that the passion that led to the American Revolution was the product not of the blind acceptance of what one learns from his elders but from the generation and embracing of one's own ideas.

It was Jefferson's conception of his University that led to its current plight. His professors, particularly Long and Key, were scholars first and educators and disciplinarians somewhere thereafter. As a result, the young University of Virginia already had more campus disturbances than any other college in the United States and certainly more than Great Britain ever saw.

This latest disturbance was the last in a series of incidents that left the Board exasperated and the faculty enraged. Jefferson clutched Long and Key's proffered resignations in his hand. Many more professors were hinting that they too were contemplating leaving. The grand experiment in education was simply not working out.

Thomas Jefferson faced similar sentiments during the formative years of the nation. At times, he himself felt that his concept of a government by the people was too idealistic to ever work. But there were many men who shared his dream. Ultimately the Declaration of Independence was signed and the country struggled to its feet and, while it tripped and limped from time to time, it managed to stay there.

But here, though many supported Jefferson's dream, no one shared his fervor for making it succeed. Jefferson no longer had the stamina to solve the University's many problems during its incubation period.

Monroe pitied his friend. So odd, he thought, that a man of so many accomplishments should look so defeated. Despite all his service, Jefferson was essentially penniless. Mired in debt and with a family of only one daughter who loved her father dearly but was married to a cruel alcoholic who blamed Jefferson for his misfortunes, Jefferson seemed to have so little to show for all his brilliance and popularity.

Chapman Johnson gave up. He sat down in his chair and crossed his arms defiantly. He failed to win over this jury with charm first and threats last. An uncomfortable silence followed. Out of the corner of his eye, Monroe saw Jefferson's head drop and his quivering arthritic hands claw through his gray mane. There was a heavy sigh and all eyes, including the students, looked at Jefferson.

Finally, the father of the University of Virginia tried to

speak. His voice was weak and could only have been heard in the cavernous silence of the hall. "I have always believed that this...would be...a place for..."

His voice trailed off and he turned toward Madison and Monroe seated to his left. Monroe wanted more than anything he had ever done to reach over and brush the tear from Jefferson's cheek. But he knew his friend's pride would not allow it. Instead, he and the fourth President rose and helped the third President to his feet and, with his arms linked through theirs, descended from the dais and shuffled down the aisle between the students. As the three Presidents made their way, fourteen extremely sober young men wiped the tears from their eyes and stood to unburden their consciences.

* * *

Massachusetts: July 1826

The Adams house in Quincy, Massachusetts was by no means the masterpiece of architecture, horticulture and innovation that Jefferson's Monticello represented. It was, instead, a simple two story home with a modest hedgerow out front. The only hint of luxury to set it apart from other typical homes in this small village south of Boston was the adjoining structure that housed the Adams' impressive library. A single room with a deck encircling shelves of books that reached the ceiling was almost intimidating to the unschooled. But few besides the second and sixth Presidents were familiar with the library. John Adams and his son, John Quincy, used the library as their sanctuary on those rare occasions that either of them actually inhabited the little house in Quincy. Otherwise the library sat empty.

The library had sat empty for several months now. John Quincy Adams was living in the President's House apparently achieving what no one thought was possible--he was proving to be a less popular President than his father. John Adams, on the other hand, was residing at the house in Quincy, but not for long. John Adams was dying. It was, of all days, July 4th.

Many years before, the Adams' installed a system of bells in their house to summon servants. There was a row of seven bells in the kitchen, each attached to a thin rope that extended to six different parts of the house and the library. The sparse Adams household staff already lost their reflexive response to turn and see which bell was ringing (or, if they heard the bell from another room, which bell was still swaying) in the last month. The only bell that rang any more was from John Adams' study.

Adams was ninety years old. He had known he was dying since he was forty. He spent fifty years making sure that his place in history was secure by meticulously protecting every bit of memorabilia that he engendered. This small house in Quincy became the living Adams' shrine to the dead Adams. He kept every letter he received from Thomas Jefferson, from his son and every other potentially historic figure he knew. His furniture was finished, refinished and preserved with the greatest of care. His domestic staff whispered to one another constantly complaining of his pathological insistence on not disturbing any small memento that might mark his fame.

He stayed irascible to the last. In fact, since Abby died eight years before he had become almost unbearable. The ego that Abby always held in check spiraled out of control. Adams alone among his Revolutionary contemporaries understood the profound nature of the country they founded and was certain that history would appreciate his enormous contributions far more than he was ever appreciated during his life.

Unfortunately for his friends, family and servants he remained lucid and able to cling to his obsession with posterity well into his ninetieth year. His bloated body failed him years before but his mind stayed sharp. He maintained a torrid pace of correspondence determined to commit to writing every last idea on every last thing that he had an idea or opinion about.

His spirits soared the year before when John Quincy became President. His son, Abby and Thomas Jefferson were the only people he ever acknowledged as capable of challenging him intellectually. He saw in his son's Presidency the chance to finally vindicate the family name and to draw attention to not only his son's brilliance but to his own personally glorified view of his own, again, unappreciated administration.

But, almost from its inception, John Quincy Adams' term went poorly. By the end of his son's first year as Chief Executive, Adams knew that he and his son's almost maniacal distrust of political parties was well-founded. Party politics was gaining momentum as politicians rallied around loosely constructed ideologies that were propped up by deals and, ultimately, money. And the Adams' long recognized in their diatribes against political parties that when elections became contests of personality and clubs (i.e., parties) rather than of ideas and principles, the Revolution was lost.

John Adams knew that his son would not serve a second term. Andrew Jackson's party machine was already attacking him mercilessly and the next election was three years away. The Revolution was lost.

In his carefully preserved study the second President had little company. Propped in his favorite chair, he wheezed in an irregular pattern. A doctor came by the day before but assured the servants that there was nothing to be done. He slipped in and out of consciousness but said little. At dawn, he awakened briefly and acknowledged that it was the fourth of July. At one o'clock he awoke again. A servant watched him closely as his eyes narrowed and an ironic attempt at a grin appeared. With a final burst of energy, he exhaled "Thomas Jefferson survives!" With that his eyes closed and did not open again. That evening as celebrations began across the country marking the fiftieth anniversary of the signing of the Declaration of Independence, the rotund little man who always begrudged the fact that Thomas Jefferson received the credit for the document they wrote together, died. The servant taking his turn watching the former President die informed the rest of the staff and they began preparations for a small funeral.

* * *

Two days later a message was delivered to the Adams house. It stated simply that Thomas Jefferson died in the early afternoon of July 4, 1826.

* * *

Tennessee: December 1828

In slightly less than three months Andrew Jackson, at long last, would be sworn in as President of the United States. At least that was his right and what every citizen in the United States expected. The Tennessee legislature nominated him for the Presidency in 1825, the same year that John Quincy Adams took office after the "Corrupt Bargain" with Henry Clay in the election of 1824. So, both literally and figuratively, Jackson campaigned throughout Adams' presidency.

Jackson's supporters were outraged by Adams' deal that made Henry Clay Secretary of State. In response, they began an onslaught of invective and slander that made it impossible for Adams to push his nationalistic agenda for a stronger central government that would procure everything from a national highway system to public education. Every move that Adams made was countered by Congress or a none too subtle Jacksonian newspaper article referencing the Corrupt Bargain. Led by the tireless efforts of James Polk of Tennessee, the young representative that owed his whole political life to Jackson, Congress managed to sidetrack every Administration initiative.

For three years Jackson's backers accused Adams of being an effeminate snob raised in Europe that, unlike their candidate, knew little of the common man and his problems. At first, Adams' partisans attempted to fight back but were restrained by the President who believed that the Jackson attacks were simply the sour grapes of the losers of an election and would subside. It was not until late in 1827 that Adams realized that the campaign for the 1828 election started in 1825. By then it was too late. In November, Jackson won in a landslide.

It was Christmas day. Jackson sat alone in his mansion overlooking his plantation, the Hermitage. As he peered out the window at the misty rain that shrouded the long drive to his door, he contemplated what he never thought possible. Not accepting the Presidency.

He spent the last twelve years positioning himself to be the chief executive. After the Battle of New Orleans, Old Hickory became a national hero that appealed to the common man as the symbol of democracy. Unlike Jefferson, Madison, Monroe and the Adams', Jackson rose from poverty to fight for his country, make a name for himself and, to some, miraculously become a candidate for President. Many were proclaiming that it could only happen in America.

For his part, Jackson publicly denied any interest in being President. But privately (and this was obvious to even the most casual observer), he wanted to live in the White House and show up every aristocratic bastard he ever cursed in his life.

The results of the election were announced just a few days before. But Jackson was not jubilant. He was told as he sat by Rachel's bedside and waived the messenger off without looking up from his wife's visage. When she died a few hours later, he reacted with bitterness and swore revenge on John Quincy Adams and every man who supported him.

Two weeks before, Rachel was well. She dreaded the thought of living in Washington but she finally came to accept the inevitable and began to prepare for the move east. Throughout the campaign, Jackson did his best to insulate Rachel from the more outlandish stories that his opponents circulated about him. By late in the campaign Adams' men realized they were in an almost hopeless situation and began to fight the Jackson campaign's inflammatory stories with fire. At first Jackson was perturbed when the story of the mulatto child that Jackson delivered into the arms of a Kentucky widow was twisted to describe the child as Jackson's bastard son by a slave. Then Jackson was incensed when a story appeared stating that Jackson himself was mulatto. But Jackson's rage reached new heights for an already legendary temper when stories began to circulate that Mrs. Jackson was an adulterer. It was a well-known fact, the stories ran, that the Jacksons had wed while Mrs. Jackson was still married to Lewis Robards. The stories did not detail the misunderstanding as to when Robards obtained his divorce from Rachel. She was purposefully portrayed as a wanton bigamist.

Despite her husband's wrath, Rachel never saw or heard of the stories due to his extraordinary efforts. In short, he threatened to kill any person that told her of the stories. So, well after the election was over, but before the results were known, Rachel took her usual trek into town. She assumed her familiar spot at the General Store on the bench by the apple barrel, a rotund old lady quietly puffing an old corncob pipe. The ladies of Nashville snickered among themselves for months at the thought of Rachel lolling about the President's mansion smoking her pipe and reading her Bible among the dignitaries and royalty. But such joking was done in the most hushed of tones for fear of arousing General Jackson's ire whose attachment to this dumpy old woman they could not fathom.

While her order was filled, she thumbed through the pile of handbills and advertisements sitting on the barrel. A pro-Adams leaflet lingering from the campaign fell out. In bold letters it asked,

OUGHT A CONVICTED ADULTERESS AND HER PARAMOUR HUSBAND TO BE PLACED IN THE HIGHEST OFFICES OF THIS FREE AND CHRISTIAN LAND?

She never responded to the storekeeper's offer of assistance. She stumbled out the door and down the street to her cousin's newspaper office. She called out in a strangled voice. No one answered. She flung current issues of the paper from a pile and read the vituperative prose that this pro-Jackson paper printed in response to the Adams press' attacks all through October. As she read she slumped farther and farther into a corner obscured by the mounds of type comprehending for the first time that she, as much as anyone or anything, was at issue in the campaign. She wept violently at first and then quietly in an almost fetal position. Hours later her cousin found her, rocking back and forth, deranged.

The first stroke came two days later. Jackson drew hope when she seemed to come around but plunged into grief when she had another and died three days before Christmas. Grief was an odd phenomenon for Andrew Jackson. He did not weep. He was not morose. There was not a man alive who could remember Jackson showing any emotions other than happiness and anger. So, his grief manifested itself in a grim but determined jaw that matched vacant yet malevolent eyes.

He sat at her funeral on Christmas eve not acknowledging or even realizing that a huge throng turned out to either support or catch a glimpse of their soon-to-be President. Some ten thousand people braved the December freeze to watch Mrs. Jackson be buried. Many came away wondering how this feral looking man could be one of them. He looked anything but common.

Now, with white hair disheveled and looking like the very flames that engulfed his thoughts Jackson was an apparition staring through the streaked pane. He did not dwell on the loss of his wife. He dwelled instead on the loss of his will. He silently cursed those that slandered Rachel. But the thrust of his venom was concentrated on Adams.

Adams could have stopped the stories about Rachel. While Jackson's men may have gone too far, they knew better than to attack a man's wife. Jackson swore in a quiet hiss that he would never forgive Adams for the murder of his wife.

It all seemed clear to Jackson now. Adams threw the "party of the decade" for Jackson after the Battle of New Orleans knowing full well that Jackson had become a viable candidate for the Presidency. Adams set aside his aristocratic breeding for a night to consort with the common man and keep his name in the forefront of Presidential aspirants. Then he and Henry Clay conspired to deny the General his rightful victory. When he was found out, Adams unleashed his last shot; the attacks on Rachel. Jackson seethed at his stupidity in ever ascribing honorable intentions to an aristocratic coward like John Quincy Adams. But, as a result, Jackson blamed his own naiveté for Rachel's death.

His mind had no room for planning his administration now; only for showering his detractors with hatred. Rachel said many a time during the campaign that she would "rather be a doorkeeper in the house of God than to live in that palace at Washington." In a perverse way, Rachel's antipathy for Washington convinced many voters that Jackson was indeed "one of them." Now, however, Jackson agreed with his wife's sentiments. He never went into a battle with less than his whole heart being in it. He was sixty-one years old and not about to change. He squinted, not to see, but to emphasize to himself that he would honor Rachel's wish. For once, he would stay at the Hermitage with her. He would not go to "that palace at Washington."

* * *

Bogota, Columbia: March 1829

General/Governor/Congressman and now Foreign Minister William Henry Harrison didn't know whether to laugh or cry. He tossed the crumpled message into the air and slumped. He laid his head back on a bench positioned in the middle of his increasingly famous garden in this mansion situated high on a hill overlooking the already absurdly high town of Bogota. At over 8000 feet in elevation, Bogota was ideal as a defensive fortress but left a lot to be desired as a capital. Having won his revolutionary war to create an independent Colombia that included parts of Spain's former provinces of Ecuador, Venezuela and New Granada, Simon Antonio de la Santisma Trinidad Bolivar was now faced with the task of setting up a government and actually governing. Like so many revolutionaries before and since, he was finding the ends to be far less exciting than the means.

Bolivar was still miraculously popular in his new country despite the widely accepted fact that things were better before the Revolution. The people of Colombia were odd, Harrison decided. They seemed to view lawlessness with a detachment that allowed them to rationalize that, while Bolivar was the cause of the slaughter and pilfering that raged among them, he was not to blame. Indeed, Harrison had been in Bogota for more than a month and had not been granted an audience with the self-proclaimed dictator for life. The press of business was the official excuse, but those near Bolivar assured Harrison that the dictator was not busy; he was sick and depressed.

For the better part of two years, Colombia's government had been in shambles. Bolivar's lieutenants staked out their bounty throughout the new country by enslaving the locals and warring with their former brothers in arms to gain even more territory for their fiefdoms. Bolivar was dismayed, but did little beyond trying to figure out what to do with his hard-fought victory and to battle the disease wracking his body. He was apparently paying the price for his many encounters with the irresistible senoritas that he "liberated" in villages throughout the republic of Colombia.

Colombians were not just harming one another, however. They were looting and robbing from anyone within striking distance, including United States merchant ships. At first, President Adams naively saw the Colombian revolution as a reenactment of his own country's liberation with Bolivar filling the role of George Washington, one of the President's few idols and mentors. As it became clear that Bolivar had very little interest in democracy as a theory much less in practice, the President lost interest. As a result, Adams' Secretary of State was able to pay back Harrison for his assistance in securing Ohio for Clay in the Presidential election of 1824. While not enough to secure the Presidency, Harrison's assistance gave Clay the leverage he needed to convince Adams that Clay's support was the key to Adams becoming President. In receiving the Secretary of State post in return, Clay was content to build up political goodwill while the President tended to foreign affairs himself. Adams made it clear from the start that he had no intention of entrusting such matters to Clay. The specter of the title with no responsibilities suited Clay just fine.

When it was clear that Colombia would be just another backward republic under despotic rule, Clay seized Adams' indifference to have Harrison appointed. Harrison gratefully accepted his orders to address offenses against United States merchants with Bolivar. His acceptance was couched with an official avowal of his pleasure in serving his country again. Privately, however, both he and Clay knew that Harrison was a desperate man. His country never fully compensated him for his military service and his years as Congressman were less than lucrative. With nearly a dozen children to feed and scores of debts, Harrison was drowning in a sea of creditors that was engulfing him more each day. A foreign minister's salary of $9000 per year would not solve all his problems but it would relieve some of the burden.

In November, Harrison boarded a creaking, retired warship/boat named the Erie in New York. After a month and a half of being tossed about by the violent autumn winds of the Caribbean, the Erie landed at the port of Maracaibo. From there the 750-mile trek to Bogota began. Along the way Harrison stayed in small villages, camped at the feet of stupendous waterfalls and feasted on wild game that was more plentiful and exotic than anything Indiana had to offer. He climbed until he was sure he must be near the gates of heaven. The scenery never betrayed such a conclusion.

Yet despite the natural splendor, Harrison was more dismayed than enthralled by what he saw. Bolivar's henchmen freely captured and subjugated men for their armies shackling them in chains until they were needed to fight. They then were sent into battle with the assurance that if they did not comport themselves with ferocity against their "adversaries," they would die. Women were also led away as slaves for even more base reasons.

Tucked away in these mountains Harrison saw children unclothed and unfed cowering at his approach. At a young age they learned that any stranger meant, at a minimum, terror and, more likely, destruction. As a man who helped tame the western frontier for United States settlers by subduing the Indians, Harrison could not help drawing comparisons between those he conquered and the "liberators" he watched now. The "savages" he battled, manipulated and negotiated with at home were frighteningly advanced compared to the citizens of this lawless republic.

More remarkable was the almost universal adherence to the legend of Bolivar. In every village, Harrison was accosted by local leaders who begged him to inform Bolivar of conditions. Harrison, through a translator, routinely replied that he had strict instructions to stay out of local affairs. Undaunted, the Colombians would press him with assurances that Bolivar would listen to a fellow soldier and be indignant at the compromise of his Revolution. Harrison would listen, nod and decline to inform these desperate people that he suspected that Bolivar saw his work as done.

Harrison's bedraggled caravan reached Bogota in early February. The minister immediately ensconced himself in the abandoned mansion of a wealthy victim of the revolution and began to make his futile overtures for an audience with Bolivar. While he attempted to feign vexation with Bolivar's snub, he already had seen enough of this country to know that there was little the dictator could do to control the piracy of American ships and travelers. While he intended to complete his assignment, he saw little urgency in the matter.

In the meantime, he came to enjoy his status as a novelty in this chaotic land. A quiet foreigner cultivating his garden of alien flora from a land he called Indiana. Harrison was amazed at how the seedlings he carried across an ocean and jungle flourished in this mountain valley. Among the locals, Harrison's garden was becoming a phenomenon.

He sat now in the splendor of herbs, flowers, shrubs and trees and stared at the clear blue sky that only occurs at such rarefied altitudes. Tomorrow, in Washington, Andrew Jackson would become the seventh President of the United States. While Harrison was not a great admirer of the hero of New Orleans, his ascendancy did not alarm the hero of Tippecanoe. Indeed, at the time Harrison left for Colombia, he fully expected that Jackson would handily defeat John Quincy Adams. This expectation was fulfilled. Still, Harrison did not believe there would be any implication for his post. He assumed that, as a soldier, Jackson would have confidence in Harrison and continue his appointment.

But the message lying in the bramble at the Minister's feet foretold another fate for Harrison. Sent in January by a Congressional colleague from Ohio, the message warned Harrison that he should begin to reassess his future. Jackson made it clear that Martin Van Buren would be his Secretary of State.

Harrison met Van Buren during his term in Congress. While he found Van Buren to be something of a dandy, he had no real dislike of the man. Unlike the soldier Andrew Jackson, however, Van Buren was first and only a politician.

Van Buren achieved power and respect in Washington in a manner that Harrison understood but could never undertake. Van Buren knew that support was built through the well timed and well placed parceling out of patronage and a cohesive, united machine. Van Buren was the new politician, not of ideas and principles, but of political parties, deals and favors. The election of 1824 and the "Corrupt Bargain" opened the door for the Martin Van Burens of officeholders to gain a foothold. The election of 1828 made it clear that they were now in control.

Unlike Bolivar, Harrison knew that Van Buren would know exactly what to do with his Revolution. The first step would be to reward every person he could think of that helped him or could help him. And there were few political plums better than a foreign ministry and its handsome salary. Harrison had already taken the message to heart. He would soon be called home without meeting Bolivar. This, however, is not what caused him to close his eyes and sigh at the sun which seemed close enough to touch. It was the question of what to tell Anna.

Chapter 2:
Andrew Jackson

Martin Van Buren climbed out of bed at 8:30 a.m. While most of Washington scurried about to start the day, Van Buren rubbed his eyes and allowed himself a soft curse at this unpleasant departure from his routine. He already wondered why he left New York, where he was the boss, to come to this soggy backwater, where Andrew Jackson was the boss.

Of course, there was some debate about who was really in charge. Jackson was the President. That much was clear. But he was only President because Van Buren deigned that it would be so and orchestrated the New York machine to assure that the most powerful of the states would be delivered for Jackson.

While Van Buren was carefully constructing Jackson's victory, he was also tending to his own political fortunes. His omnipotence was complete when Jackson was declared the President-elect and Martin Van Buren was chosen to be the new Governor of New York.

Van Buren, however, had little intention of being Governor. It was a diversion, a safety net just in case his plans for General Jackson went awry. For, in Jackson, Van Buren saw the key to the political prominence to which he aspired: A national figure of unquestioned influence. A key post in Jackson's Cabinet was Van Buren's for the asking.

Then, in early January, it appeared that Van Buren would, indeed, be New York's governor for the long term. Jackson asked his friends in Tennessee to let the leaders of the Democratic party know that he had decided against accepting the Presidency. Beset with grief and guilt over the death of his wife, Jackson let it be known that he was content to confine himself to the now all too appropriately named Hermitage.

Van Buren's initial reaction was despair. For eight years he consolidated the Democratic party, first in New York, then in Washington and the entire nation only to be undone by a mercurial soldier from the backwoods of Tennessee. Soon, however, Van Buren realized that this was not a problem outside his expertise. For an hour or two he managed to ignore the constant hum of political scheming that inundated his mind and remember that ten years before, Martin Van Buren almost gave up his life's blood, politics. What startled Van Buren was the fact that his first reaction to Jackson's message was annoyance rather than sympathy.

With the recognition that Jackson was grieving for his wife just as Van Buren grieved for the death of his wife ten years before, Van Buren set to work. He crafted an eloquent yet compassionate plea to the General.

> *I too have passed through the darkness that*
> *shrouds your days now. While it may seem*
> *that light will never grace you again, I*
> *must assure you that it will. The light, as*
> *you know, only comes when we triumph over*
> *life's most vexatious obstacles. In that*
> *light and that light alone will your*
> *beloved's memory shine and justice be done.*

With the delivery of his letter, Van Buren once again delivered Andrew Jackson to Washington. While there were rumors, it never became common knowledge that Jackson came alarmingly close to confirming his opponents' charges that he was too capricious to be President.

After salvaging the Presidency for his party, Van Buren plunged into his gubernatorial duties with dramatic vigor. He knew the President would beckon soon and he did not want to appear to be anything less than surprised when he did. The last thing he wanted was for the voters of New York to see his candidacy for Governor as a political ploy, which, of course, was exactly what it was.

In mid-February, Jackson delivered his end of the deal. He sent a private message to Van Buren asking him to serve as Secretary of State. Just as privately, Van Buren sent word that he would be honored to serve. For another month, Van Buren worked tenaciously to be the most productive forty-three-day governor in the history of the country. As a result, on March 12 when he resigned to accept the President's invitation, most of New York naively sighed and nodded in agreement that the President's appointment was high praise for such a diligent and sincere public servant like Van Buren. Those who knew better shook their heads and smiled at the latest trick by the "Little Magician."

The hours kept by Martin Van Buren were another source of wonder for his admirers, and detractors. His typical day lasted well into the morning, usually until 2:00 or 3:00. Consequently, he rarely rose before 10:00 and more often near noon. Despite his well-known habits, few grumbled. It was generally conceded that Matt Van Buren accomplished more for the Democratic party (and sometimes even for the whole country) after midnight than anyone else at any other time. He courted benefactors, he softened opponents and tended to correspondence in the wee hours. It was the life of a man with four sons who had been widowed too long.

This was Van Buren's third day in his new residence in Washington. His home sat on Lafayette Square within view of the President's Mansion. Unfortunately, the President's mansion was not within view of Van Buren's new home. Once again, Van Buren saw a problem that could be readily solved. So, he awoke early to arrange for a window to be cut from the wall of his study so he could see the mansion. The new Secretary of State had no intention of leaving Andrew Jackson's administration to chance, much less to Andrew Jackson.

Much as he did with officeholders beholden to him in Albany, Van Buren would not only use the window as a lookout but would give the President a set of simple signals to watch for from Van Buren's window to "aid" him in his duties. Like most kingmakers, Van Buren was also, in reality, King.

He lifted his head at the sound of a soft click from downstairs. He shook his head and sighed. With resignation, he hoisted his growing girth up and pushed his thinning hair back. Walking to the head of the stairs he passed the room where his eldest son was staying, temporarily. Abraham Van Buren was a somber, extraordinarily responsible young man. At twenty-two, Abraham completed his studies at West Point and was set to begin service as an Army officer.

Unlike his father, Abraham was an early riser. Van Buren was confident that Abraham had been up for hours busying himself with meeting and greeting Army officials in the Capitol city. For twenty-two years, the elder Van Buren never really gave a second thought to his oldest boy. There was no need.

Even if Martin Van Buren wanted to worry about Abraham, he was usually too busy with politics or with a true source of anxiety--his second oldest boy. John Van Buren was both his father's favorite and his father's nemesis. Slightly over two years younger than Abraham, John was everything that his older brother was not. Where Abraham was to be an Army officer, John was finishing his studies at Yale to be a lawyer; where Abraham was stolid, John was irrepressible; where Abraham was plain and shy, John was dashing and charming.

The Secretary of State watched his son stifle a belch and take a deep breath at the bottom of the stairs. As he took the first uncertain step he looked up to see his father standing, hands on hips, at the top of the stairs. Betraying his lack of sobriety John queried, "Mr. Secretary, up a tad early aren't we?"

Van Buren glared. "In a tad late, aren't we?"

John smiled. " 'Tis a relative sort of thing isn't it."

"Yes, and this relative is running thin on patience."

John chuckled. "It appears that patience is the only thing you are running thin on."

Van Buren was tempted to laugh. He always was when John was around and he usually succumbed. But this was too important. He descended the stairs and put his arm around his son and helped him climb.

"I take it you met some of Washington's more friendly

members of the opposite sex last night?" The smell of liquor and perfume was overpowering.

John answered with the sheepish grin that women of all ages found irresistible, "Nothing worse than being friendly and not having any friends, eh?"

As they reached his son's room, Van Buren crossed the floor to the window. He tapped his fingers lightly on the sill and tried to plot his course. Men as a general matter were Van Buren's foils all his life. He manipulated countless opposing attorneys, judges, jurors, political friends and foes with an ease that earned him the appellation "Little Magician." Yet this one human, his own son, utterly eluded his sorcery. Granted he was always too indulgent with his sons but he felt they were owed some leniency. Growing up was hard enough without the extra disadvantage of doing it without a mother.

Van Buren stroked his sideburns as he did whenever he was deep in thought. In a day where flamboyant sideburns were in fashion, Van Buren's were still extraordinary. Like two huge pork chops they extended to the corners of his mouth, an always inviting target for small children. As he grew more plump, Van Buren found that one of the few benefits was his heightened attractiveness to children which he found to be a pleasant trade-off.

The antics of small children Van Buren could enjoy. The antics of his own child, however, were becoming wearisome. He spoke in a measured, yet not severe, tone. "John, I do not begrudge your frolics. I would be disingenuous if I did not say that I too had my more, shall we say, intemperate episodes when I was your age. The frequency of these, uh, evenings is of concern." His hand raised and silenced John's premature response. He went on, "Done to excess, gambling, drinking and, uh, the other, uh, activities will cause you to be considered, uh, something other than a gentleman. And I hope that I have made myself clear that my expectation has always been that my sons will be first, and foremost, gentlemen." He paused and then spoke with his back to his son.

"There are other reasons for you to behave in a more dignified manner. I occupy an office now that is responsible to more than just New York where you are known and accepted. It will not do for you to embarrass not only yourself but me and, by the same virtue, the President. I'm afraid there are a good many people in this town that would rather I go back to New York. The perception that I cannot control my own son instills little confidence that I can manage the affairs of the entire country. Rest assured that that is the very impression that Henry Clay and Calhoun and the whole bunch would love to give to the American public. I must insist on your cooperation."

John's head began to pound as his hangover began to displace his inebriation. He silently wondered why his father chose this morning to deliver this oration on virtue. He smiled weakly and said to his father's back, "Let 'em say what they want Father. You've got the reins now, not them. As long as Andy Jackson is every man's hero and does what you tell him to, what can they do to you?"

John knew instantly that he compounded his folly. Despite giving his father ample reason to lose his temper over the years, John rarely saw his father employ anything other than charm and reason to make his point. Now, clearly agitated by his son's impertinence Van Buren turned and hissed, "Because they will be my opponents for the Presidency when 'every man's hero', as you put it, is gone!"

* * *

Illinois: June 1832

For over twenty years the Sac and Fox tribes were pushed ever eastward. General William Henry Harrison bribed, cajoled and, at times, warred with them to clear the way for white settlers. The tribes tried to resist their displacement with little success, the most humiliating instance occurring in Harrison's decisive victory at Tippecanoe Creek.

The leader of the tribes now, as he was at Tippecanoe, was Black Hawk. The land west of the Mississippi proved to be far less fertile than the Sac and Fox' former home on the east side of the river. As hunger began to decimate his people Black Hawk knew that he had to re-cross the river. He visited the chiefs of the Winnebago, Kickapoo and Potawatomi tribes and convinced them that only by uniting to oppose the white settlers could they cross the river and plant the spring crops necessary to save their tribes.

In the springs of 1829, 1830 and 1831 the tribes quietly crossed the river and planted without much in the way of resistance. By 1831, however, settlers were beginning to covet the land abutting the river, or, in other words, the Indians' crop lands. Black Hawk knew that prior treaties with the white man's government prohibited the tribes' presence east of the Mississippi but knew that unless he violated the treaty his tribe would be lost.

Prior to crossing the river in 1832 one of Black Hawk's scouts informed him that a band of white soldiers was sent to protect the white settlers near the river. Undeterred, Black Hawk and the tribes crossed to begin their spring planting. Upon their arrival, the scout once again informed Black Hawk of the approach of the white soldiers. The Indians' leader sent a group of his warriors to express his desire to negotiate with the soldiers. He said to assure them that the tribes meant no harm, they only wished to take advantage of the more fertile lands on this side of the river.

Two days later three of his emissaries returned to report that the leader of their mission was shot upon his approach and others were taken prisoner. Black Hawk vowed retribution. The chiefs of the Winnebago, Potawatomi and Kickapoo elected instead to re-cross the river.

The five tribes together were no match for the most rudimentary army. Black Hawk's Sac and Fox tribes alone were pitiful at best. But Black Hawk's pride and frustration clouded his normally sound judgment and, for a few days, the Sac and Fox struck back with little tangible result. The word soon spread throughout Illinois and the territories to the north that would one day be Wisconsin that the Indians were once again a threat to the security of the western frontier. Black Hawk quickly realized that after being deserted by the other tribes and having no fighting force of his own, he could not win. He withdrew and attempted to hide himself and his tribe until they could safely re-cross the river. But it was too late by then. The "Black Hawk War", as the whites were calling it, was on.

The white man's army was gathered at the mouth of the Rock River. They were actually less gathered than scattered. Torrential rains pounded their camp for four days causing them to continually move further away from the river as it swelled and invaded their tents and wagons. They were attempting to get into the river and go upstream to find the treacherous Black Hawk. But the storm continually pushed them back.

As half the men struggled with the keelboats the other half tried to negotiate the constantly shifting bank of the river to move upstream. Their progress was no better as they battled bush, swamps and darkness.

At the head of this contingent was Colonel Zachary Taylor. The Colonel had no illusions about the militia under his command. Most were not soldiers but volunteers from Illinois' southern settlements that saw an opportunity for adventure and heroism that would still have them home before the summer was out. Most thought that there would be a few fierce engagements with the Indians and a lot of card playing and camaraderie.

Taylor knew better and also knew these volunteers would present more problems for him than the Indians. Taylor not only knew Black Hawk, he respected him. He knew that Black Hawk was not likely to expose his tribe to a battle where they would clearly be outnumbered. No, Taylor was sure that there would be a random ambush or two but all he was really doing was chasing Black Hawk back across the river.

Taylor's men sorely misunderstood the life of a soldier. They deceived themselves with visions of musket fire and hand to hand combat. The reality was preparation and, then, more preparation. The spade work alone accomplished a great deal of dismay. But the flooding and mud absolutely exasperated them. Most lost their taste for army life after the first night of securing the tents and tethering the boats against the rain.

Colonel Taylor had been trying to board a keelboat for three days to no avail. He sat in a tent with water dripping in all around him. The tent sagged so that even at his diminutive height, Taylor had to hunch over. He squinted to compensate for his near-sightedness as the young captain from Springfield ducked into the tent. Taylor stifled a laugh as the gangly young man negotiated his way through the streaming leaks and water-filled pockets of sagging canvas.

The captain made the mistake of trying to straighten up to salute his superior. At well over six feet he caused a veritable tidal wave to wash over the tent top. Water coursed into new holes and the Colonel was, unfortunately, drenched. Taylor shook his head. "Captain, I am afraid I am going to have to order you to kneel down."

The captain smiled and complied, "Yes sir."

Taylor was having a little trouble taking this "war" or his troops seriously. But he did his duty.

"Captain, I understand that your men were responsible for the disturbance last night."

The captain nodded. "Reckon they were just blowing off a little steam Colonel."

Taylor sympathized but war was war even if there was no real danger. "Captain, that won't do. What would have become of us if the Indians had attacked or we had to move out quickly and your troops are lying drunk in the mud? Not to mention their betrayal of our position with all the ruckus they made." He tried to be stern but his heart was not in it.

The captain perceived that the colonel was going through the motions. He helped him along. "Yes sir. I will take responsibility. I knew they were getting into the liquor wagon and did nothing to stop them."

Taylor played his part. "Captain, this is the army, not Saturday night in Springfield. Errors of this type cannot be tolerated. Am I clear on this?"

The captain nodded again. Taylor looked at him wistfully. This man had no business in the army. He was thin and gawky. He was mild-mannered to a fault. The only reason he was a captain was his popularity back home where he was renowned not for bravery or strength but for his dry humor and ability to spin a tale.

This was not the captain's first trip to Taylor's quarters and he had only been under Taylor's command for three weeks. In his first week, the captain accidentally fired his gun in camp narrowly missing Taylor's tent. Taylor put him under arrest and gave him cook detail for a few days. Despite his haplessness, Taylor liked the captain. Indeed, it was hard not to. But the army and the captain both expected punishment so Taylor searched for the appropriate penalty.

The Colonel silently wished that the militia would disband and let him and a few of his regulars ride north and make sure Black Hawk got back across the river. But General Atkinson, despite Taylor's protests, believed this was a real war calling for hundreds of troops and even a strategy. Taylor followed orders and amused himself by allowing the neophytes under his command to believe theirs' was a noble and perilous cause. The humor was beginning to fade, however, as his charges got into mischief to compensate for the hard labor and lack of fighting.

He knew that the captain before him was not one of the troublemakers. He really saw himself as a soldier. Unfortunately, he had neither the physical agility nor mental fortitude to be much of a soldier.

Taylor wiped a trickle of water from his forehead. He tromped through the muddy floor of his tent and reached into a small chest. He withdrew a comical looking wooden sword that a friend in Kentucky made for him as a joke of sorts. He crossed back over to the captain.

"Captain, the army is no place for frivolity. I will need your musket for two days and you will have to make do with this." He presented the wooden sword to the captain who was crestfallen. Nonetheless, he saluted clumsily and responded, "Yessir. I will fetch my musket and bring it back."

Taylor hoped to be far up the river in two days. "No need Captain. Just make sure that I don't see you carrying that musket. And make sure I get my sword back." Another "yessir" and Taylor dismissed him.

Zachary Taylor watched the captain depart and smiled ever so slightly as he listened to the rain continue to pound the tent. He knew that the wooden sword would cause the young man some embarrassment but he was confident that it would be nothing compared to what these "soldiers" would experience if they ever got into a real battle. The only true danger that confronted these men was themselves. So, Taylor would let them play war for a few weeks and then send them home as heroes. Until then he would do his best to keep them out of harm's way. And keeping a musket out of Captain Abraham Lincoln's hands for a couple days could only help.

* * *

New York: November 1832

Thurlow Weed turned thirty-five years old five days earlier. For several years, however, he had been a powerful force in New York politics. As the editor of the *Albany Evening Journal* he vied with William Marcy's *Northern Budget* to cast the news to his liking. Unlike Marcy, Weed made no pretense of adherence to an ideology or political theory. Weed's ambition was not wealth, but power.

Marcy's *Budget* was less newspaper than propaganda sheet for Martin Van Buren, Andrew Jackson and the Albany Regency (a term that Thurlow Weed coined!). Weed had no particular aversion to Van Buren and the Regency. Indeed, in many respects, like ridding the state of Governor DeWitt Clinton, Weed was in quiet agreement.

But Thurlow Weed had no desire to be just another lieutenant in the Regency. The men who ran the Regency were entrenched and, by and large, young. They grew from a small faction with no unifying features, except their devotion to Matt Van Buren and their distaste for DeWitt Clinton, into a well-organized, virtually omnipotent machine.

The Regency flourished because Van Buren and Marcy understood that voters found personalities and promises of personal advancement far more interesting than issues. With well-placed publicity and articles in the *Budget* subtly deriding Clinton and championing Van Buren and his faithful, the Regency portrayed itself as the hope of the common man. With the rise of Andrew Jackson, the Regency was popular not only among the masses in New York but with the administration in

Washington.

Thurlow Weed watched the Regency's ascent and studied its success. At its most basic level the Regency owed its prominence to the most basic of human traits--the distrust of those in power. Through gentle suggestions of Clinton's character defects and by billing itself as a rational alternative to Clinton's long-standing rule, the Regency became the voice of every man who felt life treated him unfairly, whether Clinton was to blame or not.

Throughout the Regency's climb to prominence, Weed stayed non-committal. He was noted as an able writer with a solid grasp of political issues but no apparent prejudices. The Regency knew it did not own him but did not consider him a foe.

Now, however, with the Regency at the height of its puissance, Weed began his ascent and he did so in a way that even Van Buren would later have to admit was creative. When the great Cathedrals of England were being built in the seventeenth century, the stonecutters and bricklayers doing the work began to gather for meetings to discuss political events of the day and their own financial lot. They came to refer to themselves as the Freemasons. Soon they were joined by other respected members of their communities and their meetings began to take on a more formal, clandestine personality. The Freemason movement spread to other parts of the world by the middle of the seventeenth century.

The first Masonic lodge in the colonies was formed in Boston and was soon followed by one in Philadelphia. By the time the colonies declared their independence from Great Britain, there were over 150 lodges in the New World. Typically, the lodges became a refuge for a community's most prominent citizens to socialize with those of their own class. The Masons' meetings were extremely secretive and a breach of the vow of secrecy was considered the most heinous of offenses.

The Masons appeared harmless enough. The lodges generally funneled money to the poor and those in need through the charity of their well-to-do members. And the lodges provided a welcome respite from the many demands placed on the members in their outside lives. The Masons seemed to hurt no one, were openly God-fearing and, generally, kept to themselves. No one saw a reason to make an issue of the Masons.

But Thurlow Weed noticed many years before that not only the most prominent businessmen in New York tended to be Masons, so did many of the most prominent *politicians*, including the President, DeWitt Clinton and Henry Clay. He held this information as a mental note more than anything, until he saw his chance to exploit it.

Weed got his chance when he seized on the story of the mysterious disappearance of a man by the name of Morgan who published secrets of the Masons. A subsequent investigation led to the inescapable conclusion that Morgan was murdered.

Many were puzzled at first by the *Evening Journal's* unrelenting coverage of the disappearance of the not-so-notorious Morgan. But as Weed pointed out in editorial after editorial that many of New York's and the country's most powerful men were Masons, he began to get the desired response. Slowly and patiently, Weed never answered but elicited the question of what the leaders of a law abiding free nation were doing in an organization that, apparently, murdered its members? The debate soon captured the collective imagination of New York. From there Weed made the logical jump of attacking every association that counted exclusivity among its attributes, including the Albany Regency. From this narrow premise, Thurlow Weed created his own political movement, the Anti-Masons, and now, was building his own political machine.

The Regency paid little heed to the *Evening Journal's* diatribes as its members reveled in their hard-fought dominance. By the time Thurlow Weed stirred the population into a frenzy, Martin Van Buren returned from Washington and was immediately alarmed at his cohorts' failure to recognize an obvious threat to the authority of the Regency. Marcy ran some editorials castigating the *Evening Journal's* inflammatory stories but to no avail.

Thurlow Weed took the Regency's modus operandi and turned it against Van Buren and Marcy's machine. He played on the "common man's" most base instincts. He feigned suspicion with every exclusive group. The Anti-Masons railed against secrecy and privilege for those in power. Suddenly the Regency, the voice of the common man, was being assailed as corrupt and greedy. The Anti-Masons had no real political philosophy other than to denigrate the elite. It was an approach sure to appeal to enough people to allow Thurlow Weed to get his foot in the door of political power. He would worry about getting all the way in later.

Weed took a long draw on his cigar and blew smoke mostly into the face of one of his keys to political power, William Henry Seward. Seward was a state senator with a facile mind and, despite a political career that only spanned two years, he was already considered a rising star in New York politics. Of course, a great deal of Seward's prominence was attributable to Weed's frequent articles trumpeting the senator's virtues.

Unlike Thurlow Weed, Bill Seward did have his convictions. Seward was shrewd enough to realize, however, that his principles would remain unsupported and unheard without Weed's newspaper and connections. Seward's designs on prison and immigration reform, government funded highways and a host of other government driven "improvements" always lagged slightly behind Weed's political maneuvering. There was an unspoken agreement between the men that Seward's high-minded ideals were not to interfere with his duties for Weed, whether it was carrying legislation antagonistic to those in power or in conducting a direct assault on the senate floor against the same people. Of course, Seward's nastier jobs were portrayed in a far too favorable light in the pages of the *Evening Journal*.

Seward sat in Weed's office slumped in a chair. He was only Weed's junior by four years but they seemed worlds apart. Weed brimmed with confidence and, at times, charm. Seward was clearly the superior in terms of intellect but nothing else. He did not have Weed's daring or, frankly, his ruthlessness. Seward was dour and often petulant. He was not prone to being unpleasant, usually just quiet and pouty. But Weed could bring out the worst in Seward because Seward was ambitious. So, he did Weed's bidding. Oddly, however, he did not resent Weed. He admired the editor's bravado and rationalized that, ultimately, it was only with someone like Weed that he would get to where he wanted to go. So, unlike most relationships of dominance, the domineered truly appreciated the domineering.

These two young men with grand designs waited, saying little. Seward ventured, "He never did really say where he stood on anything."

Weed smiled. "That's the beauty. A candidate that is so good looking and charming that no one really cares what he believes in."

"What does he believe in?"

Weed sighed. He quickly grew bored with anything resembling principle. "I don't really know. The only thing he did in the state legislature was some bill about not imprisoning debtors or some such foolishness."

"Something of a chameleon from what I hear about him," Seward answered.

Weed held his cigar up to the light and grinned. "My favorite kind of politician." He went on. "I really believe this is the man who can give old Matt Van Buren a run for his money. He is good looking, charming and, don't be fooled, he's smart. He's already one of the best trial attorneys in the state which, you will recall, is how Van Buren started."

Seward nodded. He could never fathom Weed's fascination with Martin Van Buren, a man that Weed clearly admired but also seemed intent on displacing as the dispenser of patronage in New York. Weed took advantage of Van Buren's many absences from the state over the last few years to assemble his machine and quietly begin chipping away at the Regency. Now, with the elections over and Andrew Jackson clearly on his way to a second term and Matt Van Buren in tow as his Vice President, Weed saw his chance for unfettered mischief. He knew that Van Buren would still be calling the shots for the Regency but communication could not help but be hampered with the Regency's leader living in Washington. Shortly Weed would begin running articles vaguely critical of Van Buren and sharply critical of the Regency.

Weed needed someone to sow the seeds of discontent in the state government and Seward filled that role nicely. But Weed's ambition, like Van Buren's, did not end in New York. Granted, he had to displace the Regency first, but, again like Van Buren, he realized that dominion in New York meant national power.

Weed was not impatient. He knew that it would take time to gather a large enough band of followers to realize his aim. But when the time came, he would need a well-established cadre of henchmen to do his bidding in Washington. While he ultimately would rely on Seward to be his soldier in Washington, Seward needed time in New York to build his base. Weed was dispassionate enough to know that he had to nurture Seward's career carefully and patiently.

In the meantime, Weed needed a presence in Washington. He carefully scoured the brightest of New York's rising politicians and found his man. A man with the personal attributes necessary to draw votes but with a largely unknown public face. Weed did not share his concern with Seward that his man's fealty was still in question. Weed was confident that it would gradually dawn on him that Weed could make or break his candidacy. He surely understood that he would not be on his way to serve in the United States House of Representatives without Weed's sudden interest in his candidacy and glowing (not to mention oft-repeated) endorsements in *the Evening Journal*.

Seward leaned forward through the haze. "Look Weed. I know you don't like to be bothered with issues but you better figure out pretty damn fast where this fellow stands on at least the basics. If he gets to Washington and decides that Van Buren and Andy Jackson ain't so bad, you'll be...no, *we'll* be right back where we started!"

Weed frowned. "Bill, you just tend to Albany and we'll be fine. I'll look after our friend Fillmore."

At that instant, Weed gestured at their "friend" Millard Fillmore who was alighting the steps in front of the Journal. As they stood side by side Weed and Seward watched him through the window. Weed muttered, "Damn, how can you lose with a man that good looking?"

Seward flopped back into his chair and answered, "You shouldn't if he's smart."

* * *

Washington: April 1833

John Quincy Adams' nostrils flared in rapid succession as he hunched over his desk and wrote

*"I would not be present to see my darling
Harvard disgrace herself by conferring a
Doctor's degree upon a barbarian and savage
who could scarcely spell his own name."*

The "barbarian and savage" Adams referred to was the President of the United States, Andrew Jackson. The Boston university established itself as the preeminent educational institution in the New World years before. But the ascension of John Adams and his son to the Presidency solidified Harvard's position as the breeding ground of the elite. Now John Quincy Adams, who considered himself nothing less than elite, found himself almost apoplectic with the news that his alma mater intended to confer an honorary doctorate upon Jackson during the President's tour of the Northeast.

The Presidential campaigns of 1824 and 1828 transformed Adams and Jackson from cordial (if silently disdainful) acquaintances into bitter foes. Jackson blamed Adams for the death of his wife. Adams, on the other hand, cursed Jackson for debasing representative government with the notion that a commoner with little or no education could possibly fathom the intricacies of running a country. In Jackson, Adams saw the demise of all that his father worked for. The last hope for civility between the men came when Adams refused to attend Jackson's inauguration, just as his father slipped away to avoid Thomas Jefferson's swearing in.

After leaving Washington, Adams returned for a short while to Massachusetts with plans to retire and be the local sage. But by 1830 he was headed back to the nation's capital. His return was both voluntary and involuntary.

The first flaw in Adams' retirement plans came when Adams realized that no one was particularly interested in his views. After a lifetime of national and international service,

Adams was more of an enigma than a legend in his home state. To compound matters, many of his fellow New Englanders were embarrassed by his treatment of "Old Hickory" in both the campaign and in not attending the inauguration.

With nowhere to go Adams became the bane of all wives with retired, bored husbands. Louise and John never had a romantic or even particularly warm relationship anyway. Being forced together in their small home all day, every day, quickly became unbearable.

Adams would probably have lived out his life grumbling about his country's and wife's lack of appreciation for his efforts but for his sons' juvenile struggle for the affections of a girl. Mary Hellen was a cousin that was undeniably beautiful. Adams was sure that Mary would have been content to allow George Adams and John Adams spend the rest of their days wooing her. Never a romantic, the elder Adams grew weary of watching his boys waste their education and intellect attempting to impress a girl that Adams conceded had looks and charm but little else. He sat George and John down and demanded that his boys make Mary choose and stop wasting time on their trivial infatuation. Mary chose John.

The loser in this contest for Miss Hellen's hand was Adams' oldest son, George Washington Adams, clearly the heir apparent to his grandfather and father's legacy. Like any good Adams he attended Harvard, studied law with one of Massachusetts' most respected attorneys, Daniel Webster, and served in the Massachusetts legislature all by the time he was 28. Then he lost Mary to his little brother.

George's fondness and incapacity for alcohol always troubled his father but it now became a problem. He stumbled around the streets of Boston for weeks in a stupor. His bitterness dripped with the scorn he heaped on his father for forcing Mary into what he was sure was a premature decision.

The former President put George on a steamer to New York in the hope that a change of scenery would allow his son to sober up and get on with life. Whatever embarrassments he suffered in Boston, he was an Adams first, a drunk second. If he stopped drinking and righted himself, his father was confident that the people of Massachusetts would remember the former and forget the latter.

But Adams' plan went astray again. George boarded the ship drunk and soon was cursing the other passengers and proclaiming the superiority of the Adams'. In his inebriation George apparently gave voice to every silent grudge his grandfather and father ever harbored. The consensus of the passengers was that he was, *indeed*, an Adams.

His father soon received word that George never got off the ship in New York. The next month George's withered and shark ravaged body washed ashore on Long Island. No one saw him go overboard leading many to believe that he did not *want* anyone to see him go overboard.

A guilt-ridden father did not have long to mourn the loss of his son before George's creditors began to send notices of claims against his son. His son's legal clients called on the former President charging that their affairs were neglected for months and, in some cases, years. And a girl who worked at George's favorite tavern appeared with an infant. George's friends assured John Quincy that they had no doubt that the baby was his grandson. In a few short months, John Quincy Adams was bankrupt.

Adams never held a job outside of government and politics. He would not lower himself to practice law and he could never make the money he needed teaching. Louise hated Washington but she hated listening to her husband's remonstrances even more, so when John Quincy's supporters expressed their desire to fund an effort to elect the former President to Congress she did not object. In 1831 the Adams' were back in the Capital.

The change in Adams to those who were in Washington when he was Secretary of State and President was immediately apparent. He was still haughty when arguing a point but a new-found humility and even tranquillity seemed to prevail more often than not. His most bitter political enemies now found him almost tolerable. It was often noted that it took the death of a child, bankruptcy and crawling back to Washington as a mere Congressman to deflate Adams' ego to the point of great conceit.

Adams was at relative peace for the first time in his life.

His ambitions were all fulfilled and he found them unfulfilling. He gave up on attaining the type of model family life that his regimented mind demanded for so long. Any hope he had of financial security was also dashed.

So now he engaged in politics for nothing more than having his say in national matters and taking care of the district that he never really knew but that he always claimed for his own. He had no designs on any other office or post and that, more than anything else, gave him peace.

He was surprised by his reaction to the invitation to attend Harvard's intended ceremony for Jackson. He still detested the President but rarely was emotional about Jackson anymore. He realized, however, that Jackson was intruding into the one thing that Adams still had on Jackson and his legions of common men- -a degree from Harvard. The desecration of representative government was probably inevitable. For John Quincy Adams though, the desecration of Harvard was not.

* * *

The President and Vice President wheezed almost in unison. Martin Van Buren, the Vice President, wheezed because he was, frankly, fat. Every movement required laborious shifting and maneuvering. The constant air passing between his lips was the result of the strain of staying alive.

Andrew Jackson the President, on the other hand, had a somewhat high-pitched wheeze not because he was obese, but because he was so thin and feeble that he had long since stopped straining to stay alive. Life just wouldn't seem to let go. Whenever he appeared in public he would gather every bit of energy that he could have ever had, spend it and then retreat for several days to prepare for death. The limited circle that saw him in private (Van Buren being the principle viewer) could never adjust to the specter of the withered General who looked more like vague memories of their grandmothers than an illustrious hero and the first President from the rugged western "frontier."

Andrew Jackson was barely a month into his second term as President. The prior November Jackson was re-elected by an embarrassing margin over Henry Clay. Clay, who considered himself (and was widely acknowledged as) an expert political strategist was embarrassed because his scheme to oust Jackson completely and utterly backfired.

Early in 1832 Clay approached Nicholas Biddle, the President of the Bank of the United States, about applying to Congress for a re-charter of the Bank. The request was strategic because the Bank's charter was not due to expire until *1836* and because Andrew Jackson believed the Bank to be the root of all evil. Jackson was an ardent believer in "hard money" and distrusted Biddle's Bank's policy of issuing paper currency in lieu of actual gold or silver.

Henry Clay knew that Jackson would veto any measure re-chartering the Bank. Knowing that powerful eastern financial interests in the key election states of New York and Pennsylvania would be infuriated, Clay plotted his attempt at grabbing the reins of the Presidency by bringing the bill re-chartering the Bank to a vote shortly before delegates gathered to nominate their candidates for President. As predicted, after the bill passed Congress, Jackson promptly vetoed. Clay crowed that King Andrew was dead and announced his candidacy for the throne.

But Clay failed to understand that the two men now wheezing in Jackson's office were greater politicians than even the conniving Clay. Andrew Jackson understood that Clay's ploy was too complex. Those who appreciated the intricacies of banking and the monetary system were disturbed and even alarmed by Jackson's veto. Unfortunately for Clay, these people were few in number. Jackson was elected by the common man in 1828 and he knew that the same voters would have to elect him in 1832. The common man did not understand the Bank, but he understood Andrew Jackson. When Jackson spoke out against the Bank, the common man believed him. What Clay forgot was that there always was and always would be more common men who did not understand economics than rich men who did.

But Jackson did not stop at simply being more aware of the age in which he lived than Clay, he outmaneuvered him. When he vetoed the Bank's re-charter, he ordered all government funds withdrawn from the Bank and redeposited in state banks. The boldness and disdain for eastern financial interests that this move signaled was not lost on the voters. Clay was buried at the polls.

Like many before him, Henry Clay underestimated Andrew Jackson's political skill. This alone was probably sufficient to defeat him. But Clay's strategy was equally confounded by the fact that Martin Van Buren stood to be Vice President if Jackson was re-elected. Even Clay's substantial prowess was no match for Van Buren when it came to political gamesmanship, especially when Van Buren's own political well-being was on the line.

Clay's whole plan hinged on the disaffection of the financial interests in New York and Pennsylvania with the President after the veto of the Bank's re-charter. When Jackson took the further step of withdrawing federal funds from the Bank, Van Buren immediately set out to allay the fears of those with a stake in the Bank. Through deft coordination where Van Buren's hand was never seen (but always felt), the government money made its way to state banks favorable to the most financially potent. When Jackson took New York and Pennsylvania handily in the election, Clay was one of the few who knew (without being able to prove it) that he fell prey to the Little Magician's latest trick.

Van Buren's ascent to the Vice Presidency took a route that even his manipulative mind could not have conjured up. After his brief tenure as Governor of New York, Van Buren arrived in Washington to assume his post as Jackson's Secretary of State. While he made it clear to his fellow New Yorkers that he was sacrificing the profound honor of being New York's Governor for the noble calling of national service, those who knew Van Buren knew that he intended to use his Cabinet post in just the same way as Madison, Monroe and Adams. He fully expected to be the eighth President of the United States.

But two things happened that forced Van Buren to change his course. One was a revelation, the other an opportunity. The revelation caused Van Buren anxiety and consternation at his own lack of cognition. For over twenty years he worked to create a system where a man like Andrew Jackson could be elected President. Yet once Jackson *was* elected, Van Buren started his quest for the Presidency by relying on the system that existed before Jackson. He still could vividly recall the evening in early 1831 when his head began to throb as he read the words over and over in Thurlow Weed's *Albany Evening Journal*:

> *Millard Fillmore's recent move to Buffalo is a sure signal that one of New York's brightest and most energetic political stars is set to enter the national stage.*

The fact that Millard Fillmore was moving to Buffalo was of little consequence to Van Buren. What disturbed Van Buren was that he met Fillmore and determined quickly that Fillmore was neither bright nor energetic. He *was* handsome and mildly charming which meant that Fillmore fit the profile of a typical Van Buren candidate perfectly. It was at that moment that Van Buren knew that relying on his position as Secretary of State to catapult him to the Presidency was a mistake. *He* transformed politics from a game of credentials to a game of personality and image. As Secretary of State he was playing the game of credentials.

Martin Van Buren was also acutely aware that he could never command the public adulation that Andrew Jackson could. In a game of personality and image, Van Buren's image of eastern sophistication would not serve him well. By the time he laid the *Journal* article down, he knew the key to the Presidency lay not in being Jackson's trusted Secretary of State, but in being Jackson's trusted heir apparent.

Up to that time Van Buren was certainly one of Jackson's closest advisors and Cabinet members. But their relationship was grounded in mutual respect and political expediency. Van Buren knew that whoever Jackson supported to succeed him as President would also have to be Jackson's friend. It was only then that Van Buren saw the path out of the Cabinet and into Jackson's chair. Her name was Peggy Timberlake Eaton.

Andrew Jackson was a shrewd politician with a novel approach for his era. He was not a deal maker like Van Buren or Henry Clay. Jackson, more than any politician in the United States' brief history drew his strength from his appeal to the people. He was not forced to compromise nearly as often as most office holders because of his immense popularity. As a result, much to their consternation and bitterness, many a politician found themselves bowing to Jackson's will.

When Jackson first assumed office he followed the precedent of George Washington and each subsequent President. He tried to name a Cabinet that reflected divergent views to foster so-called "healthy debate" on issues that confronted his administration. The most dominant figures in his Cabinet were his Vice President John Calhoun and Martin Van Buren, his Secretary of State. Jackson appointed an old friend from Tennessee, John Eaton, as his Secretary of War. The remainder of the Cabinet consisted of essentially weak figures favorable to Calhoun, Van Buren or Eaton.

Jackson's initial problem was that Van Buren and Calhoun were bitter political rivals. They were both hopeless intriguers that schemed endlessly to bolster their own image while currying favor with Jackson. It was Calhoun's misfortune to be pitted against Van Buren, a man that Calhoun could never match when it came to subtlety or cleverness. Within months of his inauguration, Jackson realized that he and Calhoun were philosophically at odds and, at a more basic level, he simply did not like Calhoun very much. This attitude was not the least inhibited by Van Buren's plentiful yet sufficiently abstruse hints about Calhoun's more clandestine activities. Unlike George Washington's constant struggle to maintain Alexander Hamilton's and Thomas Jefferson's services despite their enmity for one another, Jackson simply ignored the members of his Cabinet for whom he had little regard. In the official Cabinet's place, the "Kitchen Cabinet" was inserted.

The Kitchen Cabinet consisted of Van Buren, Eaton and a handful of influential newspaper editors that were favorable to Jackson. Official Cabinet meetings became meaningless exercises where the decisions of the Kitchen Cabinet were announced and implemented. Not surprisingly, Calhoun and the other members of Jackson's Cabinet were not pleased with their impotence. Resignations were out of the question. To resign would be a clear admission that they were out of favor with

Jackson, the most popular man in the nation. In short, to resign would be political suicide.

Calhoun and his fellow political eunuchs also knew that there was little they could do to Jackson directly to force him to recognize them. Taking on Van Buren was also fraught with danger simply because too many before tried and failed. Partly by circumstance and partly by design, John Eaton became the object of their wrath. More precisely, John Eaton's *wife* came under fire.

Margaret Eaton went by the nickname Peggy. She was many years younger than John Eaton. She was the daughter of the proprietor of a Washington tavern where both Jackson and Eaton lived when they first arrived in Washington. Peggy frequently tended bar and served the patrons at her father's establishment. This is what she was doing when she first met the charming Senator from Tennessee, John Eaton. Their flirtations and her fascination with his close friendship with the great General Jackson soon led to repeated visits.

Eaton and Peggy had one problem. Peggy was married. Her husband, John Timberlake was a clerk in the Navy's Washington office. This inconvenience was soon resolved by a discreet visit by Senator Eaton to the War department. He let it be known that he felt that the talents of a bright young man like Timberlake were being wasted in Washington. He should be at sea where his administrative acumen could only benefit the orderly disposition of naval business. Timberlake, a shy and timid man, was delighted by this unexpected recognition of his efforts and the opportunity to show his beautiful wife that he was a man of consequence.

Peggy Timberlake *was* beautiful. Years of serving liquor to politicians who were far from home and desperate for companionship allowed her to hone her skills to flatter both politicians and her own looks. She accentuated her dark eyes and exquisite skin with jewelry (collected as gifts from star-struck patrons) and clothes that never failed to compliment her extraordinary figure. No sooner did John Timberlake set sail than John Eaton became more intimately familiar with Mrs. Timberlake's figure.

About the time Peggy had her first child by John Eaton,

John Timberlake learned of his wife's philandering. Though Peggy was telling Washington that the child was Timberlake's he knew this could not be true. *He* had not enjoyed her figure for several months before he went to sea. Alone on the deck of his ship in the Mediterranean Ocean, the Navy's sudden interest in his heretofore insignificant career and his wife's enthusiasm for his "adventure," as she put it, crystallized. He was found shortly before dawn slumped against the railing with blood still dripping from the gaping wound he gouged in his throat. His eyes were still open but vacant. After most of the crew inspected the corpse the Captain ordered him slipped quietly overboard. He never understood why the Navy insisted on Timberlake being on board the ship anyway.

Peggy dutifully observed a public period of mourning after her husband's death while continuing her liaison with Eaton privately. A few months after Timberlake's death, however, Peggy was again pregnant. Andrew Jackson had already declared John Eaton his Secretary of War. Eaton approached the President with notion of marrying Peggy, failing to mention that she was also pregnant. Eaton's affair with Peggy was common knowledge in Washington social circles but Jackson took great pride in having little to do with such circles. He was also still reconciling the loss of his own wife, Rachel. When Eaton made vague reference to Peggy's somewhat unsavory reputation, he was relieved to hear Jackson advise him, "If you love her John, pay no mind to gossip. You must marry her." A few weeks later, on January 1, 1829, Eaton did just that. After an appropriate amount of time the couple announced with pride that they were expecting their "first" child.

Cabinet posts are, understandably, prestigious and potentially powerful jobs. Equally understandably, they are viewed by their recipients as stepping stones to greater prestige. What was less understandable (at least to the long-time widower Van Buren) was the change wrought on the wives of newly appointed Cabinet members. Invariably the same women that helped their husbands realize such success by lending their own charming dispositions became snobbish and insufferable once entrenched as part of the Administration.

The wives of those members of Andrew Jackson's Cabinet who were not privy to the Kitchen Cabinet were (again, understandably) alarmed at the lack of deference paid to their husbands by the President. Just as Vice President Calhoun was premier among Jackson's outcast Cabinet members, Floride Calhoun was premier among their wives. Together, the Calhouns saw in the scandalous relationship of John and Peggy Eaton their only hope of bringing the President to brook.

Peggy Eaton did her part to fit in as any self-respecting Cabinet member's wife. She made sure to remain aloof and distant from all but those who mattered most--that is, the President and Martin Van Buren and the wives of other Cabinet members. But soon after Floride Calhoun ensured that every member of the Cabinet and their spouses knew the ignominious nature of the Eatons' union, Peggy found herself the *object*, rather than the purveyor, of snobbery. She was omitted from all receptions and her visits to other wives were refused. At the President's functions, she was ignored by all but the President and Van Buren.

The Calhouns hoped that the Eatons would bring disgrace to the President forcing him to disband the Kitchen Cabinet and to call for Eaton's resignation. Their plan misfired woefully. Jackson was enraged and, to the Calhouns' and other Cabinet members' amazement, he leapt to the defense of Peggy Eaton. He called a special Cabinet meeting to discuss the issue at which Calhoun denigrated Peggy's virtue and feigned disbelief at Jackson's support of her. Van Buren winced when the President retorted by exclaiming that Peggy Eaton was "as chaste as a virgin!"

If Calhoun asked Van Buren how the President would react to an assault on Peggy's character, Van Buren would have told him that there was no doubt in his mind that the President would defend her honor. Andrew Jackson almost declined to accept the highest office in the land because of venal attacks on his own wife's virtue. To a man like Jackson, who still fancied himself a General more than a politician, a woman's honor was worth any price. And *that* was why Andrew Jackson was such a popular *politician*.

Van Buren watched the "Eaton malaria" as he called it with amused detachment until it occurred to him that this silly little melodrama held the key to Presidential succession. Absorbed with his own predicament of how to assure his succession to Jackson, Van Buren was jolted from his malaise on a ride with Jackson through the countryside outside of Washington. Van Buren was not much of a horseman and was not particularly enthralled when Jackson suggested that Van Buren should get more exercise and accompanying the President on his weekly rides would be the perfect opportunity. Van Buren soon agreed, however, that it was the perfect opportunity but not because he cared any more about exercise but because he soon realized that his rides with Jackson allowed him unfettered access to the President for hours at a time. It was on these rides that most of their political strategy took shape.

It was on just such a ride shortly after the Cabinet meeting concerning the Eatons that Jackson ventured, "I cannot allow Calhoun to torment John or Peggy. I am inclined to ask for his resignation. That's the lunacy of having a Vice President. He has no real function other than to create trouble for the President."

Van Buren's eyes widened and he reined in his mount. He sat silently as his plan formed with lightning speed. Jackson realized that his Secretary of State had stopped and returned fifteen yards to the spot where Van Buren's horse grazed while his rider gazed impassively. Jackson queried, "Matt, what is it?"

Van Buren replied in a soft but measured cadence, the clicking sound of his voice subsiding temporarily, "No, Mr. President. It is I who must resign."

Jackson's head snapped up. "Ridiculous. I can't do without you and why in tarnation should you resign?"

Van Buren was encouraged. "For several reasons. First, Calhoun is right. Whether you wish to believe or not, many people are disturbed by your support of Peggy." When Jackson's eyes flamed, Van Buren held up his hand. "I know, I know Mr. President. You know that I, like you, am fond of Peggy. She is, of course, harmless. But there is some unseemliness and that is more important to many people than it should be. As long as John remains as Secretary of War, Calhoun will assure that the issue plagues you."

Jackson, calmer, began to listen intently. Van Buren continued, "Next, I am not sure that you can get rid of Calhoun if he refuses your request to resign. He is, after all, the Vice President, duly elected just as you were." Jackson nodded. Van Buren concluded, "Asking John to resign would humiliate him and be a clear victory for Calhoun. But if *I* resign on the basis that the Administration needs a fresh start, that clears the way for John to follow my lead and, who knows, maybe even Calhoun. At a minimum, it allows you to ask the rest of the Cabinet to resign which, if they refuse, will appear unpatriotic. Even if Calhoun does not resign, he will have lost his support within the Administration. But not at the expense of you, John or Peggy."

Jackson, genuinely concerned, asked, "What would become of you?"

Van Buren shrugged, "I will return home. I will practice law. If you were so inclined, I might consider the English ministry."

Jackson sighed and said that he needed time to think about Van Buren's idea. He commented again that he valued Van Buren too much. But Van Buren knew that he saw the genius of Van Buren's resignation and was not surprised the next day when they rode again and Jackson, fully energized, agreed to the plan. John Eaton was quickly persuaded as well. Much to Jackson's dismay John Calhoun did not resign but at least he was left with no way to embarrass Jackson.

Van Buren left for England but not before leaving every hint necessary to let Jackson know that he was available for the Vice Presidency. Then Calhoun played into his hands again. When the vote to confirm Van Buren as Minister came up in the Senate it resulted in a tie. Calhoun dramatically cast the deciding vote to reject Van Buren's appointment. Calhoun trumpeted throughout the Senate that he had his revenge on Van Buren. Jackson fumed. But Van Buren rejoiced. Again, Calhoun made a grave miscalculation. With Martin Van Buren in England there was little harm to be done. Instead, Calhoun's vindictiveness proved his undoing. In three months, Martin Van Buren was back from London orchestrating what would ultimately result in the election of Jackson and himself as President and Vice President. John Calhoun smoldered for almost a year after being outwitted by Jackson and Van Buren before he found another issue on which to challenge the President.

Throughout the first term, Jackson and Calhoun had a philosophical difference over state versus federal power. This philosophical debate became reality when Calhoun encouraged the South Carolina legislature to pass a law stating that it would not comply with the new tariff signed into law by Jackson. Calhoun further publicly stated that any attempt by the federal government to enforce the tariff would lead to secession by South Carolina. Jackson responded by declaring that secession was treason and he would not hesitate to use force to enforce the tariff *and* to keep South Carolina from seceding. In a move designed to throw the gauntlet down in front of Jackson, Calhoun resigned the Vice Presidency and prepared to lead South Carolina out of the Union. Again, Calhoun became Jackson and Van Buren's foil.

Immediately after Calhoun resigned, Jackson (at Van Buren's urging) contacted Henry Clay, still reeling from his defeat by Jackson one month earlier. Jackson proposed a compromise tariff. Clay, eager to rehabilitate his image, agreed. Together they took the credit for averting a crisis over secession.

By the end of 1832, in a sequence of events too rapid for Calhoun to assimilate, his arch-rival Martin Van Buren would replace him as Vice President and enjoy the same public perception of being in favor with the indestructible Jackson that Calhoun once enjoyed. And Calhoun was left with no issue to rally around to challenge Van Buren for the Presidency in 1836.

And so it was that Van Buren sat before Andrew Jackson one month into Jackson's second term secure in the knowledge that there was little that could come between him and sitting on the other side of the desk in front of him in four years. Then Andrew Jackson almost ruined four years of masterful scheming.

Van Buren watched Jackson shift uncomfortably in preparation for what he assumed would be a typical strategy session on the mundane issues of government that held far less appeal to Van Buren than politics itself. Jackson labored to get comfortable. The metal ball that Charles Dickinson shot into him twenty-seven years before was still lodged dangerously close to Jackson's spleen and seemed to cause him more trouble than ever. Van Buren knew that Jackson's doctors long before deemed it a miracle that the old General was still alive. For two decades, he fought off recurring infections in the area of the wound. It was a rare day that Jackson did not have at least a mild fever and, quite often, it was alarmingly high.

Despite having the well-earned right to complain, Jackson rarely mentioned his various maladies. So, when he started off this conversation with "Matt, I am old and not in the best of health these days" Van Buren's instincts were stimulated. Jackson's next words almost made the new Vice President faint.

"I think quite often of my successor and, obviously, I am hoping that it will be you. While I have little doubt of your ability to be elected in your own right, as you are well aware, a lot can change in four years. It also is not at all likely that I can survive another four years. If I die, I am worried that our common enemies will do what they can to block you from assuming the Presidency. I have determined to return the favor you bestowed on me. I am going to resign from office and ensure that you will become President."

Van Buren's nimble mind screamed. His finely tuned instincts told him immediately that this was not just a bad idea, it was potentially disastrous. Now he just had to collect himself sufficiently to keep from telling Jackson that his plan was incredibly stupid so that he could rationally and logically explain *why* it was incredibly stupid.

Van Buren knew himself well enough to realize that the most common criticism of him was that he was manipulative and opportunistic, which, of course, he was. To assume the Presidency in the manner Jackson suggested would be the most solid confirmation of his detractors' opinions imaginable. He would serve out Jackson's term with no hope of reelection. He would never exert influence in political circles again after an almost certain thrashing at the polls.

For years Van Buren methodically planned and executed his ascent. Jackson was right in one sense. Four years *was* a long time. But Van Buren knew the lay of the land well enough that it would take a cataclysmic set of circumstances to prevent his election. He and Jackson just had to be cautious the next four years and the office would be his.

Van Buren regarded Jackson for a moment more to give the President the impression that he was seriously considering the offer than anything else. He took a breath and hefted his weight forward. "Mr. President, I am truly flattered and grateful but I have to ask you to reconsider. First, the country elected you, not me. To the extent you are able, you *owe* the people that. Second, you know as well as I that my ability to govern would be weakened immeasurably if I succeeded you in such a manner. Finally, I am not ready. My tenure in your Cabinet was brief and I would prefer more time to watch and learn from your example." Van Buren knew this was not his most persuasive argument but it was the best he could do under exigent circumstances.

He knew that Jackson grasped the situation and Van Buren's aversion to the idea when Jackson replied, "I will do as you wish and reconsider. But I am not as strong as I once was which tells me that the people may not have elected the man they thought they did. We will talk again."

Van Buren wheezed his relief. He understood the President well enough to know that the subject was closed and that, even in his decrepit condition, Jackson still considered himself the toughest man in Washington. Jackson tried to repay a favor in kind but Van Buren felt confident that he was as happy that his offer was rejected as Van Buren was to reject it.

***

January 1835

Congressman Frank Pierce's eyelids slid far enough over his eyes to block some of the light that was intruding upon his preference for a gray morning. He swallowed to try and stimulate some moisture in his mouth as he stood for the invocation. He did not know the dead man very well. Davis was a quiet man, a Congressman with a long and thoroughly unremarkable record.

Pierce reflected briefly that this could easily be *his* funeral forty years hence. At thirty years-old Pierce was something of a curiosity. He had been a Congressman from his home state of New Hampshire for two years and for half a dozen years before that he was a dominant figure in the state legislature in Concord. Even though he was just reelected to Congress by an overwhelming margin, he was still hard pressed to identify what he accomplished in two years in Washington. For the most part his contribution was limited to his accessibility for anyone looking for a partner for a night on the town.

The night before Congressman Davis' funeral was particularly active. His best friend, Nat Hawthorne, showed up unexpectedly and Pierce could do no less than give him a tour of the Capital. Together they took in most of the taverns Washington offered, embellishing on tales from their college days reminding themselves how irreverent and virile they once thought they were. Their days at Bowdoin College were the two friends' only common thread but that seemed to be enough to sustain a somewhat improbable devotion between them. Pierce immediately commenced practicing law (a job that he did with notable indifference) and launched his political career shortly thereafter. Hawthorne, on the other hand, continued to write. His college manuscript *Fanshawe* was published to no acclaim as were a few short stories. To the casual observer Pierce's willingness to pay for an uninspired author's meals and drinks and the author's willingness to accept had the stench of opportunism. But Pierce valued this friend too much to quibble over a meal here and there. And the drinks paid handsome dividends in rollicking and piquant conversation.

Frank Pierce believed that Nat Hawthorne was the one person that understood Frank Pierce. He was the one person who knew that, despite being one of the youngest members of the House of Representatives and despite rising to the pinnacle of his state's legislature by the age of twenty-six, Pierce was not an ambitious man. Pierce succeeded in politics mainly because it came naturally to him. His personal charm and boyish good looks opened many doors for him. At least the doors that his father had not already opened.

Benjamin Pierce was nothing short of a legend in New

Hampshire. In the Revolution, he was on the front lines at Bunker Hill and subsequently camped alongside General Washington through the winter at Valley Forge. Ten years later he retired from the military as "General" Pierce. From there he served at the state constitutional convention for New Hampshire and was ultimately elected Governor where he served until 1829. Since then Benjamin Pierce's avocation was the promotion of Frank Pierce's political career.

As Benjamin Pierce's son, election to the office of his choice was a foregone conclusion. At his father's direction Frank declared himself a Democrat in the tradition of Thomas Jefferson, Benjamin Pierce's idol and occasional benefactor. The younger Pierce made vague allusions to States rights and his support for Andrew Jackson. The first time he ran for Congress no one even bothered to oppose him. In 1834 he was opposed but only half-heartedly. No one was going to beat Ben Pierce's boy and, in reality, no one really wanted to.

Before he left for Washington Frank's father gave him simple advice: "Vote Jackson." Frank took the advice to heart and voted with the President on virtually everything except an occasional trivial bill, to demonstrate his independence. The arrangement worked well as it left him plenty of time to establish himself as a favorite at Washington's numerous taverns and frequent receptions. In short, without really trying, Frank Pierce's future was extremely bright.

During the first campaign for Congress, Benjamin Pierce warned his son that continued bachelorhood would ultimately doom his political career. Although his father's legacy and his handsome appearance served him well with the ladies, he was not enamored with any specific woman. In one of his few original thoughts he decided upon Jane Appleton, the sister-in-law of one of his college professors and, more importantly, the daughter of a Man of the Cloth. Somewhat plain, devoutly religious and inordinately shy, Jane was stunned by Frank's marriage proposal. It did not occur to her until much later that their brief courtship resembled a business deal more than a romance.

General Pierce was pleased with his son's choice for a spouse. In Jane, he saw the perfect antidote to Frank's sometimes wayward habits. In two months of marriage, however, the remedy seemed to be having little effect. Frank continued to indulge himself rather than applying himself, usually leaving Jane alone to quietly long for the steady predictability of New Hampshire. Her inquiries into returning to New Hampshire had not yet reached the impassioned stage that they would and, until they did, Congressman Pierce ignored her.

Frank realized upon their arrival in Washington that, while Jane complimented him perfectly in New Hampshire where her shy manner was considered an asset, she was a liability in Washington. On the few occasions that she accompanied him to receptions the evenings were excruciating as she recoiled and shuddered from the bombastic and gregarious personalities that populated the Capital.

Nonetheless, Frank began the subtle process of trying to assimilate Jane to Washington. General Pierce made it clear that in 1836 he expected his son to assume his pre-ordained spot in the United States Senate. Gently, Frank informed his new bride that this city would be their home for a long time to come. Jane did not protest but, so far, she did not smile either.

What Nat Hawthorne understood more than Frank's family and the colleagues that surrounded him was that Frank Pierce really did prefer to be in New Hampshire. Matters of state bored him and, despite his ability to enchant, he disliked the social obligations of a Congressman. Nat Hawthorne knew that Pierce was never happier than when he was in the Granite Hills in the White Mountains plying a fishing rod or listening to a good friend like Hawthorne spinning a yarn while they shared a flask.

Congressman Pierce looked about him and wondered if any of these men had the same lack of moral and philosophical rectitude about their offices that he did. To his right was Jim Polk of Tennessee. No, there was no doubt in Pierce's mind that Polk was as dedicated a Congressman as one was likely to find. For ten years Polk assiduously mastered the arcane procedural rules of the House of Representatives and labored to the point where he was assured of being elected Speaker of the House at the end of the year. At the age of forty.

Polk was not particularly likable but Pierce could not help

but admire him. His passion for his job led him to work harder than any other public servant that Pierce ever knew. It was true that Polk had the charm and magnetism of a prune but he was seldom bested because he was *never* unprepared. It was this quality that Pierce admired and could not comprehend. The mountains of details that Polk seemed to be able to marshal effortlessly dumbfounded Pierce. Even for a man as colorless as Polk, all the minutiae he stored in his apparently brilliant mind had to be *boring*.

Because Pierce *was* popular and because he blindly supported the President, Polk seemed to tolerate him better than the many other Congressmen that attacked their duties with infinitely less zeal than the future Speaker. Polk's devotion to the President had already led some to refer to him derisively as "*Young* Hickory." Pierce was intelligent enough to recognize that he could only benefit from being associated with Polk. He was Jackson's prodigy and his indefatigable work ethic made it improbable that he would be on the losing side of an issue.

Pierce watched the distinguished man who was seated before him move forward to deliver what was sure to be a moving eulogy. Senator Daniel Webster of Massachusetts was a man who, at once, was the antithesis of Jim Polk and Frank Pierce. Webster was, like Pierce, originally from New Hampshire. His keen mind and mellifluous baritone set him apart and above from every other lawyer or politician in the country. After making a fortune with his dazzling oratory in the courtroom, Webster was elected to the House and then the Senate. He was no less eloquent in Congress and quickly came to wield the kind of prestige that Pierce knew he would never attain.

Webster was clearly no slacker but, like most men, he was no match for Polk's work ethic. Nor was he as charming as Pierce. But Daniel Webster was and always would be more than his young colleagues. He had an aura that gave him a reputation as a man of principle. He was as ambitious as the next man, but somehow he gave the impression of being above politics. Frank Pierce and Jim Polk had their principles but everyone knew they largely hinged on the whims of the old General in the White House.

Pierce glanced at the bald head that settled into the seat next to Webster's vacated chair. Another man of towering ambition who not only exuded being above politics but believing he was above *men* as a general proposition was the former President, John Quincy Adams. It still struck Pierce as unseemly that Adams returned to Washington as a lowly Congressman but, in spite of his anti-Jackson sentiments, Pierce was glad Adams was here. He enjoyed Adams' irreverence for much of the pomp that pervaded the floor of the House. Those who knew Adams for many years assured Pierce that the former President was a changed man. He still had the icy stare that defined him in his rise to and during his Presidency, but it was now combined with a sardonic wit that somehow endeared him despite his petulant nature.

For all of Adams' lack of regard for the formality of his office and for the intelligence of his peers, however, Pierce knew that Adams had a passion for the concept of government that was rivaled only in intensity by Pierce's apathy. Pierce often watched Adams napping at his desk on the floor of the House as bills were debated and wished that he had the self-assurance to doze off at his leisure. Yet when a bill of consequence came to the floor, the old man would rise and unleash a fury of logic and witticisms upon the unfortunate miscreant that dared to oppose him. Upon further reflection, Pierce would often realize that he disagreed with Adams, but at the time of debate Pierce sat frozen with awe and no small degree of intimidation at Adams' withering exposition. And it occurred to Frank that just as he could never relax like Adams, nor could he become as inflamed as Adams.

No, Frank concluded that he could never work like Polk, mesmerize like Webster or confound like Adams. What worried him was not that he could never attain what he saw as greatness but that his lot was worse than that. He worried that he may be like the Congressman to his left, Millard Fillmore of New York.

Pierce did not know Fillmore very well. He had heard the caustic references to him as "Dullard Fillmore" when some of his colleagues imbibed more than their share. From what Frank understood, Fillmore was bright and hard working. Oddly enough, he was backed by Thurlow Weed who was not known as the savoriest man in politics. But the stain apparently did not stick to Fillmore.

He was, like Frank Pierce, a handsome man. But, unlike Pierce, he did not drink or play cards, two passions that consumed many Congressional hours and cemented friendships in a city populated by temporary residents. Combined with Fillmore's haughty sounding voice and his wife Abby's propensity for speaking her mind, Millard Fillmore was not disliked among his colleagues, just ignored. Neither Fillmore or Pierce had accomplished much during their tenure in Congress, but at least Pierce could claim a modicum of popularity.

Weed was apparently trying to boost Bill Seward in the Senate and Fillmore in the House to become political kingpins like the Vice President Martin Van Buren became in New York. Pierce knew, at least as to Fillmore, Weed would fail. Fillmore did not have the personal charm or scheming mind of Van Buren but, more critically, Fillmore was given to fits of idealism, a weakness that Van Buren never succumbed to. In Fillmore, Pierce saw everything he did not want to become--a caricature of little consequence.

Daniel Webster's voice resonated as he summed up his eulogy imploring the Lord to accept the soul of the dead man before him. Pierce smiled inconspicuously at the thought that if anyone could persuade God to do something He was not otherwise inclined to do, it was Daniel Webster.

The House Chaplain presided over an extended prayer and invited the mourners to view the body. Pierce turned to his left and fell in line two men behind the man who *was* unpopular in Washington, the President. But the old General was almost a deity to voters and, to the extent Frank Pierce cared about such matters, he was aligned with Jackson's political philosophy of strong state governments and a minimal central government to provide for the common defense.

Pierce was astonished when he arrived in Washington at the amount of asperity that the members of the legislative branch had for the President and how little of it stemmed from a divergence of ideas. Much to his colleagues' dismay, the President turned out not to be a bumbling neophyte, but a shrewd and cunning politician. Coupled with his unprecedented popularity, Jackson was too much for a gathering of such monumental conceit to bear.

Pierce watched him labor toward the casket. He walked with a cane which clicked and echoed up the rotunda as he thrust it from beneath a flowing black cape as if to catapult each step. His face was whiter than the unruly hair that was still thick and flowing. The contrast with his cape gave him a ghost like appearance that may not have been far from reality considering the deliberate pace he was setting in getting to the open casket.

At first Pierce was not struck by the fidgeting man standing behind the Chaplain during the ceremony, especially since the Chaplain seemed to be paying him little mind. But now the man was standing at the end of the casket, *running his finger along the soles of the dead man's shoes*. It occurred to Pierce that he must be the only one who noticed this, as no one made a move to stop him. Pierce leaned to his left and watched the President look briefly at Congressman Davis' withered countenance and turn to commence the tapping of his cane and the long journey back to the Presidential mansion.

There was one tap, but no more. Pierce cut short his viewing of the corpse as he realized that the slow-moving procession had ground to a halt. The man stepped from the end of the casket and was pointing a small pistol at the President. As this fact registered, he fired. In the cavernous rotunda the discharge reverberated like a cannon. As the shocked mourners stood motionless, the President gaped down at his midriff awaiting signs of his demise. The man used this opportunity to withdraw *another* pistol from his waistcoat and pointed it at Jackson. In a voice tinged with rage, terror and delirium, the man announced, "King Andrew must die. I and I alone will rule Great Britain."

The words were so nonsensical that they had the effect of further delaying action on the bystanders' part and, once again, the man fired. Again, the report was deafening.

As remarkable as the scene was to that point, Frank Pierce was even more amazed to see that Andrew Jackson was still standing. As dozens of younger, healthier men gaped, the President raised his cane and lunged at his assassin. The first swing of the cane missed the man who was now being wrestled to the ground by an army officer. As the President raised his arm again two more military men hoisted him and dashed from the building with the writhing old man spewing invective on his assailant. The President's color was suddenly quite good.

In the days that followed Frank Pierce heard much about the President's good fortune. *Both* the assassin's pistols misfired. No bullet ever left a gun. There was a great deal of talk about divine providence in Andrew Jackson's life. How he carried a musket ball from a duel with the well-known marksman Charles Dickinson in his chest to this day and so on and so forth.

Pierce was impressed by these details. But he was more concerned about Jackson's reaction to the attack. Pierce knew that, in a similar situation, he would have done whatever he could to clear himself from harm's way. Yet a man thirty-seven years his senior who was reduced to shuffling from spot to spot chose to defend himself. For years to come Frank Pierce would be haunted by the syllogistic thought that if he was incapable of defending his own *life*, how could he ever defend an idea or a principle?

***

December 1835

In Jim Polk's mind, Andrew Jackson had one trait that was both a blessing and a curse. The President was as loyal a man as one could ever hope to meet. For Polk, this was a blessing because he probably would not be enjoying his new mantle as Speaker of the House but for Polk's reputation as a man very much in Jackson's favor. Jackson's faithfulness was a curse because just as he took a somewhat paternalistic view of Polk's political well-being, he also developed an interest in the career of Jim Buchanan of Pennsylvania.

From their first encounter, Polk and Buchanan circled one another like two predators trying to stake their territory. By the time Jim Polk arrived in the House of Representatives, Jim Buchanan was a veteran of the lower house. As in everything he did, Polk assumed his duties as a Congressman fully prepared. He became an expert on the House rules and their many intricate and sometimes mysterious uses. In the first bill he brought to the floor Polk attempted to take advantage of an arcane and long ignored rule to force a vote on his bill without debate. Buchanan requested that the new Congressman forego his request and allow Buchanan to comment. Polk refused. The normally placid routine of the House floor resounded with silence as Buchanan stared at the upstart from Tennessee. After Polk's proposal to forego debate was soundly defeated, Buchanan rose and, barely containing his fury, prefaced his comments on Polk's bill by stating, "I apologize to this honorable body for the time that has been taken to allow me to comment on Mr. Polk's bill. Of course, this inconvenience would not have been necessary but for the *young* man from Tennessee's ungracious attitude. Apparently, he is unwilling to consider the contributions of minds other than his own."

Polk was a planner, a lumbering strategist that prevailed through preparation and detail. He was not a gifted orator nor was he particularly likable. In other words, he and Jim Buchanan could not be more different. While Buchanan did not have the melodic voice of a Daniel Webster, he spoke with an ease and confidence that belied his lack of precision with facts or issues. The misfortune of being farsighted in one eye and near-sighted in the other caused Buchanan to close one eye or the other depending upon whether he was reading or attempting to see at a distance. This had the unintended ancillary effect of causing him to look as though he was earnestly absorbing every word that was being said to him, which was rarely the case.

Buchanan's personal charisma and his imposing presence served him well as a lawyer and now as a politician. Polk was a devoted husband. Buchanan was a confirmed bachelor. Polk was ambivalent about religion. Buchanan was an active church member and theologian of sorts. Polk disdained social gatherings. Buchanan relished both formal and informal gatherings. Polk was humorless and something of a plodder. Buchanan was quick-witted. Polk did not drink. Buchanan enjoyed a fine Madeira or other wines frequently. Polk was not just a politician, he was a student of politics and the political process. Buchanan had a rudimentary understanding of the procedures of the House and Senate and viewed political office as a series of rungs on a ladder toward the zenith of power, the Presidency. If one pondered his current task too long, he was apt to lose sight of more meaningful goals.

Jim Buchanan was far too mild mannered to harbor lasting resentment against Polk from their first encounter, but Polk was not. While Buchanan was outwardly pleasant to the Congressman from Tennessee, Polk was civil only to the point of necessity. He was relieved when Buchanan left the House to serve as Minister to Russia for a couple years. By the time Buchanan returned from St. Petersburg, Polk had consolidated his position in the House and knew that his dream of being Speaker would soon come true. As a result, Polk was not disturbed to hear that Buchanan would return to Washington as a Senator from Pennsylvania.

Ideologically, the two men were in agreement. They supported President Jackson first and foremost in all phases of policy. So, Polk was pleased that the Senate would have another member that shared his political philosophy, even if they were less than enamored on a personal basis.

Polk expended little mental energy on Buchanan's return until shortly after his election as Speaker. On a rainy evening in late March, a message was delivered requesting that he and Buchanan come to President's mansion the following day. When he arrived the President was engulfed in his faded shawl that those who saw him often knew to be a fixture as much as his indomitable white mane. Buchanan was already seated chatting amiably with the General/President. Polk, as always, was perfectly punctual. Neither too early or a moment late. Time spent chatting amiably was wasted time.

Polk was growing used to being summoned by the President. They often discussed legislation and the best ways to promote Jackson's and Vice President Van Buren's agenda. But Buchanan was a new participant in the process which Polk viewed with some apprehension.

As it turned out the President did not want to discuss House or Senate business. He wanted to talk about political business.

Polk was aware that in 1834 a handful of House and Senate seats were captured by candidates from the newly organized Whig party. By early in 1835 these new senators and representatives descended on the Capital and their message became clear. They were closely aligned with Henry Clay and Daniel Webster and their unifying theme was that they opposed anything and everything to do with Andrew Jackson.

At first Jackson was indifferent about the new party until its ideology became manifest. Jackson seethed about their name now recognizing it to be the taunt that it was--like the Whigs of the Revolutionary War that opposed King George, these Whigs vowed to battle King Andrew. They abhorred Jackson's vice-like grip on the reins of power that he manipulated by flouting his own personal popularity with common citizens and through unbridled use of the Presidential veto. His detractors argued that the veto was an emergency measure that was never intended to be used offensively. They declared that this was evidenced by the fact that in his first term alone Jackson vetoed more bills than the six Presidents that preceded him *combined*. Jackson was unmoved by such reasoning. Like his prodigy Jim Polk, Jackson believed that the veto, like any other tool or rule, was meant to be used unless the Constitution said otherwise.

Buchanan and Polk listened to the President's diatribe against the Whigs in a voice dripping with rancor for the better part of an hour. He likened their malicious inference about his monarchical tendencies to the attacks on his late wife and swore retribution against "the instigators of this defamation!" Although neither knew it, Buchanan and Polk were of the same mind. They were externally polite and attentive and internally anxious to reach the point.

Jackson concluded more like a General than a politician. "I'm telling you boys that this is not a matter to be trifled with. Getting control of this country out of the hands of aristocratic elitists like the Adams' was a long time coming. *By thunder,* I will not see a bunch of gossip-mongering, eastern snobs drag these great people back down that road." Buchanan was impassive while secretly deploring the President's predilection for melodrama.

Jackson paused, for effect, and told Buchanan and Polk, "You are the future of the Democratic party. It is the party of the people. You must not become so enraptured with your own ambition" and he looked at Buchanan "or your asinine rules and responsibilities" and he looked at Polk "that you forget what you must do. You *must* fight these people. Henry Clay is no fool. Keep your eye on him or the next person sitting in this chair will be him and all your ambition, rules and responsibilities won't amount to a hill of horse dung." He told Buchanan he wanted monthly updates from him on the activities of the Whigs in the Senate and likewise from Polk in the House.

Either he was unaware of the enmity between the two or chose to ignore it but the Jackson concluded with, "You two must work together to make sure that we leave no lie unanswered, no treachery unpunished and no opportunity to do battle unexploited. I suggest that you meet weekly to make sure *all* of our interests are protected!"

Now, nine months later, Polk trudged off to meet with Buchanan as he had been doing every week since the lecture from the President. Both men left the President's office stinging from the implication that they were somehow not attentive to their political obligations. They agreed to meet a few days later at which time Buchanan suggested that they were wasting time appeasing the old man and should simply prevaricate and tell him that they were meeting from time to time and let it go at that.

But Jim Polk knew that Andrew Jackson took his legendary status as a General far too seriously. An order was an order and Jackson would not be favorably disposed toward wayward soldiers. So, they met. And, as 1835 progressed, they came to appreciate one another's talents. They were not friends. They did not trust each other. But they were allies.

***

Virginia: February 1836

Tazewell Tyler climbed up onto his father's lap. Both father and son were engrossed in their own thoughts to the point that neither was aware of the other. "Taz" Tyler was six years old. He was quiet, almost studious (if such a thing is possible for a six-year old). In a family with a Mary, a Robert, an Alice and two Johns, "Tazewell" was an odd departure. But his father wanted to name his child for his good friend and the current governor of Virginia, Littleton Tazewell. So, Tazewell it was.

Taz twisted a piece of string around his finger until he reached the small figure of a man tied to the end. Then he pointed his finger down allowing the doll to fall free, spinning madly in its descent as the string snapped against its neck. The motion intrigued Taz, it did not entertain him. He leaned his head against his father's chest and repeated the experiment, over and over.

Taz was forty years younger than his father. Senator John Tyler reclined in his chair to accommodate his third son and seventh child. In the twenty-seven years since he became a member of the Bar, John Tyler practiced very little law but was now facing the dim prospect of actually being a lawyer. He moved into the Virginia legislature almost immediately, then rose to prominence by serving as Governor of Virginia just like his father. From there he moved on to the United States Senate.

John Tyler stayed true to his roots. His political career was marked by a tenacious devotion to the principles of his idol, Thomas Jefferson. He championed agrarian causes and battled any measure designed to make the federal government more powerful. For four years he helped thwart every attempt by President John Quincy Adams to pass measures to have the national government oversee the construction of canals, railroads and highways. Tyler argued in true Jeffersonian fashion that the responsibility for internal improvements belonged to the states. Washington's only obligation was to provide for the national defense.

To an idealistic aristocrat like John Tyler, Andrew Jackson represented the Jeffersonian ideal. A candidate for the common man. He joined in the gory campaign of 1828, attacking Adams' nationalist agenda and heralding Jackson's devotion to States rights.

Tyler was not oblivious to Jackson's capacity for erratic conduct. As a Senator, he voted for Jackson's censure when the

General exceeded President Monroe's orders by invading Florida and executing two British citizens. Unlike Henry Clay and John Calhoun, however, Tyler voted for censure not for political reasons but because Jackson exceeded the Commander in Chief's orders. After all, Washington's one legitimate function was to provide for the national defense and it would not do for soldiers to disobey their civilian commander.

As a young man, John Tyler's political baptism consisted of long hours spent listening to the ideological discussions of his father and his father's contemporaries like the great Jefferson himself. Tyler took their musings on States rights and the evils of a central government to heart, never accepting that these eminent men would compromise to attain other goals. As a result, his reputation was that of a naive idealist who was due some respect both for his father's legacy of good character and his own gentle demeanor.

John Tyler's troubles started by believing that *Andrew Jackson believed* in Jeffersonian code without qualification. Even Jefferson himself knew of Jackson's aptitude for political expediency along with unpredictable behavior. In short, Tyler never understood that while Andrew Jackson labored to portray himself as the man in Thomas Jefferson's sermons on the American ideal, Jefferson knew two things before he died. First, he knew that Andrew Jackson's devotion to States rights was exceeded only by his own ambition. Second, Jefferson knew that *Jefferson's* own ambition caused him to abandon the Jeffersonian code on more occasions that he cared to admit.

When John Calhoun and the President squared off over Calhoun's threat to lead South Carolina out of the Union if the President enforced the tariff on southern exports, John Tyler seemed to be the only member of Congress or the Administration unwilling to concede that Jackson and Calhoun were locked in a political duel that could only wound any bystander caught in the cross-fire. The President sent a message to Congress seeking authority to send troops into South Carolina to enforce the tariff. Thirty-two senators approved the President's request despite the fact that many of them *and* the President described themselves as champions of States rights. Fifteen senators that could not support the request were conveniently absent from the senate chamber when the vote was taken rather than run the risk of directly alienating Jackson. The final vote was 32 to 1 approving the President's request. The "1" was John Tyler.

Friends and foes alike were aghast at the Virginia senator's temerity. It was one thing for a northerner or a Whig to directly contest the President but it was positively suicidal for a Southern Democrat. Tyler was begged, cajoled and threatened to persuade him to renounce his vote. But with quiet determination he maintained that he meant no disrespect to the President. He simply could not abide federal troops being used against the very states that authorized the existence of federal troops.

Then Jackson recklessly gutted the Bank of the United States and deposited money in his "pet" banks around the country. Tyler was against the National Bank but he could not abide Jackson's slanderous attacks on the Bank and its officers. Tyler served on a bipartisan committee that reviewed the Bank and found its operations to be sound, much to Jackson's and his Congressional supporters' ire. The withdrawal of funds piqued Tyler's disenchantment with the President as Jackson accomplished through audacity what he could not through Congress.

Tyler no longer made any pretense about respect or deference to the President. He openly declared the President to be guilty of megalomania and voted in favor of censuring the President when the resolution was presented on the floor of the Senate by Henry Clay. In the process, Tyler became the rarest of creatures. He was a southern Whig.

Despite his open defiance of the Administration and the increasing enmity that southerners outside Virginia developed for him, John Tyler was still respected in his home state. But Tyler's rigid adherence to the principle of States rights proved to be his undoing. Not only did he believe that all power that could be vested in the states *should* be vested in the states, he firmly believed in the Virginia legislature's right to direct the performance and positions of Virginia's elected national officials, such as himself, under the state Constitution's peculiar "instructions" provisions. Under these provisions, Tyler believed he was beholden to the will of the legislature.

Tyler was no John Quincy Adams. Adams believed that he was elected because national issues should be decided only by those capable of understanding such issues. Adams would no more seek or accept orders from the Massachusetts legislature than he would from the King of England.

John Tyler, on the other hand, could not flaunt the mandate of his state legislature. Because of this basic tenet, Tyler was prepared to sacrifice his political career once and for all at the altar of States rights. The legislature directed its two senators to renounce their votes in favor of Clay's resolution of censure. His fellow senator and Whig from Virginia, Benjamin Leigh, refused to comply. But Tyler could not do this.

For weeks his closest friends anxiously awaited his response to the legislature. Those who knew him well knew that he would not decline to follow the legislature's directive which left him with only one option; to resign. When his friend Bill Gordon guessed that Tyler was contemplating resignation, Tyler was candid, "Bill, you know that the legislature's power of instruction was never intended for a matter such as this. I'm afraid I have no options." Gordon and others beseeched him to wait until the spring elections and see if the voters agreed with his vote of censure but Tyler found such political machinations distasteful.

Henry Clay came to Richmond and attempted to browbeat Tyler into telling the legislature what to do with its instructions in language that only Henry Clay could weave. But Clay discovered for himself that Tyler was as stubborn in private as he was in public on questions of principle. To a political soul such as Clay, Tyler was incomprehensible.

Tyler shifted Taz up on his lap and leaned forward to look at his letter of resignation again. Addressed to Vice President Van Buren as President of the Senate, Tyler did not like the message implied; that he was capitulating to the Administration. But he had little choice in the matter. The letter was too long, but his critics would expect nothing less. He was given to ornate prose and oratory. Yet even with its length, Tyler searched for an appropriate closing.

He looked at Taz who was humming a tune his mother liked to hum. Letitia was concerned about what John would do to support her and seven children if he left the Senate, but she also knew better than to question his judgment on matters of principle. The naiveté that confounded others attracted her to John Tyler.

Tyler nodded at no one or thing in particular and, leaning forward again, began to write:

> *I shall carry with me into retirement the principles which I brought with me into public life, and by the surrender of the high station to which I was called by the voice of the people of Virginia, I shall set an example to my children which shall teach them to regard as nothing place and office when either is to be attained or held at the sacrifice of honor.*

The irony of the February 29 date on his letter was not lost on the soon to be former senator from Virginia. He leaned back once more to watch Taz let the little man on the string plunge, twisting and twirling as he fell.

***

June 1836

For a man who never weighed much over a hundred pounds his entire adult life, James Madison was struck by how light he felt. He knew this sensation was significant because he had felt ponderous and listless for the better part of a year. For the last five months he rarely left the bed where he lay propped up on a mountain of pillows. His meager frame was all but lost in a sea of linens.

He knew the day was typical for late June because several of his blankets were turned back. This was good since he was incapable of moving the heavy quilts once he was trapped beneath them. He knew that Dolley, his nieces (who came to stay from time to time to help their beloved "Aunt Dolley and Uncle

Jemmy") and faithful servants and slaves were taking great care for his comfort. He did not bother to tell them that he felt no real effect from changes in weather or temperature anymore.

He opened his eyes briefly wondering if his vision might have returned and, for one last day, was disappointed again. The man that treasured the clause in his Constitution requiring the separation of church and state could not help pondering why the Lord had left him with an alert and lissome mind trapped inside a body with eyes that did not see, legs that could not stand, hands that could not write and a mouth that barely spoke. He accepted his condition with few complaints but did wonder what purpose he could possibly be serving.

His father named the family plantation Montpelier. James renovated the residence many times with his friend Thomas Jefferson's help. Despite this, just as Madison was always compared to Jefferson and found to come up short, so Montpelier failed to seriously rival Monticello. But this was of little moment to Madison. He treasured his memories of Monticello and, for the last ten years, seldom passed a day without thinking about his lost friend. He knew that despite all the adulation heaped on Jefferson and the many wonders of Monticello, neither Jefferson nor his fabled house had the one thing that Madison and Montpelier had and that Jefferson wanted. Dolley.

There was a consensus that James Madison would be remembered for his work in helping form the Union and writing the Constitution, not for his Presidency. By the same token, however, Dolley Madison would not soon be matched as a First Lady. Even now, almost twenty years after her husband left office, the residents of the nation's capital still yearned for her grace and style. Elizabeth Monroe's and Louisa Adams' parties were typically stiff, uncomfortable affairs. Even worse was the common view among Washington's elite that Andrew Jackson's niece was incapable of curbing the inherently base instincts of the people who consorted with her Uncle. With Dolley there was fun, but it was proper.

Dolley was still the belle of the Union. She aged but was still radiant. And people still puzzled over what caused her to become enamored with James Madison. As he lay on his deathbed he was more shriveled than ever which was truly a remarkable statement. For forty years people described Madison as a "shriveled little man." Yet this withered man won the affection of the woman that Aaron Burr, Thomas Jefferson and, ultimately, most of the United States adored and, in some cases, lusted after.

What Burr and Jefferson and most others never understood was that Jemmy Madison allowed Dolley to be Dolley. She was a clever, charming and vivacious woman who would never have relished the role of the quiescent, subservient wife. Men such as Burr and Jefferson relied on their own charisma and warmth to make their way--a woman was simply for companionship. But in James, Dolley saw a man discomfited by social by-play yet hopelessly immersed in politics. A man such as that needed a woman to help pave his way. As the years passed, James came to realize that Dolley was much more than adept at throwing parties and greeting guests. She was his best confidant, advisor and friend.

One of his oldest and most faithful slaves, Annabelle, propped him up signaling that feeding time had arrived. He started to wave her off but realized that his niece would insist that he eat *something* and thought it better not to argue. He watched the dim outline of Annabelle's black face while she jostled him about with the same ease that she lifted the pillows she was arranging.

He felt himself slipping and wondered what would become of Annabelle. He was glad that Tom Jefferson missed the last ten years in the country they worked so hard to form. While Jefferson saw the dangers that slavery posed to the young republic, he would have been deeply saddened by the events of the last decade. These "abolitionists" were bound to destroy the Union to "free" the slaves. Naturally, southerners resisted and both sides spoke openly of secession.

Madison knew that slavery could not survive in a country committed to the principles of the Constitution that Madison drafted. Yet he could not abide dissolution of the Union into an endless succession of states or countries with shifting alliances that never realized their collective potential, much the way

Madison and Jefferson always viewed Europe.

Madison was firmly convinced of the Negro's inferiority. But it was not this that caused his exasperation with the abolitionists; it was what he saw as their hypocrisy. While Negroes were ostensibly "free" in the north, they were typically abysmally poor and outcast. The abolitionists seemed hell-bent on assuring that *all* Negroes lived in *equal* squalor.

It was clear that, as an economic proposition, slavery was ultimately doomed. Machinery was being invented on what seemed like a daily basis that could do the work of several slaves. But southerners were proud and refused to accede to the preaching of the moralists of the North. Additionally, many of Madison's less courageous neighbors did not relish the thought of freed slaves roaming in their communities.

Even more distressing was his fellow southerners' apparent willingness to sacrifice the country when their views did not square with those in the North or even with the federal government. John Calhoun's irresponsible cry for secession just four years earlier over the newly enacted tariff struck Madison as the most ominous threat to the future viability to the Union. He told all who would listen that in preserving power to the states in the Constitution it was not his intention to allow the states to ever dissolve the Union. But this was not what the inflamed citizens of the South wanted to hear.

Madison's attempts to alleviate the nettlesome problem of slavery failed. Two years after he left office, he founded the American Colonization Society which, in turn, founded Liberia in West Africa as a colony for deported slaves. The Society's success was sporadic at best and, to Madison's stupefaction, was chiefly opposed by the abolitionists!

He argued in support of the Society's work telling both northerners and southerners that deportation was the only way to save the Union. His southern brethren were not interested in parting with their slaves simply because a handful of zealots in New England thought they should. Abolitionists chided him for relegating Negroes to a land where they were not guaranteed a voice in government as they would be in the United States if they were only set free. Madison countered that freedom went hand in hand with opportunity and that Negroes would never enjoy equal opportunity, especially if their freedom was gained by the northerners dictating to southerners. The Negro would be doomed to years of repression and discrimination. Madison proclaimed that it was only in their *own* country with their *own* people that the Negroes could truly be "free." Abolition of not only slavery, but the Negro problem was the only way the United States could stay united. His pleas fell on deaf ears.

Madison lay in his bed on June 28, 1836 knowing that he would die without confidence that the Union would endure. In six days it would be the sixtieth anniversary of the signing of the Declaration of Independence. The second and third Presidents, John Adams and Thomas Jefferson died on the fiftieth anniversary. Five years later, the fifth President, James Monroe died on the fifty-fifth anniversary.

Madison's doctor pulled a chair to the fourth President's bedside the night before and quietly assured him that, if he so desired, he could keep Madison alive long enough to join his predecessors on July 4th. Madison shook his head and declared that it was better not to trifle with a man's destiny.

But now, he knew he would not live six more days and he was disappointed. He would not change his instructions. He somehow knew that this sensation of etherealness was not to last. It was a sign just as he was sure that Adams', Jefferson's and Monroe's deaths were signs.

His niece cheerfully laid a newspaper over his legs so that she could read to him while she fed him his breakfast. A small piece of bread was offered which he started to chew but then, with great effort, reached up and removed from his mouth. Why eat when one was about to die?

His niece smiled at him quizzically, "What's the matter Uncle?"

Madison raised his head and replied in a gravelly yet light tone, "Nothing more than a change of mind, my dear." His head dropped. For the last time, James Madison came up just short of Thomas Jefferson.

PART III

THE LITTLE MAGICIAN, TIPPECANOE AND TYLER TOO

(1837-1845)

Chapter 1:
Martin Van Buren

Ohio: May 1837

The coach carrying Daniel Webster pitched rhythmically up and to the right with an almost soothing repetitiveness. Coupled with the monotonous southern Ohio landscape, Webster dozed intermittently. The spring blossoms failed to engage Webster and he seemed to care little that he could gaze across the Ohio River and see parts of Indiana and Kentucky, if he wished.

Like his fellow statesman from Massachusetts, John Quincy Adams, Webster's singleness of purpose allowed little time for idle sightseeing. He understood enough about Ohio, Indiana, Kentucky and these other western states to know that this was the frontier, peopled by adventurers, fugitives, homesteading farmers, trappers and all the other types of humans that elected Andrew Jackson to be President. Daniel Webster was not in the West to revel in the spring. He was here to make sure that the next President would be a Whig, not another Jacksonian Democrat.

The Whigs were led by Webster and Henry Clay. While Webster was not an admirer of the senator from Kentucky, they were bound together by a deep, abiding disdain for Andrew Jackson and the dictatorial power with which he imbued the Presidency. Together, Clay and Webster intended to assure that Martin Van Buren would serve but one term as President and that sanity and *representative* government would be restored in Washington.

The most offensive of Jackson's many misdeeds in office was already haunting Van Buren. Jackson's unilateral dissolution of the Bank of the United States and withdrawal of massive funds from the institution led to rampant speculation in western lands. The speculation was fueled by easy credit terms for what would turn out to be virtually worthless paper money. Much of the land that Webster was now surveying was settled by speculators who took advantage of Jackson's chaotic monetary system. Banks issued their own currency at their own values often lacking any sort of substantive backing in gold, silver or anything else of value.

The danger of the system he created finally became manifest by the time Jackson was ready to hand over the Presidency to his hand-picked choice, Van Buren. In a final rash act, Jackson issued the Species Circular requiring public land purchases to be paid in gold or silver. Speculators were left holding paper money that could not be accepted *or* redeemed. As quickly as the western land boom was born, it went bust. But now Martin Van Buren was President and, incredibly, less than three months into his Presidency, *he* was being blamed for the country's economic collapse. Clay and Webster were, of course, elated by Van Buren's misfortune but were nonetheless incredulous at the degree to which Andrew Jackson could escape criticism.

The outcome of the election of 1836 was pre-ordained the moment Andrew Jackson declared that Martin Van Buren was to be his successor. Webster and Clay and the other leaders of the Whigs were realistic enough to know that they would not defeat Van Buren or anyone else that had Jackson's support but they did not squander the election. Instead, they previewed the election of 1840.

While Van Buren was invulnerable in 1836, the Whigs knew that the Little Magician did not have enough hocus-pocus to overcome his effete nature and appearance. He was, in short, the antithesis of Andrew Jackson. When the first crisis arose, Webster and Clay knew that Van Buren was a far more inviting target for blame than Old Hickory. They did not reckon on the crisis arriving as soon as it did.

The Whigs did not throw their support behind any single candidate in the recent election. They ran many candidates, essentially holding a Presidential election just within their party and conceding the actual office to the Democrats and Van Buren. Even Webster's name was included on the ballot in several states.

Somewhat to the surprise of the Whigs and a great deal to their dismay, the election proved the obvious. The nation loved war heroes like Andrew Jackson. Because of this, William Henry Harrison polled more votes than all the other Whigs combined. Unlike Jackson, however, Harrison was not a forceful presence nor was he much of a politician. But the election told Clay and Webster that Harrison was the best hope of dislodging Van Buren and the rest of the Jacksonian Democrats. Thus, Daniel Webster, under the auspices of a western "inspection" tour, was in route to inform General Harrison that, even though the election was over three years away, Harrison was the likely Whig nominee. It was "likely" because both Webster and Clay wanted the Presidency for themselves but knew that they probably could not garner enough support for the nomination. Yet. They would work on their own behalves knowing that in the worst case, they would step aside to have Harrison elected.

Webster thought it remarkable that because Jackson and Harrison were revered for their battlefield exploits, they were automatically considered statesmen. While Webster did not wish to quibble about the two generals' valor (although he suspected that much of their legend was grounded in hyperbole), he was confounded by the general population's inability to understand the true nature of these men.

Jackson proved to be a statesman of the lowest form. More than once Webster stood on the floor of the Senate to lambaste Jackson's disregard for the Constitution and, consequently, for Congress. "King Andrew" usurped every power he could to have his way. James Madison's thoughtfully crafted but not unduly antagonistic system of checks and balances between the executive and the legislature devolved into a colossal war of wills under Jackson. But the voters were unsympathetic to Webster's disdain for Jackson's methods. The great General was still the great General, not a scheming politician that found the Constitution inconvenient.

William Henry Harrison could not have been more

different from Jackson. Nonetheless, the election of 1836 made it clear that the voters saw Harrison in much the same light as Jackson. They admired a military hero who could, theoretically, exhibit the same leadership in Washington as he could with an army. But General Harrison was as malleable as Andrew Jackson was firm. While both Webster and Clay would much prefer to be President themselves they wanted to take no chances with the sure thing they had in Harrison.

Webster and Clay decided that they would take a page from Jackson's book and begin the campaign of 1840 immediately, just as Jackson had done to John Quincy Adams in the aftermath of the Corrupt Bargain in 1824. Webster would inform Harrison that he would be the Whig nominee. But Harrison was not to campaign, Webster and Clay would take care of that. Harrison would stay at home while the Whigs sowed the seeds of discontent over Van Buren's policies (not to mention over Van Buren's aristocratic lifestyle). Then, once Harrison *was* elected, Webster and Clay would assume prominent roles in the Cabinet and guide the country away from Jackson's dictatorial disaster.

Webster and Clay never gave a thought to whether Harrison would be amenable to their strategy. He had no choice. He had raised nine children, had never been reimbursed for his military service, and was a marginal farmer. In other words, he was broke. To compound matters, he was supporting the widows of two of his sons and his grandchildren. John Harrison died of typhoid fever in 1830. At 36 years old, William Henry Harrison, Jr. had grown tired of hearing of his legendary namesake and died a hopeless alcoholic.

As a result, Harrison's reputation in Washington bore little resemblance to the esteem in which he was held throughout the country, especially here in Ohio. Around the Capitol he was a pathetic figure beseeching anyone who would listen to pay him for his military service and to give him some meaningful post consistent with his stature. But his pleas grew old and he was, for the most part, ignored.

Webster made note of the General's garden for the purposes of small talk and nothing else. Webster cared little for such mundane hobbies but he knew that Harrison was an accomplished horticulturist. So sad that the Whig candidate for the Presidency probably knew infinitely more about plants than politics or matters of state. For that matter, he probably knew more about plants than he did about war.

The garden was impressive with some exotic strains that Webster was sure came from Harrison's worthless mission to Colombia. Webster was not at all impressed that Harrison had a knack for raising flowers and vegetables. After all, the General was, basically, retired since he returned from South America, occasionally making a speech in between letters to Congress asking for money or a job. Webster thought, with as much free time as he had, Harrison damn well should be good at *something*.

The coach slowed to a halt in front of the Harrison family's smallish but well-kept home. Harrison's home was one of the larger residences in North Bend but did not compare favorably with Webster's own mansion in Massachusetts. It was an appropriate home for a "common" military man, but not for a renowned lawyer like Webster. Webster gathered more material for small talk and alighted from the coach.

The General quietly opened the door and was sidestepping down the front steps before Webster realized that Harrison saw him arrive. Harrison did not look particularly well. He had always been extremely lean but his cheeks had a sallow, drawn quality that made him look abnormally narrow. His dark eyes were still furtive, darting from Webster to the coach and back again several times as he walked from the bottom step to greet his guest.

Harrison extended his hand and said in a deep yet somewhat airy voice, "Senator, welcome to Ohio."

Webster's great voice boomed (knowing that the General's hearing was fading), "Thank you General. Am I to believe that all days are this beautiful in the west?"

Harrison smiled. "If you do believe that, I have several acres for sale that you might be interested in."

Webster laughed and with a charm bordering on genuine he launched into his litany of carefully logged items for conversation that would serve as a prelude to the purpose of his visit. Harrison had a servant take the Senator's bags to a guest room and before Webster and Harrison ever talked about the Presidency, Webster took a nap, received a full tour of Harrison's modest estate spending well over an hour discussing the various flora of the General's garden, met many children and grandchildren, ate a meal under the baleful glare of Harrison's wife Anna who knew all too well why Webster was in North Bend and, finally, retired to Harrison's study to sip brandy and talk.

Webster surveyed Harrison's modest library and thought it not at all surprising that a man with the General's modest intellect should have a library to match. He finally got to the one subject that he genuinely cared to discuss with Harrison.

"General, Senator Clay and I think the country made it clear that you will be President after the next election."

Harrison did not feign surprise or modesty. He knew that his showing in 1836 combined with the recent economic woes besetting Martin Van Buren made his election much more probable. And no matter how Anna felt about living in Washington, he needed the job for his family. Maybe, as President, he might be able to prevail on Congress to pay him what he was owed for his military service.

He did make a small concession to propriety. "Senator, isn't it a little early to be making predictions?"

Webster answered as though lecturing a dull-witted and forgetful adolescent. "General, Martin Van Buren may be a gifted politician but he is Martin Van Buren, not Andrew Jackson. The people will blame him for the Panic and we will certainly not dissuade them. When people are poor, they always want to blame someone else and the President is well-suited to the role. They will long for the more prosperous days they enjoyed under their hero, Jackson and that's where you, the conquering hero, will come in."

Harrison was a little irritated that Webster assumed that he did not understand why he could be elected President, but held his annoyance in check. "Yes, yes, I see. But the election is over three years away. Surely the Panic will have subsided?"

"Possibly. But even if it does, there will have been some hard times courtesy of the President."

"Surely Van Buren already understands how this will affect his candidacy?"

Webster came as close as he could to grinning. "Oh, I'm sure he does but I believe Matt is learning that you can't be a political boss *and* President at the same time. And if Martin Van Buren is not calling the shots, we can beat him."

Harrison made a lame attempt at sounding statesmanlike, "Well, certainly, if called, I will serve."

Webster resisted the temptation to roll his eyes. He responded matter-of-factly. "General, we assumed as much."

Harrison inquired, "What can I do?"

Webster was relieved. It was the question he came to North Bend to answer. "Absolutely nothing. Senator Clay and I have matters in hand."

"How should I answer questions about my candidacy? It happens, you know."

"How about 'Well, certainly, if called, I will serve.'"

Harrison nodded, unable to reconcile Webster's sarcastic humor with Webster's dour countenance. "Should I comment on Van Buren?"

Webster's eyes widened as he answered quickly and emphatically, "No. As a matter of fact, the less said, the better. I believe that the country's situation is bad enough that we actually will need to do little to get Van Buren out of Washington other than stoking the fires of discontent."

Harrison looked perplexed. "And how will you do that?"

Webster snorted. "Not to fear General. Not to fear. There is one issue that you should keep in mind that we hope you will, briefly, should the occasion arise, express support for."

"That is?"

"The government is running a substantial surplus. We believe it should be returned to the people." Webster watched Harrison's reaction carefully and was pleased. He knew the government surplus would be Van Buren's undoing. People were starving and the government had more money than it needed. To a consummate beggar like Harrison, this was an issue he could understand.

Harrison replied, "Yes, it is only fair." He rose hoping to

bring the conversation to an end. "Well, Senator I will do my best to not upset your obviously well-laid plans. I'm sure you're tired from your journey and I know you must travel early. May I get you anything before you retire?"

Webster declined politely and there was more directionless banter before the Senator made his way to his room.

Harrison stepped out to his porch to breathe the fresh spring air before going to bed himself. He heard his grandson crying and his daughter-in-law scurrying to keep him from disturbing Anna. Anna was not happy with the prospect of being First Lady but Harrison knew she would adapt. She always did. And he saw no other way to provide for his family. He was 64 years old and was dismayed that he still had to provide for a family but the death of his sons left him no choice.

What appalled him more, however, was the audacity of Henry Clay and Daniel Webster in treating him like a puppet for their political schemes. For years he tried to get Henry Clay to prevail on Congress to simply pay him what he was owed. Clay never delivered. Now Harrison finally understood that he was too valuable as a political tool to Henry Clay. If Clay just arranged the appropriation that Harrison sought for so long, Harrison would not be beholden to the Senator any longer. Harrison figured out too late that he was Clay's only hope, just as Clay was *Harrison's* only hope.

He closed his eyes and listened to the warbling call of a bird high in the sycamore above him. He would do as Webster and Clay wanted. If they wanted him to be President, they could probably make it so. But he would be a far different President than what they were expecting. Of that, he was sure.

***

Florida: December 1837

For generations, the Seminole Indians were unequivocal about their disdain for the United States. Unlike tribes in the West that just kept getting pushed farther west, the Seminoles were surrounded by white settlers to the north and east for decades. Starting out as a loose congregation of Creek and Hitchiti Indians in the 18th century, the Seminoles wrested control of the most fertile lands of northern Florida from the ambivalent Spaniards that occupied them and created a thriving agricultural community.

It was not long before the white settlers of Georgia began to covet the Seminole lands and made several ill-fated feints into the Spanish territory. The Seminoles were not about to yield their prosperity without a fight and they seized every opportunity to weaken their white neighbors. They supported the British in the War of Independence; they raided the border settlements of South Carolina and Georgia, stealing, butchering and raping with a savagery that struck fear in the hearts of the most courageous frontiersmen; and they gave shelter to escaped Negro slaves. In fact, the Seminoles now counted a large number of mixed race members among its tribe. They found that the Negroes not only were capable farmers able to share the techniques learned in their servitude, they could supply the Seminole warriors with invaluable information about the habits and routines of the white men, allowing for the most opportune attacks.

The United States tried for the better part of three decades to eradicate the Seminole threat and, incidentally, eliminate a refuge for fugitive slaves. Demands were made on the Spanish government to control actions within its territory to no avail. Ultimately, the First Seminole War began when Andrew Jackson was dispatched to drive the Seminoles from Georgia, which he did. But he then continued into Florida, razing Seminole settlements and executing two British subjects. The Spanish were convinced that they could not exercise control over Florida and John Quincy Adams negotiated a purchase of the wayward territory. Much to the Seminoles' dismay, President Monroe appointed Jackson to be the first governor of the territory.

Under Jackson, the Seminoles were subdued but not controlled. The General was ruthless in executing tribal members and making it clear that aggression against whites would not be tolerated, whether provoked or not. Jackson and his successors were adamant that the Seminoles must join the other Indians and move west. The territories east of the Mississippi River were to be reserved exclusively for white settlers. All Indians were to be relocated west of the Mississippi.

In 1832, the battered Seminoles agreed to move west of the Mississippi by 1835. But a small band of Seminoles led by a half-breed named Osceola refused to recognize the treaty and were arrested. It appeared that the Seminoles were finally pacified and preparations began for their emigration to the west.

A few months after the treaty, however, Osceola was released from prison. He stirred the Seminoles from their apathy, berating them for giving up the fertile lands of their home in Northern Florida for the dry wastelands west of the Mississippi. The son of a British trader and a Creek chief's daughter, Osceola was articulate, clever and brave. As 1835 approached the Seminoles revolted and refused to honor the removal treaty.

The Seminole repudiation was more evidence to President Jackson that the Indian tribes could not be trusted. Never a man to forget a slight, Jackson was determined to show those in Congress that criticized his excursion into Florida in the First Seminole War that not only was he right in proceeding into the Spanish Territory, he should have gone farther. He dispatched army and cavalry troops to quell the insurrection and to march the Indians out of Florida. The Second Seminole War was on.

The trouble with chasing the Seminoles into Southern Florida was that the American troops were, literally, marching into a quagmire. The swamps grew deeper and darker. And there was no end to the places to hide of which the Indians readily availed themselves. Osceola stirred their souls into revolt but they were led in battle by an Indian whose name described his method of battle with cold precision: Alligator.

Alligator's given name was Halpatter-Tustenuggee. When the Seminoles were "asked" by the United States if they would willingly relocate west of the Mississippi River in Arkansas, most of the Seminole chiefs said they would comply rather than risking bloodshed. Osceola inspired five chiefs to lead their people into the swamps to resist relocation. One of the five chiefs was Halpatter-Tustenuggee and he soon gained a new identity for stealth and lightening-like surprise attacks like the huge reptiles that he inhabited the swamps with. For over two years the

Seminole War was really a series of ambushes to which the hapless white troops fell prey like sheep wandering off a cliff.

After two years of soldiers mysteriously disappearing into the swamps, the army decided to send a less conventional commander to Florida. Colonel Zachary Taylor remembered the jungles of Florida from years before when he was ordered to make Florida ready for Andrew and Rachel Jackson. He doubted the wisdom of President Monroe in sending Jackson to be the first governor of Florida at the time. Now he was certain of the mistake.

The Seminoles' distrust of the whites was the most acute of the many Indian tribes he fought and Zachary Taylor made a career of fighting Indians. Taylor knew that Andrew Jackson despised Indians second only to the British. So, he was not surprised that the Florida Indians were not inclined to believe that Arkansas would be an improvement over Florida. And, having been to Arkansas, Taylor knew they were right.

As much as the terrain that they had to fight upon, the white troops were hampered by the renegade slaves that sided with the Seminoles. If the Seminoles were conquered, the slaves knew that they would not be joining the Indians on the march to Arkansas. They would be *lucky* to return to their white masters in Georgia and South Carolina. Taylor already knew of several instances where captured slaves were tortured by the frustrated white troops who, even more than being annoyed with their crafty Indian foes, were outraged by the effrontery of the fugitive "niggers." Zachary Taylor owned slaves and knew slaveowners, especially here in the deep South. He knew that he would not be chasing the Seminoles through the muck and the marshes if there weren't so many runaway slaves hiding out in Indian country. But it was getting more and more dangerous these days to admit that you were fighting to keep your slaves in line.

Colonel Taylor was dismayed to find that over half his troops in Florida were volunteers, mostly from Missouri. He knew from his days chasing Black Hawk back across the Mississippi that volunteer troops were far better runners than fighters. But at least he had some professionals under his command. Enough to fight a small, wayward band of Indians by his reckoning.

It was Christmas morning. The camp was stirring with men ready to follow orders and finish their march to Lake Okeechobee. For once, the men were subdued. Even the men without families kept quiet in deference to the irritation of the men who did. Colonel Taylor spent so many Christmases in army camps that he couldn't remember what it was about Christmas that he missed, but he still knew that he belonged with Peggy and their two daughters and son.

As much as he missed his wife and three children, he missed Knox even more. She was the daughter that he could not resist; the daughter that charmed him and could get anything from him. They were the most alike of any of his children with the exception that he was a short yet gangly old soldier with an oversized head that no one would ever accuse of being handsome and she was, quite simply, beautiful. She was also strong-willed and defiant yet disarmingly charming.

With her military father away in the swamps of Louisiana and fighting Indians in the Northwest, young men flocked to the Taylor plantation to pay their respects. She made them all feel that they should hold out some hope that they might be blessed with her affection but only one stood a chance. He was an army lieutenant named Jefferson Davis. Davis served as Taylor's aide in the much-heralded but uneventful Black Hawk War.

Jeff Davis' charisma and dashing personality made him popular with many young women but Knox Taylor was the prize he coveted. Zachary Taylor responded to the announcement of their intention to marry with unexpected ferocity. He was adamantly opposed to the suggestion that his daughter, especially *this* daughter, would marry a military man. No, he declared, his child would not endure the prolonged absences and neglect that his own Peggy endured. Peggy Taylor was a semi-invalid from raising four children on her own while managing a plantation. To thwart the proposed union, the colonel repeatedly sent his lieutenant on far-flung and often meaningless expeditions to keep the young lovers apart. But when Davis was ordered to report to Fort Smith, Arkansas, Davis made a quick trip back to Louisville. Jeff Davis and Knox Taylor eloped.

After their marriage Knox and Davis made their way to Mississippi where Jeff Davis planned to become a country gentleman and plantation owner. But in less than three months after they secretly married, Davis and his young bride both contracted malaria. A severely weakened but recovering Davis wept as he watched Knox die. Davis resigned from the army but returned Knox' body to Kentucky and begged Zachary and Peggy Taylor's forgiveness. The colonel never forgave him.

Knox' death left a void that her father was unable to fill. Instead of drawing him closer to his other children and home, he plunged into his soldiering duties with a zeal that bordered on reckless. He became more cavalier and aggressive in his strategy. The results were often more dramatic, but there was no satisfaction. He drove his men relentlessly seeing young Jefferson Davis in every one of their faces. Ultimately he relented realizing that his soldiers should not pay for Davis' mistakes. But he privately swore that he would never forgive Jefferson Davis for taking his daughter from her home where she would still be alive today. To celebrate Christmas.

He knew that today would be the last Christmas for several of the young men under his command. His troops would win the battle that would undoubtedly take place on this Christmas Day but not before they were ambushed by the handful of Seminoles that he knew were waiting in the swamps that lay all around Lake Okeechobee.

A private from among the Missouri volunteers appeared at Taylor's side as the colonel wrestled with his saddle. The young soldier requested permission to lead the men in a prayer for Christmas morning. Taylor glanced furtively about realizing that they were undoubtedly being watched by an Indian scout. He grunted his assent as he jerked on his cinch. "Then be ready to move out," he growled.

He leaned on his horse's rump and watched a small circle of men gather around the private, nervously shifting back and forth with the discomfort of men declaring their faith out in the open where not only God, but everyone else could see. Taylor would rather be on his way but he understood the need to make some concession to Christmas and, unknown to the Missouri volunteers, he figured they would need all the divine assistance they could get. It was Taylor's plan to have them lead the march into the swamp. The colonel had little faith in the volunteers and assumed that they would break and run at which point his regulars could take up the charge. At best the volunteers would be used to flush out the Seminoles, at worst they would serve as target practice for the Indians.

Colonel Gentry approached and inquired about Taylor's plan for the march to Okeechobee. Taylor did not look at him but said quietly and firmly, "You will lead the Volunteers. You'll be followed by the fourth and sixth infantries."

Gentry grew noticeably pale. "A direct assault sir? Have you considered a left and right flank?"

Taylor swung himself into his saddle and looked down at Gentry. "I don't want any cross-fire. Good Lord Gentry, you're not scairt of a few Indians are you?"

Gentry flushed. "Certainly not sir. Just trying to minimize losses."

Taylor stared at him with flinty directness, "So am I, Colonel. But I also need to teach these Indians that we mean business. Now let's get."

The Missouri Volunteers marched at the head of the column trailed by the regulars and officers on horseback. As the ground grew soggy, Taylor and his officers dismounted, tethering their horses and securing supplies. The column marched on. It was almost noon as they climbed a small hill to see Lake Okeechobee glimmering in the Florida sun. Between them and the lake there was a meandering stream that wound its way into the lake. Grass taller than any of the soldiers and a stand of pine trees lay on the other side of the stream stretching to the banks of Lake Okeechobee.

Gentry pursed his lips and looked at Taylor. Taylor nodded him forward and Gentry stepped down into the marsh. His first step brought water up above his ankle. His second step flooded his boot with water. For five more steps he sloshed as quietly as he could but still make progress. He took no more steps. From the timber on the far bank of the stream a clap of rifle fire fell Colonel Gentry. He pitched forward into the muck and his blood began to blend with the black water of the swamp.

Taylor paid no mind to the Missouri Volunteers that were splashing away from the stream in retreat. He assumed that they would run. Instead, he watched as the Indians moved into the swamp. Taylor knew that Alligator believed that the white soldiers were in such disarray that he could advance unnoticed. Three groups of Indians and a band of Negro warriors slid into the tall grass and moved with the ease of, well, an alligator.

Taylor alone among the white soldiers watched the maneuver with admiration. Volunteers continued to fall into the water which now was a kind of sickly purple. Taylor raised his hand and yelled as quietly as he could to Colonel Thompson to move the Fourth Infantry into the swamp and prepare to engage the enemy. Taylor muttered to himself. He knew he was about to lose a lot of men but the Indians could not ultimately defeat his superior numbers and firepower. With the enemy in his sights, his job as a soldier was victory. He would not have men die in vain if he could help it.

The swamp halfway between Taylor and Lake Okeechobee became a turbulent mass of blood and water as men fought with the ferocity that only men fighting for their lives can muster. Gentry's carcass was already being ravaged by real alligators. Taylor watched Colonel Thompson spin in agony, clearly hit, as he descended into the water. Indians began to fall too. The Volunteers that made it out of the swamp began to slow with some turning to watch the regulars and the Indians, first in horror, and then shame.

The regulars began to get their bearings and spontaneously began fighting as a unit. All but one of Taylor's officers were floating in the swamp as their troops fought on knowing that there was no way out of the swamp alive without fighting. The Seminole and Negro warriors sensed their loss of the advantage and splashed to the flanks to retreat.

Gentry was right. A direct attack was allowing the enemy to retreat. Taylor's land lubber troops haplessly attempted to pursue but their foes almost glided across the water. There would be no more major battles. One of the many things Taylor admired about Indians was their unwillingness to fight meaningless battles. Now Alligator knew that, even with advantage of surprise, he could never match the white troops in numbers or weapons. He would be a nuisance, but nothing more.

The Seminoles were defeated. By capturing Lake Okeechobee, Alligator was cut off from the rest of his tribe that would soon be marching to Arkansas. As time permitted, Colonel Taylor would find Alligator and send him and his handful of rebels west as well. But now there was no rush. The soon-to-be General Taylor knew Florida was as safe as it would ever be. And his fellow slaveowners could rest easier knowing that their slaves would soon learn that, if they ran to Florida, the Seminoles would not be waiting.

***

Washington: February 1838

The Speaker of the House of Representatives gave no visible sign of discomfort. Jim Polk obtained his current post through dogged perseverance. He served on countless committees including being the chair of the House Ways and Means Committee. He demonstrated repeatedly that few were his equal on questions of procedure. It also did not hurt that Andrew Jackson trusted him implicitly and went to great lengths to show his support for the 42-year-old Congressman from Tennessee.

Polk liked the mechanics of politics and governing. Unlike his mentor Jackson, Polk did not rely on personal charm or the loyalty of others to achieve his goals. He methodically and, at times, maddeningly, *worked.* He was prepared to the point of absurdity at times but it earned the grudging admiration of even his foes.

What the Speaker did *not* like was the emotion and sophistry of politics. As a result, the House became a model of efficiency with a minimum of rhetoric under his stern leadership. At least it was.

The issue now pending before the House had come to dominate debate despite the best efforts of Polk and his fellow southern Congressmen. It was the Gag Rule. It was a resolution that Congress could not interfere with slavery in any of the states so it should table and not receive any petitions concerning slavery without discussion. The resolution received obvious support from southern Congressmen but also was supported by several northern Congressmen who either favored the states' right to determine the legality of slavery within their own borders or simply were tired of hearing anti-slavery petitions that they knew they could not act on for lack of votes or power.

The petitions had become an ongoing nemesis for both the House and the Senate. The charge was being led by the American Anti-Slavery Society, a group that grew to about 150,000 members from its inception in Philadelphia in 1833. The Society was headed by William Lloyd Garrison, a newspaper editor with a moralistic bent. Garrison and other members of the Society like Arthur Tappan produced articles, pamphlets and handbills at a furious pace denouncing the practice of slavery and deriding the slaveowners as the most wicked of citizens. President Jackson declared that the abolitionists and the Society, in particular, must be silenced for their "incendiary" activities. He openly praised the anti-abolitionist mobs that raided Society meetings and demanded legislation punishing postmasters that delivered abolitionist propaganda.

As its sources for expression dwindled, the Society hit upon its constitutional right to petition, a right that even the fearless Jackson would be hesitant to trifle with. Its members inundated Congress with petitions to outlaw slavery in the District of Columbia, which, unlike the states, was clearly under the province of Congress.

Southern Congressmen viciously opposed the prohibition of slavery in the nation's capitol for both symbolic and practical reasons. To ban slavery in Washington D.C. gave credence to the abolitionists' claims of the South's moral turpitude. It also removed the buffer that separated Virginia from Maryland, a half-hearted slave-holding state and Pennsylvania, home of the Society and some of the most zealous abolitionists.

But the Society was tenacious. It had its Congressmen from the North introduce petition after petition resulting in the virtual paralysis of business on the floor of the House much to the

Speaker's consternation. In all, the Society's Congressmen introduced over 130,000 petitions in the last year.

To Polk, the endless speeches cursing or praising slavery were torturous. Important work lay fallow while the stream of petitions was presented, debated and, uniformly, rejected. Finally, in 1836, when Polk could take no more, he encouraged Henry Pinckney of South Carolina to present a resolution calling for all petitions or bills concerning slavery to be immediately tabled and sent to a committee that would report back on such petitions. Polk, in turn, having the power to appoint such a committee made sure that its members were predominantly southern or sympathetic to the South's States rights arguments. The committee met for three months while other non-slavery work was done and came back with a recommendation that all slavery petitions be tabled and that the House allow no further debate on the issue of slavery.

Polk allowed some short debate by southern Congressmen, including a few who said Pinckney's proposal was too *weak.* They argued that the proposal failed to point out that Congress, in their view, had no power over the question of slavery. But Polk was unconcerned with the constitutional issue and wanted only to dispose of the issue of slavery. He was more concerned with the constitutionality of not allowing debate on the subject of slavery within the House. He knew that few of his fellow representatives could articulate the constitutional objection to Pinckney's resolution. One of the few who could had started to struggle to his feet, alarming Polk. The old man raised his hand and called for recognition. Polk quickly turned to George Owens from Georgia who, by prior arrangement moved for a vote. Polk called for a vote.

The old man thundered "Am I gagged or am I not?!!!"

Polk replied tersely, "Debate has been terminated. You are out of order."

The old man appealed stating that debate was improperly concluded. He lost. The vote proceeded. Pinckney's "Gag Rule," as it would come to be called, passed.

Polk called for new business but not with the sense of satisfaction he anticipated. He realized he made a mistake. The "old man" was John Quincy Adams. He dutifully presented his abolitionist constituents' petitions in the years preceding the Gag Rule, but without much fanfare. He clearly opposed slavery but seemed to share Polk's antipathy toward purposeless debate.

When Adams rose to speak, Polk assumed that Adams was prepared to question the constitutional propriety of Pinckney's resolution and Polk was correct in this assumption. By failing to recognize Adams, however, Polk knew that he unleashed the tiger. Adams did not suffer such an affront quietly. Having disposed of incessant debate of slavery, Polk realized that he sparked a new lightening rod for the abolitionists in the Gag Rule. And he created the worst possible adversary in Adams, one of the few Congressmen that could match Polk procedural move for procedural move.

Here, almost two years later, he listened as Adams delivered yet another dissertation on the Gag Rule, slavery and the horrors of the South. Southern Congressmen shouted objections but Polk dared not rise to Adams' bait. Adams found a home among the abolitionists and was clearly delighting in it. They came to refer to him as "Old Man Eloquent" and the former President who, much like his father, never enjoyed any measure of popularity, stoked his ego on the flames of the abolitionists' fanaticism. Polk found it ironic that the son of the man that imposed the Alien and Sedition Acts now was fighting passionately for his freedom to speak and not be "gagged."

For two years Polk presided as southern Congressmen spewed invective upon Adams and, in turn, Adams tormented the southerners. Polk was not sympathetic to Adams but he despaired of getting his hot blooded southern brethren to contain their fury with the former President.

Shivering on the dais surveying activities in the well, Polk sat musing about the possibility of returning to Tennessee to run for the soon-to-be vacant post of Governor where he could get back to doing some real work. This infernal debate over the morality of slavery had grown wearisome. Back home in Tennessee the issue was settled. As Governor, he would not be forced to endure the irrational harangues of the abolitionist zealots. Sarah would not object and might even enjoy the more prominent post of First Lady of Tennessee. He would discuss this with Jackson.

The Speaker's reverie evaporated with a jolt as John Quincy Adams' words came into focus. The bald old man leaned against his desk addressing the House. He was attempting to introduce yet another Society sponsored petition offered by nine black female slaves from Virginia. As usual, his arguments were articulate, logical, persuasive and ignored. Typically, he would begin by discussing the Gag Rule but then would stray to the evils of slavery eliciting the hisses and objections of southerners who called for Adams to be ruled out of order for discussing slavery in violation of the Gag Rule. Polk would occasionally reprimand Adams but he knew that the rebuke only fueled the fire.

On this day, Adams broached the subject of slavery again and the catcalls and insults began anew. But to the astonishment of even the most ardent abolitionist Congressmen in response to the argument that slaves (particularly slaves of "infamous character") had no right to petition, Adams declaimed, "If these were infamous women, then who is it that made them infamous? Not their color, I believe, but their masters! I have heard it said in proof of that fact, and I am inclined to believe it is the case, that in the South there existed great resemblances between the progeny of the colored people and the white men who claim possession of them. Thus, perhaps, the charge of infamous might be retorted on those who made it, as originating from themselves."

Adams' sly grin told Polk that Adams knew that his speeches had become too routine. A bit of controversy was needed to reclaim control of the debate. Polk watched Adams stand with the smug satisfaction of knowing he hit his mark as southern Congressmen leapt to their feet and heaped the vilest insults they could muster on the Massachusetts Congressman. One particularly bellicose Georgia representative demanded satisfaction before it apparently occurred to him that a duel with the diminutive Adams would not create a legacy for bravery. Polk marveled that his fellow southerners would create such a stir over what they knew to be true. Many slaveowners *did* have relations with their female slaves. Why give Adams the gratification of denying what was undeniable?

Polk pounded his gavel, but without conviction. When some order was restored he called for a brief recess. He climbed down from the dais and headed for the cloakroom. A scowling Jim Polk was not unusual but his dismay was transparent on this day.

Polk was a harsh taskmaster, especially on himself. He could not assess what he detested more, Adams, or himself for having ever wakened the old man into fighting the Gag Rule. If these fools were satisfied to engage in interminable debate over something as meaningless as the status of a bunch of illiterate Negroes, so be it. He would go back to Tennessee.

***

December 1838

Millard Fillmore sat in the front row of the Senate Gallery. His arms were folded on the railing as he leaned forward to get a fuller view of the chamber. A few senators shuffled papers at their desks in the Well but, for the most part, it was quiet. Soon, others would join Fillmore to listen to Senator James Buchanan speak.

Fillmore had just been elected to another term as a member of the House of Representatives. There was no doubt about getting reelected. He was in the Whig Party and the economic panic of 1837 proved to be politically catastrophic for the Democrats. Whigs were swept into office all over the country. For a reasonably prominent Whig like Fillmore, there was little need to campaign.

Thurlow Weed was in his glory. Bill Seward was the new Governor of New York and both the Senate and House as well the New York legislature were filled with Whigs. More importantly, they were Weed's Whigs. The newspaper editor realized his dream of displacing Martin Van Buren as the king of New York politics.

Weed cared little about national politics. He knew that New

York's influence on the makeup of the national government was a given. If he controlled New York, he automatically wielded tremendous influence nationally. *That* was the syllogism that Martin Van Buren forgot when he left New York thinking that he could control New York and Washington *from* Washington. Weed knew better and patiently built a machine to replace Van Buren's Albany Regency. He stayed in New York and was now firmly in control.

Despite Weed's new preeminence, Millard Fillmore was a problem. Shortly after the election, Weed summoned Fillmore to offer him the position of Comptroller of the State of New York. The Comptroller was the second most powerful post in the state next to the Governor. With Fillmore as Comptroller, Weed would have the two most well-known politicians in the state in control. Both Seward and Fillmore owed their prominence, in turn, to Weed. He offered Fillmore the post despite the fact that Fillmore worked against Seward's election. Weed was able to easily forgive this affront to the Machine since, first, there was little chance that Seward (or any other Whig) would lose and, second, Weed really did not mind that his top two lieutenants were antagonistic. It lessened the likelihood that they would conspire against him.

But Weed misconstrued Millard Fillmore's motivation. Fillmore liked politics and actually viewed himself as public servant. Power did not have as much allure to Fillmore as a good challenge. He was loyal to Weed because it helped him get into politics and stay there but he had no interest in the powerful but undemanding duties of the Comptroller. Fillmore was popular enough to be elected to the House of Representatives without Weed's help as long as he wanted. Maybe even the Senate. He was wealthy and was not disturbed in the least by the prospect of returning to the practice of law. In short, there were advantages to being aligned with Weed, but Fillmore would not sell his soul.

Weed was dumbfounded by Fillmore's rejection. His short-lived gloating over the election results was replaced by a furious outburst, cursing Fillmore and threatening reprisals. It took all of Fillmore's charm and weeks of maneuvering to convince Weed that *his* power was not in danger and that Fillmore was not breaking ranks. Fillmore was still faithful, he just did not want to be Comptroller. Weed was perturbed but finally withdrew his vow of political ruination for Fillmore. Nonetheless, Fillmore understood the significance of the rift and knew that he could never count on Thurlow Weed or Bill Seward for support again.

Fillmore lifted his chin above the railing enough to see that Senator James Buchanan had entered the Well and was standing shuffling through a thin stack of paper on his senate desk. A few other senators filed in exchanging greetings, dipping snuff and, of course, furtively checking the gallery to see if there were any constituents for whom they could perform. But the gallery was empty except for Fillmore and Senator HerBest's mother who sat quietly knitting something. She was a regular, much to Senator HerBest's dismay but to the delight of his fellow senators who took great pleasure in making sport of the Senator.

Henry Clay and Daniel Webster appeared below Fillmore. Even though Fillmore, Clay and Webster were all Whigs, their lack of regard for one another was typical of this loose amalgamation that was created and, at least temporarily, flourished, on one unifying principle--opposition to anything Andrew Jackson and Martin Van Buren favored. While the public still was partial to the old General, it had grown to despise Van Buren.

While Clay and Webster held similar views and were united in their disdain for Jackson and Van Buren, they were both ambitious and worked together warily. The subject at hand for the Senate was of little interest to the public but could have profound consequences for the Federal Government. Webster and Clay's scheme was to pass legislation removing the power of the President to dismiss his own appointees and, instead, to place the power to fire in the hands of the Senate which, of course, Clay and Webster controlled.

Even to a Whig like Fillmore, Webster and Clay were making an audacious grab for power. It made little sense that they would worry about Van Buren since the Little Magician stood almost no chance of reelection. It was already a foregone conclusion that General William Henry Harrison would be the next President. To Fillmore, it was a telling statement about the

Whig party that even with their own President in the White House, Clay and Webster were not inclined to leave their dominion to chance.

As a politician, Fillmore was disenchanted. As a lawyer, he was intrigued. He did not know James Buchanan well. Despite a reputation for unbridled personal ambition, Buchanan emerged as a leading Democrat and an acknowledged authority on the United States Constitution. His training as one of Pennsylvania's premier trial lawyers served him well in attacking his foes. And, apparently, the viability of the Constitution was one of the few concrete passions Buchanan held.

Fillmore served briefly in the House with Buchanan where the Pennsylvanian successfully argued against legislation that would have prohibited the Supreme Court from reviewing state legislation for conflicts with the U.S. Constitution. Buchanan's position then was courageous because his benefactor, Andrew Jackson himself, was supporting the legislation. Buchanan was expected to support the legislation like any good States rights democrat. But Buchanan saw the legislation as short-sighted and, knowing full well that the states' various positions on slavery could lead to questionable legislation vis-à-vis the Federal Government, he took his political life in his hands and helped defeat the bill. Fillmore assumed Buchanan was much relieved when President Jackson, in a rare moment of humility, conceded that Buchanan's view had merit.

Having established that he would argue in defense of the Constitution even if it meant imperiling his own political neck, Buchanan was the logical choice to lead the charge against Webster and Clay. In Van Buren's plan to oppose this bill designed to enervate his power, Fillmore was sure that Van Buren had not forgotten Buchanan's daring challenge to the Jackson administration. It was typical Van Buren to remember someone's past position to serve a current need.

If Buchanan was effective and defeated Webster and Clay in the Senate in this new attack on the separation of powers, Fillmore would not have to face this issue in the House. The lawyer in Fillmore was silently pulling for Buchanan hoping that he would not have to confront this issue as a politician. It was going to be difficult enough to stay in Thurlow Weed's good graces without running afoul of Henry Clay and Daniel Webster too. But Buchanan was not doing the unpredictable in this skirmish, he was defending the position of his party's President and his party was in the minority in the Senate.

Buchanan cleared his throat and cocked his head to the side as he signaled to be recognized. Vice President Richard Johnson hailed Buchanan, right on cue. Fillmore mused that it must have pained President VanBuren to have to rely on Richard Johnson to assure that Buchanan gained and controlled the floor. Johnson was a classic Jackson/Van Buren nominee. He was an ex-soldier from the backwoods of Kentucky that served under General Harrison at the Battle of Thames and boasted of having killed the Indian Chief Tecumseh. He was a notoriously unkempt and uncouth man thus making him the perfect antidote to the fastidious Van Buren. Even though Van Buren enjoyed some popularity in the South, he could never match a common, Indian-hating soldier like Johnson at gathering votes in that region.

But two years after Johnson was elected to be Martin Van Buren's Vice President, the South learned what a handful of northern Democrats knew all along. Johnson was not a bachelor as was believed. At home in Kentucky he resided with a Negro woman and their two children. Richard Johnson went from folk hero to the most vilified man in the South. And he was another reason that Martin Van Buren would not be reelected, even though everyone (including Johnson) knew that Johnson would never be renominated. In a country that was beginning to fray at the seams over slavery, the South viewed Richard Johnson as the epitome of what the future would hold if the abolitionists had their way.

Fillmore gazed at Johnson recalling how Thurlow Weed crowed about the "nigger-lovin' Vice President" that insured that a Whig would take over the White House. He remembered how Bill Seward left the room in disgust over Weed's crass back-handed endorsement of Southern morality. But Seward was too close to becoming Governor of New York at that point to stand completely on morality and shuck Weed altogether. This was one of many things Fillmore disliked about Seward--he was self-righteous, but only when it was safe.

The irony of the Whigs relying on the South's vituperative assault on the Vice President was not lost on Fillmore. Among the most solid of the Whigs' constituents were the abolitionists who railed for black freedom and, to some extent, black equality. In an act that even many abolitionists would not consider, Richard Johnson took a black woman as his mate. The Whigs were now more than happy to capitalize on this fact to play on southern prejudice and fear to further their political goals. Fillmore was no abolitionist, but the hypocrisy was unsettling.

James Buchanan spoke in an effortless voice that filled the chamber, not because it was loud, but because it was powerful. He did not have the gift of eloquence that graced his opponent Daniel Webster, but he was steady and confident. He worked through the provisions of the Constitution with disarming ease establishing his mastery of the subject. He then discussed the proposed bill itself and its logical inconsistency with the provisions he just detailed. He did not accuse Webster and Clay of manipulation and power mongering, which were precisely their goals, but instead managed to imply that they were simply the victims of an oversight. He apologized if his own analysis suffered from a similar defect, but if not, he hoped that his fellow senators would consider withdrawal of their bill given its hopeless collision with the Constitution.

The speech was short, but effective. Fillmore did not expect that Clay and Webster would capitulate quickly, but he was comfortable that Buchanan and Van Buren were prepared to make sure that this was not a battle they would lose. Millard Fillmore breathed easier knowing that this was not his fight, nor would it be.

***

Tennessee: September 1839

The newly elected governor of the state of Tennessee cast a fiery glance at his wife as she audibly gasped. Jim and Sarah Polk were sitting in the library of the Hermitage, Andrew Jackson's decaying estate. Sarah quickly regained her composure as the former President shuffled in agonizingly slow steps across the room to a worn, black wooden rocking chair. The ancient man did not hear her exclamation because he was engaged in cursing the equally ancient slave that tried to assist him across the room. The old black man stopped and folded his hands before him knowing that he would be blamed if his master fell despite his efforts to prevent such a calamity. When Jackson finally descended into his chair there was a collective sigh from the soon-to-be Governor, his wife and the old slave.

Sarah Polk's surprise had less to do with Jackson's pace (which slowed to a crawl several years before) than with his appearance. His withered countenance was narrower than ever with the famous white, unruly hair giving him the appearance of a madman which many were saying was an apt description. The gray pallor of his skin gave the blank, chalky gaze of his blind right eye a frightening effect.

Mrs. Polk surveyed the decrepit house which was rife with dust and mildew to avoid staring at the pathetic figure of the great hero of New Orleans. She shuddered as she fought off the notion that a grave would be a more hospitable setting than where she sat now. It struck Sarah as pitiable that the most popular man in the country now lived with a few slaves in this ghost-ridden mansion. His estate was in a state of ruin with more weeds than crops. Jackson's debts were many, or rather, the debts of his adopted son Andrew Jackson Jr. that Jackson assumed, were many.

Andrew Jackson Jr. was a nephew of Rachel Jackson. Rachel and Andrew Jackson adopted him as an infant when his mother's weak constitution would not allow her to nurse both him and his twin brother. Because they were unable to have children of their own, the General and Rachel spoiled their son unmercifully. He grew to be an irresponsible lush and playboy that his father felt obliged to support beyond all reason. The result was what sat before Sarah Polk now. A bankrupt and lonely former President. The only reason that he even still resided at the Hermitage was the unwillingness of his creditors to incur the public's wrath for foreclosing on Old Hickory.

This was an homage call. Her husband grew tired of the relentless self-righteous bickering about slavery that enveloped Washington and returned to Tennessee intent on being Governor. Andrew Jackson was disappointed that his prize pupil shunned national office but agreed to help him get elected Governor. Help he did and now the Polks were obliged to pay their respects, express their gratitude and listen to the old General talk about his glory and his many enemies who still sought their revenge against him.

Sarah understood the importance of the General's paternalistic interest in her husband, but she still had never grown comfortable with Jim Polk's dependence on Andrew Jackson. Jackson's fame was built on more fiction than fact, more bravado and boasting than actual daring. Despite his fondness for being called "General," he really was never anything more than a masterful politician.

Her husband, on the other hand, *preferred* to be known as a politician. But he really was an administrator. He was not a gifted speaker, he despised social occasions and despite being only forty-three years old, his penchant for working himself to exhaustion made him look like he was well into his sixties. His demanding personality was only compensated for by the fact that he was never wrong about details or facts, making him an invaluable ally and a dangerous adversary.

As fond as the General was of Jim Polk, he was even fonder of Sarah. Using his pet name for her he whispered loudly, "How are we, Daughter?"

Sarah smiled and replied, "We are well General. Both Mr. Polk and I are so happy to be back in Tennessee. Hopefully we will be able to see more of you, now that we are home."

Jackson's head nodded slightly as he closed his eyes to muster the strength to respond. "Yes, I reckon that it is better to be here than in the Congress. But you know that Jim belongs in Washington keeping an eye on things. You know that. . ."

Sarah laughed as Jim shifted with annoyance. "General, I'm afraid the Whigs and abolitionists will act as they are going to act whether Jim is there or here."

"Oh Jim will be a fine Governor, don't take me wrong. But Sam Houston is almost begging to join the country and he needs someone like Jim to bring 'em in."

"'Em" was Texas. For over a year, Texas had been an independent republic with Andrew Jackson's old friend Houston as President. After rejecting the government of Mexican dictator Santa Anna, the numerous Anglos that immigrated to Texas declared their independence. There was strong support within Texas to join the United States but Mexico still refused to recognize Texas as an independent republic and the northern abolitionists vowed to fight the admission of another slave state, especially one the size of Texas. To push for the admission of Texas was a sure path to war; either with Mexico. . .or between the states.

Jim Polk pointed this out to Jackson with all due deference. The eyelid over Jackson's one good eye fluttered and his sallow jaws worked to form the words, "Jim, so what? Matt Van Buren will never use our army to fight for the abolitionists and if we can't whoop Santa Anna and a bunch of Mexicans we ain't worth spit as a country anyway, now are we?"

"No, sir. I suppose you're right."

"Course I'm right. It's our destiny. I've been to Texas Jim. There is more land there than you can imagine. Green hills and water. People can settle whilst barely havin' to clear a weed. We lock up Texas and California all the way up to Oregon and, you mark my words, them Brits will never be able to set foot in America again."

Jim nodded. He heard this speech before. He agreed with it even though he was more cautious and less phobic about the British than Jackson. But like so many of Andrew Jackson's themes, it was not really Jackson's. For a man of such passion and notoriety, Jim found it odd how few *original* thoughts Jackson generated. The notion that it was the United States' divine calling to extend from the Atlantic to the Pacific Ocean and form the Gulf of Mexico to Canada, emanated from the brain and tireless mouth of Senator Thomas Hart Benton.

Benton was originally from Tennessee. Along with his brother Jesse, the Bentons were prominent in Nashville until

1813 when Thomas Benton made the mistake of publicly maligning the already popular and soon to be heroic Jackson. The ill will began when Andrew Jackson agreed to act as second on behalf of a man that Jesse Benton challenged to a duel. Jesse proved to be as much of a blowhard as his brother but, unfortunately, not much of a marksman. Upon reaching his mark, Jesse chose to tumble to the ground rather than firing his pistol. To the amazement of his opponent, Jesse chose to roll away rather than standing his ground or even running. Jackson stood by and watched as his friend raised his gun and fired a round directly into Jesse's posterior.

The Bentons did not suffer humiliation lightly and Thomas insulted Jackson at every opportunity, clearly hoping to vindicate his brother's ignominy. Jackson, never much of a fighter but always spoiling for a fight, let it be known that he intended to publicly horsewhip Thomas Hart Benton when next he saw him. His opportunity soon came as he walked down the main street of Nashville. He spied the Bentons and with his usual calm but fierce determination, he approached Thomas from behind and grabbed the back of his coat and spun him around pointing a pistol between Benton's eyes. As he backed him toward the door of the Nashville Hotel, Jesse slipped inside ahead of his brother and Jackson. When Jackson and Thomas stumbled through the entrance, Jesse shot Jackson in his left arm.

For nineteen years, Jackson carried the slug in his arm that Jesse Benton fired. While he was President, the wound developed its most serious in a long line of infections. Doctors decided it was time to risk removal but Jackson's arm never healed and now lay largely useless on his lap.

After his brother shot Jackson, Thomas Hart Benton discovered how popular the mercurial Jackson was as he was shunned at every turn in Nashville society, such as it was in 1813. Soon, friends of Jackson let it be known that Jackson wanted Benton out of Nashville even if it meant killing him. Benton had seen enough of the loyalty that Jackson's friends had for him to know that his days in Tennessee were numbered.

It was no small indication of Benton's personal charisma that he was elected as Senator from Missouri within a few years after moving there to escape Jackson's wrath. He joined the Senate at the same time his old nemesis Andrew Jackson was elected to represent Tennessee. Even more painful was his first committee appointment--to the committee headed by Jackson. Benton knew he could hide no longer and approached Jackson who, much to Benton's amazement, was quite ready to put their acrimonious history behind them. Benton's fascination for the loyalty of Jackson's Tennessee followers evolved into understanding. A politician first and foremost, Benton quickly realized that Henry Clay (who Benton was supporting) could never engender the type of fealty that General Jackson could. Benton pledged his allegiance to Jackson and became one of his closest allies during Jackson's Presidency. With Benton's prestige and influence in the Senate, Jackson could always count on support when necessary.

Thomas Hart Benton was about power. And, to him, Andrew Jackson was power personified. With a President like Jackson and a country which controlled all its borders, the United States would become the colossus of world history. This was precisely the type of vision that appealed to Andrew Jackson and Thomas Hart Benton preached it relentlessly. So, Jim Polk had heard this "*destiny*" spiel before but he was still amazed that this wretched shell before him was able to articulate his grand vision for the United States when Jim knew that he couldn't even see Sarah and Jim's faces.

Polk started to speak but stopped when he realized that the General was asleep. Jackson's edema had grown more pronounced in recent years. A byproduct of this affliction caused him to nod off in mid-conversation from time to time. It was unsettling but Sarah smiled at Jim knowing that the old man would awaken shortly picking the dialogue up right where he departed. Sarah rose and crossed quietly to adjust the shawl that Jackson could never quite get situated across his shoulders and that he would not allow the slaves to assist with either. She knelt beside him and took his hand. He awoke and tried to focus on her managing to lift his lower lip just enough to indicate that he was pleased.

Polk leaned forward earnestly. "Well, General, but what if

Matt Van Buren is not President? The Whigs will owe the abolitionists and they will never stand for Texas coming into the Union. As the Congress stands now Texas doesn't have a prayer."

Jackson's head shook ever so slightly. "Jim, it is our *destiny*. That means it is not up to Democrats or Whigs or anyone else. If we control all our coasts, we will be the most powerful country on earth. To compare the Lord's ordained station for us with the misguided sympathy of a bunch of northern bookbenders for our niggers is just foolishness. This ain't no question of what can happen, it *has to* happen."

Jackson drew a deep breath. He was near his limits. "And Matt Van Buren will be President. He's the best politician the good Lord ever made. He could never lose to a beggar like Harrison."

There was another silence punctuated by labored breathing before Jackson went on. "Jim, with you at Matt's side our destiny will be fulfilled."

Polk looked perplexed. "General, you know I support the President."

Jackson inhaled and exhaled through his nostrils several times. This was the only way he could laugh. His head nodded down and then he tilted it back, "You don't understand. You and I and Matt all know that he can't keep that nigger lover Johnson. You gotta be Vice President."

Sarah slumped and stared up at Jackson. Perhaps the General *was* mad. No one could believe that James Knox Polk could tolerate a meaningless post like the Vice Presidency. She didn't even need to look at her husband. She knew that he was dumbstruck. She interceded.

"But General, we just got back to Tennessee. . ."

Jackson coughed and responded, "Daughter, Tennessee doesn't need Jim, the country does. After a few years with Matt he'll be ready to move you into the White House with him, just the way Matt followed me."

Now she was truly dizzy. The General was always able to read her mind. Sarah always believed that Jim belonged in the White House ultimately but her husband was taciturn on the subject. He would grow surly and claim that there was too much talk and not enough do involved in being President.

Sarah knew that the bigger problem was that her husband could never command the affection that Jackson did nor the loyalty that Van Buren established. And he simply would perish as Vice President. But if the General insisted, Jim would comply.

Even though the General's instincts were still generally sound and the Democrats would still do his bidding, there was one problem that, unknown to one another, Jim and Sarah both eventually dwelled upon. The General was wrong about one thing which made him wrong about everything else. Martin Van Buren not only *could* lose to a beggar like William Harrison, he *would*.

***

Washington: March 1841

The new Vice President of the United States folded the notes for the speech he just concluded and slid them into his pocket. He shook hands with a few senators who uniformly seemed pleased that he would be presiding over their deliberations and that Richard Johnson would be going home to Kentucky. Most of the chamber, however, was hurrying to get the best seat possible on the East Portico of the Capitol for the inauguration of the new President, William Henry Harrison.

After an illustrious career as a senator and Governor of Virginia, John Tyler was almost embarrassed to be elected Vice President. He knew very little about Harrison but that mattered little since the entire election was orchestrated by Henry Clay with the purpose of installing a political neophyte who would do Clay's bidding as President (of course, this was only Clay's strategy once it was clear that the nomination would not be extended to Clay himself). As strong a showing as Harrison made in 1836, it was clear that no ticket could be elected without some southern support. That was where Tyler came in.

John Tyler was a Whig in name only. The one trait he shared with the Whigs was his disdain for Andrew Jackson. He was not even unfavorably disposed toward President Van Buren.

But the Whigs needed a southerner and Tyler was their only real choice in the sense that he was the only one acceptable to Henry Clay and Daniel Webster. Even though no one said as much to him and they never would, Tyler knew that the sixty-eight-year old Harrison would not be ascending the steps but for John Tyler's willingness to call himself a Whig.

But Tyler was a Democrat. To the extent Harrison managed to speak his mind on an issue, he and Tyler were at odds. With the Panic of 1837 still fresh in the collective conscience of the country, the main plank in the Whigs' platform was to establish a strong national bank, an institution that Tyler fought against bitterly in the past and still opposed. Tyler rationalized that the Vice President did not fill a substantive role anyway and, frankly, he needed the job. He just hoped that Harrison would not allow the Presidency to be completely usurped by Clay not only because he believed in the independent executive like any good Jeffersonian/Madisonian Democrat but, on a more practical level, because William Harrison could not achieve the success for the Whig platform that Henry Clay could. Harrison did not have that kind of political influence. Clay did.

Tyler stepped onto the balcony behind Harrison and shivered. The air was still damp from the drizzle that greeted him on his way to the Capitol this morning. The sky was overcast with just enough breeze to make the day not just cold, but chilling. Tyler noticed that Harrison had neither hat nor gloves and apparently intended to remain that way. He didn't know whether this was more theatrics to demonstrate Harrison's earthiness or if Harrison simply didn't have the sense to remember to wear something warm on a cold day.

Even though he was a willing participant, Tyler was still somewhat abashed by the campaign of 1840. The Whigs essentially nominated Harrison and then told him to shut up. Tyler, who didn't even agree with most of the Whig platform, gave more speeches than the old General. The fact that Harrison was an old General seemed to be the most important fact of all. Despite the Democrats' attempts to embarrass Harrison into taking a position by referring to him as "General Mum", Clay and Webster managed to keep him quiet.

The Whigs' strategy was simple. They were doing exactly what Martin Van Buren did in getting Andrew Jackson elected. Harrison could never match Jackson for force of personality but the fact that he was the hero of the Battle of Tippecanoe was enough. As far as the masses knew, Old Tippecanoe was the second coming of Old Hickory. "Tippecanoe and Tyler Too!!!" became the Whig rallying cry and the theme for many a hard cider gathering on the American frontier.

Tyler knew General Harrison was not General Jackson. Unlike Jackson who remained a hero from the moment the Battle of New Orleans was over until he became President, Harrison enjoyed glory for a few short months after the Battle of Tippecanoe and then began a gradual descent into the ranks of near ignominy until his resurrection by the Whigs. Almost overnight, he went from unemployed diplomat and disgruntled government pensioner to "Gentleman Farmer" and Indian fighter overnight. The Democrats were aghast at the Whigs' temerity in painting the supplicant Harrison as a hero on par with the great Jackson and tried to set the record straight. But to the hordes of settlers trying to tame the western frontier, maligning a man who fought Indians seemed indecent. More than the reincarnation of Harrison, however, the Whigs gained the White House by turning the tables on Martin Van Buren.

Tyler watched Van Buren shake Harrison's hand and step back while Harrison began speaking. The Presidency had not been kind to Van Buren. His hair was snow white and deep lines creased his face. He was more rotund than ever, but he no longer looked jolly, just tired. The most powerful politician in the country, ironically, lost all potency once he attained the highest office in the land.

The Panic of 1837 was the main reason Harrison unseated Van Buren. But the Whigs' manipulation of the Panic was Van Buren's undoing. Van Buren built his Albany Regency by shrewd handling of the press and adept distribution of patronage. After the Panic, the Whigs took the lessons they learned from their arch foe Van Buren and used them against him. First, the Whig press made indirect assaults on Van Buren by portraying him as a man living the life of a King while the citizens suffered the hardships brought on by the Panic. The symbol of the Van Buren administration's royal persona was Angelica Van Buren, the President's daughter-in-law.

Angelica was introduced to the President's stoic eldest son and personal secretary Abraham by her cousin, Dolly Madison. After James Madison's death Dolly returned to Washington to become the empress of the Washington social scene. Angelica was the beautiful and refined daughter of a wealthy South Carolina planter. Washington and, in particular, the President, were enchanted. Upon Abraham and Angelica's marriage in November of 1838, Angelica was installed as the official White House hostess.

She took her duties seriously and insisted upon a tour of Europe and returned to the states with new notions on how to host White House events. The throngs of "common people" that raided Andrew Jackson's fetes were no longer welcome. Admittance was by invitation only and, as to those guests that *were* invited, Angelica now refused to greet them or shake their hands. She arranged herself on a mounted chair that looked disturbingly like a throne and nodded at her visitors just as she had been taught by her new friend, Queen Victoria of England. The affable Van Buren did not seem dismayed by the display. After all, Angelica was also pregnant with Van Buren's first grandchild so he was inclined to allow her some latitude.

By the time the President realized that he had let Angelica get out of hand and persuaded her that what was expected in Europe was not necessarily acceptable in the United States, the myth of the palatial President was taking root. In April of 1840, it reached full bloom with the "Gold Spoon Oration."

Charles Ogle was a Congressman from Somerset, Pennsylvania who had loftier aspirations than his intellect or personality would probably ever allow him to achieve. In this election year, he decided to make his mark in a fashion that was sure to endear him to vanguard of the Whigs. He took the floor of the House and began a speech that he obviously spent some time preparing. He reported that a fellow Congressman dined with the President over the winter and was dismayed to have a place setting with golden spoons set before him. The "fellow

Congressman" asked for the floor briefly and said that the story
was untrue. Ogle smirked and regained the floor, simply ignoring
the disclaimer. Ogle first thundered that it was unconscionable to
have the people who voted Van Buren into the White House
struggling to overcome the Panic that Van Buren wrought while
the President himself dined with golden tableware. Ogle then
began a litany of Martin Van Buren's opulent possessions and
habits and he did not stop for three days. The gallery was full by
the middle of the second day as word spread through Washington
that there was an entertaining harangue unfolding in the House of
Representatives. Clerks, tavern keepers, reporters, laborers and
all other types begged off their jobs to watch the spectacle.
Washington was, in all respects, a small town.

Even the most dedicated Whigs were troubled by Ogle's
speech which was, for the most part, patently false. Van Buren,
weary from the loss his new granddaughter at only five months of
age, tried halfheartedly to dispel the mistaken portrait painted by
Ogle but to no avail. The son of a saloon keeper from the
backwoods of upstate New York was now the emblem of eastern
elitism.

Despite their discomfort with Ogle's methods, the Whigs
were not above capitalizing on the disdain for Van Buren's
"palatial" lifestyle to distinguish General Harrison as a war hero
who had overcome his impecunious origins. John Tyler found it
ironic that the voters were unaware, or forgot, that Harrison was
the son of a signer of the Declaration of Independence who, like
Tyler's father, was a wealthy Virginia plantation owner. In order
to gain the trust of the voters, the Whigs were careful to avoid
any illumination on Harrison or Tyler's illustrious ancestry.
Andrew Jackson had made it more acceptable to be an orphan
from a log cabin than the child of a reputable, successful family.

Of course, even given his antipathy for Jackson, Tyler had
to admit that it wasn't Old Hickory that made paupers out of the
well-to-do and vice versa. It was Van Buren himself. Tyler did
not have the personal aversion to Van Buren that he developed
for Andrew Jackson so he felt some sympathy for the way the
Whigs turned Van Buren's tactics against him. Unlike Jackson,
Van Buren's ego was held firmly in check. Tyler knew that Van

Buren could be trusted to keep his word and would always place his country and his party before himself. But Van Buren was a master politician who was burned by the very lessons he taught his foes over the last decade.

Van Buren knew that issues did not win campaigns. As the country expanded westward, communication lagged behind. The ability to accurately disseminate one's position became more and more difficult. It was Van Buren that perfected the cult of personality which became the cornerstone of all sophisticated campaigns. Andrew Jackson was his master work.

While Van Buren did not have the appeal of Jackson, he positioned himself to receive Jackson's fervent endorsement which was the next best thing to being the subject of a cult of personality. By 1840, the Whigs had seen enough to know that politicians like Henry Clay or Daniel Webster could not generate the type of enthusiasm that Andrew Jackson could, but another war hero might. *Then,* if all went well, Clay or Webster might be able to hitch a ride into the White House just like Van Buren.

Harrison held a thick stack of prepared text from which he read. For a man that was called "General Mum" by his foes throughout the campaign, Harrison had a lot to say. There was a great deal of melodramatic drivel apparently intended to establish that Harrison was an educated man not to be trifled with. Unfortunately, Tyler sensed that the effect was just the opposite as he spied Henry Clay rolling his eyes and smiling at everyone and no one in particular. Tyler knew from talking with his friend Daniel Webster early in the day that Webster spent the better part of the night editing Harrison's speech. Tyler smirked thinking what the speech must have been like before a gifted public speaker like Webster worked on it. As Harrison began holding forth on the Roman Empire, Tyler smiled as Webster's comment that he killed seventeen "Roman proconsuls" overnight made sense.

As the speech dragged on, the murmur of the crowd grew gradually louder until Harrison's platitudes were all but washed away by the conversations of his audience. Even on the platform, Tyler could hear people rubbing their hands to stay warm and speculating about who the old General would appoint to various government posts. As Old Tippecanoe entered the second hour of his address, Tyler slowly pulled his scarf tighter and discreetly rubbed his gloves together to try and generate warmth. He was determined to display respect and courtesy for the new President even while everyone else did away with all pretense. But Harrison's long-windedness was making it difficult.

After an hour and a half, it appeared that Harrison was showing signs of stopping. The dissonance of the crowd began to wane. Tyler could see from where he stood that Harrison was having difficulty turning the pages of his text as his hands grew red and numb. But he did manage to turn the page and silence the crowd with his next words.

"We are told by the greatest of British orators and statesmen that at the commencement of the War of the Revolution the most stupid men of England spoke of 'their American subjects.' Are there, indeed, citizens of any of our States who have dreamed of *their* subjects in the District of Columbia? Such dreams can never be realized by any agency of mine."

Tyler forgot about the cold momentarily. Conversation ceased. Harrison was taking on slavery in the nation's capital, the political equivalent of a raging inferno. Harrison babbled on about the Romans again before declaring his position. "Our citizens must be content with the exercise of the powers with which the Constitution clothes them. The attempt of those of one State to control the domestic institutions of another can only result in feelings of distrust and jealousy, the certain harbingers of disunion, violence and civil war."

Henry Clay rolled his eyes again but, this time, without the attending smile. Martin Van Buren remained as he had throughout the ordeal of Harrison's speech with a thin smile but his eyes betrayed his amusement. There were some hisses from the abolitionists in the crowd but even more cheers.

The Democrats excitedly muttered to one another that Harrison was intentionally showing up Henry Clay. Clay would never allow the subject of slavery to be raised if he was truly in control. Among the Whigs, there was stunned silence that Harrison was asinine enough to raise the one subject certain to inflame the populace.

John Tyler, for one, was pleased. He was a politician to be sure but he could never sacrifice the principle of States rights which was at the core of Harrison's comment. He was also a southern slaveowner who was glad to see that the new President apparently did not intend to allow the extreme views of a pack of idealistic abolitionists to temper his actions. Henry Clay had to be worried.

William Henry Harrison raised his red, trembling right hand in the air to allow Chief Justice Roger Taney to swear him in as President. John Tyler watched Harrison cast a quick furtive glance toward Clay as he placed his left hand on the Bible. If John Tyler knew Henry Clay, he was doing some swearing of his own right about now.

Chapter 2:
William Henry Harrison and John Tyler

Washington: October 1841

Henry Clay helped himself to some of Congressman Adams' brandy and lowered himself into a chair in Adams' parlor. Despite his relaxed appearance and the easy manner he moved about Adams' home, Clay did not consider any visit with Adams social in nature. The thought of turning to Adams was as distasteful to Clay as raw molasses but his desire to be President was all consuming.

Clay and Adams' failure to find any personal charm in one another did not keep them from understanding that their vision for the country was very similar. They both believed in a strong national bank and provision for internal improvements such as highways and canals to strengthen the country's ability to trade. Their foes (who they lumped into the single category of "Jacksonians" rather than "Democrats") were ardent states righters that held that the federal government had no authority under the Constitution to effect such programs. The responsibility for internal improvements resided with the states. As for a national bank, the Jacksonians would sooner revert to British rule than willingly accept a plan that would revive the monopolistic monetary practices of Nicholas Biddle.

From negotiating with the British to end the War of 1812 to negotiating to put Adams in the White House instead of Andrew Jackson and *then* negotiating to minimize what they saw as the disastrous policies of Old Hickory, these two men were thrown together for the last thirty years to the point that they finally had grudging respect for one another despite their lack of personal affinity. With the election of William Henry Harrison, they were sure that their long mutual struggle was over and the changes they championed would become reality. For Clay, this included the Presidency because Harrison gave his word that he would serve only one term to clear the way for Henry Clay. Then Harrison died.

It started with Harrison's confounding and tedious inaugural speech. Within a couple of days, the President was complaining of a sore throat and fever. He continued to work and held Cabinet meetings on an almost daily basis often running from 8:00 in the morning until 10:00 at night. As Whigs descended on the White House in droves with letters recommending them for various posts, Harrison began to falter under the strain of distributing the spoils of victory.

Clay's always uneasy alliance with Daniel Webster began to falter as well. Harrison appointed Webster as Secretary of State and relied on his counsel increasingly in awarding patronage posts mainly because it was easier than sifting through the mountains of applicants himself. Whether it was because of his fatigue and ill health or because he was acceding to Webster's flattery, Harrison finally turned on his long-time sponsor, Henry Clay.

The first instance was when Clay objected to Harrison's nominee for the Secretary of the Treasury. To Clay's astonishment Harrison snapped, "Mr. Clay, you forget that I am the President." Clay decided against reminding Harrison that this was true only because Clay allowed it to be true. The disagreement about the appointment could easily be ascribed to undue influence on the part of Daniel Webster, Thurlow Weed and Bill Seward. He shrugged off the rebuke and comforted himself with the knowledge that the old General would remember himself once he was faced with the proposition of passing legislation without the cooperation of the omnipotent Senator Clay.

Two weeks later though Clay had enough of the suddenly intrepid Tippecanoe. He believed that Congress should be called into an extra session to begin the work that the Whigs had been fighting for since before there were Whigs. He sent a note to

Harrison enclosing a proclamation that he recommended Harrison sign. In return, Harrison wrote,

My dear friend,

You use the privilege of a friend to lecture me and I take the same liberty with you. You are too impetuous. Much as I rely upon your judgment there are others whom I must consult and in many cases to determine adversely to your decision. In the matter to which your communication of this morning refers there is no difference of opinion as to the manner and there would be none as to the time but for the situation of Tennessee to whom we owe so much. Her feelings and interest must not be sacrificed if it can be avoided. The question will finally be settled on Monday having been adjourned over from a discussion which took place this morning. I prefer for many reasons this mode of answering your note to a conversation in the presence of others.

If he was honest with himself, Clay would have admitted that his resulting rage had less to do with the extra session than with the fact that it was clear that Harrison had no intention of dancing to Clay's tune as Clay, and everyone else for that matter, expected that Harrison would. Clay dashed off a note of the nature that all men with any conscience come to regret and told his friends as he climbed into a wagon that he would be in "Kentucky if that old son of a bitch should need to pass any bills."

In another two weeks Harrison was dead. Shortly after Clay rode out of Washington, Harrison's condition deteriorated to pneumonia. As he was throughout the only month of Harrison's Presidency, Daniel Webster was at the President's side when he died. He sent his son Fletcher Webster to notify John Tyler of the President's death.

At first Henry Clay regarded Tyler's succession of Harrison with mild optimism. To be sure, Tyler was a states righter and could be stubborn, but he, like Clay, was from a border state which tended to foster moderation between the ever-growing extremes of North and South and, unlike Harrison, Tyler had some understanding of politics and loyalties. From their years in the Senate together, Tyler and Clay became friends. They were often on the opposite side of issues but were adept at finding middle ground on all but the most fundamental of their beliefs.

Clay was also sure that Tyler surely would not have the temerity to act like a Democrat. In Clay's view, it was nothing short of absurd to think that the Vice President would do anything other than carry out the intended goals of the President he was succeeding. If the Vice President was to follow his own ideas, then the voters' mandate would be thwarted simply by the passing of one life. Clay and Harrison's Cabinet informed Tyler that he would carry the Harrison torch. One member of Harrison's Cabinet dissented: Daniel Webster.

Not surprisingly, Tyler agreed with Webster. He informed the Cabinet and then Henry Clay that, like William Henry Harrison before him, he "was the President." While many in Washington fretted and fumed about Tyler's unwillingness to simply accept the mantle of "acting President," Clay set to work on the Whig agenda confident that Tyler would not act contrary to the will of a Whig dominated Congress and Cabinet. But he was wrong. Dreadfully wrong.

Once it was clear to Henry Clay that he would not be nominated by the Whigs to run for President in 1840, he started setting his agenda for the twenty-seventh Congress. To demonstrate that he was in charge whether he sat in the White House or in the Senate *and* that Andrew Jackson's influence counted for little in Washington, Clay put the issue most likely to inflame the Jacksonians (and Andrew Jackson himself) at the head of his list: The Bank of the United States.

The Whigs' denunciation of the failure of Jackson and Van Buren to re-charter the Bank of the United States rang in both houses of Congress as the Democrats were charged with plunging the nation into the Panic with their chaotic money policies. The cure was to return to the prosperity of a central money system. The Second Bank of the United States was approved by the Senate and the House.

Even considering his most incensed moments with William Henry Harrison's churlishness, Clay never envisioned the depths of rage which he was soon to reach. John Tyler, the *Whig* Vice President who just happened to be living in the White House, *vetoed* the Bank bill. Even worse, there were still just enough Democrats left in Congress that Clay's troops could not override Tyler's heresy.

Now the senator from Kentucky was worried. For all of Harrison's impudence, Clay knew that he would not stand in the way of Whig legislation, especially legislation backed by Clay. But with Harrison gone, Clay made the mistake of giving Tyler too much credit. He came to the stark realization that Tyler's resignation from the Senate in lieu of reneging on his vote to censure his *own* party's standard bearer, the great Jackson himself, was in deadly earnest. Tyler was not a Democrat in the modern sense at all, he was a Democrat in the *Jeffersonian* sense. He was not only in favor of States rights, it was *all* he favored. It occurred to Clay that on those occasions where he recalled Tyler behaving as a rational politician and compromising, there was never a potential collision with the sacrosanct protection of States rights.

Clay came to understand the incomprehensible (at least to Clay). Tyler did not resign from the Senate because of a personal grudge against Old Hickory that would not allow him to reverse his vote of censure, but because he believed that his state should have the right to dictate how he should vote. Since Tyler was unwilling to follow Virginia's instruction to him to expunge his vote of censure, he was duty bound to resign and allow Virginia to appoint a senator that would comply with its wishes. John Tyler stood on the principle that a national government official must bow to the wishes of his state. And he was willing to destroy his own career to vindicate his belief. Clay was aghast. Instead of a muddle-headed old soldier, he installed a zealot in the White House.

Clay's apprehension as to Tyler's state of mind soon

proved well-founded. In the wake of the Bank bill veto, the entire Cabinet that Tyler inherited from Harrison resigned except for Daniel Webster. Clay quickly forced other essential Whig bills through that Tyler promptly vetoed. Clay took to the Senate floor and delivered righteous harangues about the blasphemy being visited upon the will of the American people by their traitor President. Yet Tyler continued his skein of vetoes. And with each veto, Henry Clay saw more clearly the futility of even attempting to get Tyler to honor Harrison's promise to step aside after one term. John Tyler wanted to be elected President in his own right and he was doing all that he could to show the country and Washington that he was in charge.

As always, John Quincy Adams was direct. "What's on your mind Henry? There are card games going on all over Washington so it must be something serious for you to be here."

Clay tried to smiled. "I'm beginning to understand why your father was always at odds with Virginians."

Adams laughed, "Yes, they can be insufferable. But I'm sure Tom Jefferson and Jemmy Madison are twisting in their graves to hear their names fraternizing with John Tyler's. Those men were thinkers and, to a certain extent, politicians. Tyler is obviously not of that caliber."

"This is not news to me Adams. The question is what to do about him? Your father already tried the Alien and Sedition Acts."

Adams laughed again. He wasn't fond of Clay but did find him entertaining at times. When he wasn't being boorish and obnoxious.

"Henry, what do you want me to do? We all know that it was never anybody's intention that he would become President, but he is all the same."

Clay rose and walked over to Adams and jabbed him in the chest for emphasis. "You can stop reading those damn slavery petitions and help me corner Tyler."

Adams' trace of a smile vanished. "As long as I am gagged from presenting the interests of my constituents for the consideration of the House, I will present the petitions." For four years Adams had been fighting the Gag Rule which prohibited the introduction of petitions denouncing or calling for the abolition of slavery, with little success. But he had become the darling of the abolitionists and was enjoying the irritation he inflicted on the southern Congressmen who jeered his every word.

Adams went on, "As for the President, he will not be cornered easily. Don't forget he has the best lawyer in the country advising him."

Clay shook his head, "Webster is making a real mistake. If Tyler would betray the people that elected him, he'll betray Webster."

Adams smirked and said, "No he won't. Webster is a man of principle and Tyler believes that he is a man of principle. The President admires Webster's patriotism and loyalty in not resigning along with the rest of the Cabinet over the Bank bill. Daniel, of course, was the only one of them smart enough to realize that being rid of Harrison's Whig Cabinet was the best thing that could happen to the President. Alas, the man closest to the President right now is Webster and he is a Whig, which I guess we should be somewhat thankful for."

Clay wasn't convinced. He knew that Webster wielded great influence with Tyler because of his decision to stay on as Secretary of State. But Webster made sure to spread the story that when Webster announced he would not resign, Tyler responded by saying, "Give me your hand on that, and now I will say to you that Henry Clay is a doomed man." Clay's guess was that Webster's "loyalty" had less to do with duty than with Webster concluding, perhaps accurately, that Clay and Webster's plan to have Harrison serve as their puppet exploded in their faces and that Webster's best hope for still getting into the White House was by trying to salvage what he could with Tyler. Being the veteran gambler that he was, Clay knew that Webster was banking on a longshot.

Clay blurted it out. "We gotta impeach the bastard."

Adams seemed unperturbed and asked studiously, "On what basis?"

Clay waived his hand and said, "Ah hell Adams. The man has laid waste to everything that the Whigs promised the people who elected him *to be Vice President* and his own party wants nothing to do with him because he ran as a Whig. He has no votes. You'll think of something."

Adams couldn't resist needling Clay, "I remember very few promises. As I recall the election was mostly about hard cider and rich men pretending to be poor. Mr. Tyler was noticeably silent to my recollection."

Clay said nothing but looked at Adams as if to say his comments were beside the point.

Adams stroked his impressive sideburns. He was intrigued. "I'm not sure it is that easy. Tyler *has* abused his prerogatives and abandoned the very ideals that landed him in the job he holds."

Clay clapped his hands. "Precisely!"

"I'll give it some thought Henry. Having been President, I can tell you that I will not pursue something as serious as impeachment lightly. . ."

But Henry Clay was not listening. He knew that Adams could not resist a dramatic fight. Clay slapped the brandy snifter onto a table, grabbed his hat and headed for the door pausing only long enough to mutter over his shoulder, "You give it some *hard* thought. This man must be stopped. Hell, I'd rather have Matt Van Buren up there. Least I could work with him."

Adams watched Clay close the door behind him and had a rare twinge of pity. Henry Clay was desperate to become President. Unless he could reverse Tyler's unintentional but nonetheless real challenge to Clay's authority, Clay would never get near the Executive Mansion. The last time he made a deal with Henry Clay, it ruined any hope of a successful administration for his Presidency. But now, he did not care if he ever saw the inside of the White House again. Adams smirked as he headed upstairs thinking about how ironic it was that Henry Clay thought Adams would be doing him a *favor* by helping him to become President.

***

New Hampshire: October 1842

Former Congressman and senator Franklin Pierce twirled a fish hook between his thumb and index finger picking with his other thumb and index finger at the piece of cotton he glued to the hook. He rationalized that this was a good thing. Certainly, doing some legal work would be a better thing since that was how he was supposed to be making a living. But he was a member of Congress for nine years and it could be argued that he should have dedicated more time to studying legislation than he did. No, it couldn't be argued. It was a fact.

Yet Frank Pierce was not living in Concord as a well-known but marginal lawyer because the citizens of New Hampshire refused to re-elect him. He resigned his seat as Senator. He could have returned to Washington as many times as he pleased. His father's name still held great sway in the Granite State as its premier revolutionary hero and the son continued to benefit as a result. The people of New Hampshire neither knew nor cared that Frank Pierce was popular in Washington not for his diligence or statesmanship but because he was a readily available socializer that was a pleasure to have around whether at a White House reception or at the City Hotel's tavern.

But Jane Pierce cared. For nine years, she endured life in a city that she considered amoral and diseased both literally and spiritually. She grew accustomed to her husband's late nights and liquor induced torpor. She even entertained from time to time despite her disdain for the banal depths to which political small talk could sink on such occasions. But her faith in Frank Pierce was perversely restored at one such party when she realized that her husband seemed to be as bored at such functions as she.

They lost two children in Washington. They named each Frank. The first died within weeks of his birth. The second died when he was but four years old. Jane blamed both deaths on feculent atmosphere of Washington which bore no resemblance to the fresh White Mountain air of the Pierces' youth. By the time their third son arrived Jane was determined to not subject another child to the scourge of Washington life. As her husband wrapped his scarf about his neck to brave a bitter Washington winter night, she announced in a flat, desolate voice that she intended to return to New Hampshire in the spring. Forever. With or without him.

Pierce did not argue with his wife. He wondered how long she could tolerate Washington in general and his high jinx specifically. Now, he had an answer. He simply nodded and said, "I'll be late" and proceeded to get extraordinarily drunk.

Pierce also did not argue because the idea of returning to New Hampshire appealed to him. The thought of practicing law held little attraction but he assumed that his name would afford him the opportunity to make a living trading favors and maybe even taking on minor political posts in lieu of performing more typical and mundane legal services. The fact that Pierce was willing to return to the practice of law highlighted how weary Pierce with his senate duties.

In his time as senator, Pierce befriended many southern senators and Congressmen. They tended toward the easy-going manner that was Pierce's hallmark and he mixed with them comfortably. Pierce liked their practical style and adopted it as his own, relying on loose pragmatic reasoning and disdaining emotional appeals. And of all those who favored emotional theatrics on the floor of Congress, none cut against Franklin Pierce's grain like the abolitionists.

The abolitionist movement started in Great Britain in the eighteenth century by members of a wealthy religious cult known as the Clapham Sect. It took the Sect fifty years to persuade Parliament to outlaw the West Indian slave trade. This occurred in 1833, just about the time that William Lloyd Garrison started printing the *Liberator* in Boston.

Just barely thirty years old, William Lloyd Garrison was the most strident of a strident lot. There was little in his background to explain his fervent passion for the plight of the downtrodden. He never knew his father since he deserted the family when Garrison was only three years old. Having been raised by a strong-willed mother helped explain Garrison's almost heretical insistence that women be allowed to vote, but it did little, in Pierce's view, to explain Garrison's preoccupation with the liberation of southern slaves.

For several years Garrison wrote anonymous anti-slavery

pieces for different publications. Garrison decided to start the *Liberator* as an exclusively anti-slavery work. The banner on Garrison's journal dramatically trumpeted *"I am in earnest. I will not equivocate; I will not excuse; I will not retreat a single inch; and I will be heard"* and *"The compact which exists between the North and South is a covenant with death and an agreement with hell"* along with other moral proclamations.

The abolitionists were divided into two camps: The Gradualists and the Radicals. The Gradualists differed from the Garrison-led Radicals by arguing for progressive eradication of slavery. This view was not a new one. It stemmed from Thomas Jefferson and James Madison's grand vision of deporting all Negroes to Africa reasoning that the black and white races could never co-exist after the years of subjugation of one race by another. In the first issue of the *Liberator* Garrison threw down the gauntlet that wrenched the country ever since. In rejecting the Gradualists (with whom Garrison once sided) Garrison wrote:

> *Assenting to the 'self-evident truth' maintained in the American Declaration of Independence, 'that all men are created equal, and endowed by their Creator with certain inalienable rights-among which are life, liberty and the pursuit of happiness,' I shall strenuously contend for the immediate enfranchisement of our slave population. . . [O]n the Fourth of July, 1829, in an address on slavery, I unreflectingly assented to the popular but pernicious doctrine of gradual abolition. I seize this opportunity to make a full and unequivocal recantation, and thus publicly to ask pardon of my God, of my country, and of my brethren the poor slaves, for having uttered a sentiment so full of timidity, injustice, and absurdity. My conscience is now satisfied. . .*

And later he stated:

Of this I am sure: no man, who is truly willing to admit the people of color to an equality with himself, can see any insuperable difficulty in effecting their elevation. When, therefore, I hear an individual-especially a professor of christianity-strenuously contending that there can be no fellowship with them, I cannot help but suspecting the sincerity of his own republicanism or piety, or thinking that the beam is in his own eye. My bible assures me that the day is coming when even the 'wolf shall dwell with the lamb, and the leopard shall lie down with the kid, and the wolf and the young lion and the fatling together'; and, if this be possible, I see no cause why those of the same species-God's rational creatures-fellow countrymen, in truth, cannot dwell in harmony together.

Garrison railed in issue after issue that any union with the South was immoral and insisted that the Northern states could only achieve absolution by dissolving the Union. Ironically, northern abolitionist Congressmen quoted Garrison's works extensively on the floor of Congress to support their charges of southern depravity while southern Congressmen read from the *Liberator* to demonstrate the abolitionists' insanity. By 1840 Garrison's zeal caused him to appear at abolitionist rallies and demonstrate his conviction by burning copies of the United States' Constitution while thundering that any Constitution that condoned slavery was *per se* void.

Despite the intensity of the debate within the nation's capital, Pierce was acutely aware that the abolitionists did not reflect the sentiments of the public in general. Indeed, the abolitionists were few-in-number and concentrated chiefly in New England and those belonging to the Quaker faith. Franklin Pierce himself spoke for most Americans when he referred to them as "reckless fanatics" on the floor of Congress in 1833. By then Garrison and his followers were inundating Congress with petitions to outlaw slavery which ultimately led to the "gag rule" that John Quincy Adams continued to contest to this day.

To Pierce the abolitionists took on greater significance than they warranted. Most northerners were simply unconcerned with the Negroes' plight and many figured that slavery helped reduce competition for paying jobs. At any rate, while many in the North were disturbed by the incongruity of slavery in a nation founded on freedom, they were not sufficiently dismayed to favor disunion. To most citizens, with Pierce being prominent among them, the notion of disunion over something as peripheral as slavery was lunacy.

Pierce knew and worked with many southern slaveowners and found that they were not Satan incarnate as urged by Garrison but industrious farmers that were coming to accept that slavery was growing less and less economic. But they were loath to free their slaves in the face of the abolitionists' condemnation of their moral composition and, frankly, because they were frightened to find out what slaves might do once free. Even the Negro abolitionist Frederick Douglass found fault with Garrison's insistence on disunion since it would merely exonerate the North from its association with the South but leave the slaves to fend for themselves against the slaveowners.

So, slavery continued. But Pierce was confident that, left to its own devices, the demise of slavery was certain. The number of slaves voluntarily freed by their southern masters increased each year since George Washington himself left instructions in his will to emancipate his slaves. It was an institution doomed to extinction.

With the ascent of the Whigs to the White House and leadership in Congress, however, slavery became the central topic of discussion. No legislation, no appropriation, nothing seemed to be able to move forward without some analysis on whether it would help or hinder the institution of slavery. Even with the slave owning John Tyler in the White House, Garrison and his followers managed to submerge the entire government in a never-ending and never productive dialogue on slavery. Sympathetic Whig Congressmen would stoke the fires of controversy and hot blooded southern senators and representatives responded by raging and cursing at their northern foes. While he did not actively speak on behalf of the South, Pierce grew disillusioned with the tactics of the abolitionist Congressmen to the point of entrenched apathy. When Jane issued her ultimatum, he was far more willing to accede to her wishes than she imagined. The ceaseless orbicular debate on southern morals that once merely simmered now boiled. The heat was too much for one as tepid as Senator Pierce.

But Pierce never reckoned that the tedium of life in Concord would become as wearisome to him as the abolitionists. There was no shortage of jobs being offered to him but most required him to leave Concord which Jane resolutely refused to do. Consequently, he toiled with his law office referring away many more clients than he accepted (though he kept Jane blissfully ignorant of this fact) keeping only the matters on which he thought he could make the most money in the shortest amount of time or which actually interested him, although the latter were few and far between.

He fished a lot and did not drink nearly as much as his days in the senate. He lingered longer on the lakes and rivers and still would stop for a whiskey or brandy before heading home on most days. But the all-night sprees were simply not prudent in Concord. And while he did not relish seeing Jane, she *was* happier and he *did* relish seeing his son, his one true source of joy.

After the loss of his first two sons, Pierce was determined to spare himself from the devastation he felt after each death. He kept himself distant for Bennie's first few months of life, protecting himself. But he gradually warmed as Bennie's smile and peaceful demeanor attracted and captivated him. Pierce convinced himself that Jane was right in wanting to get their son away from Washington. He began to dream of showing his son the wonders of New Hampshire's White Mountains and their many mountains and streams. And of Bennie living in a country free of abolitionists and their self-righteous ignorance.

***

Virginia: February 1844

In an administration that lent itself to a metaphor of storm tossed seas, President John Tyler found himself enjoying a smooth, if short, voyage that gave him some respite, if short, from the political tempest that awaited him ashore. The ship was the *Princeton* commanded by Captain Robert Stockton who chose what turned out to be a glorious day to demonstrate the latest in battleship design. Captain Stockton was as much politician as seaman and knew that John Ericsson's new ship was bound to impress the luminaries now sipping champagne aboard the *Princeton*. It was no coincidence that Captain Stockton's guests all, directly or indirectly, exercised some influence over how the United States government spent its meager funds for defense of the country. Never mind that this was probably the first time most of the notables on board had been on a boat, much less a warship.

Tyler was not alone in noting that the brass fixtures and other equipment gleamed from what was undoubtedly an enormous amount of polishing in preparation for this visit. Like others on board, however, Tyler found it somewhat amusing that the military mind reveled in cleanliness and order when their ultimate occupation of war was the most dirty and chaotic activity humans engaged in. In a perverse and arrogant way people like Captain Stockton seemed to dare their enemies to try and sully their splendid weapons by making them glistening targets. To weather a battle and still have a clean deck was clearly the coveted denouement of the professional warrior.

The President descended carefully down narrow steps and seated himself as the guest of honor before a simple spread of game and fruit. He fulfilled his obligation to chat amiably with his fellow guests but was sufficiently distracted so that he managed to avoid anything beyond the most superficial discussion. The object of his distraction stood at the far end of the cabin near the stairs. Julia Gardiner's arm was linked through that of her father. Together they were talking with Captain Stockton himself and Senator Thomas Hart Benton of Missouri. Up on the deck another of the Princeton's guns was fired as they were periodically throughout this trip to remind the politicians of the serious nature of the Princeton's mission. The cabin reverberated from the blast and all the guests exclaimed the appropriate ooohs, aaahs and twittering, nervous laughs.

It would take more than gunfire it seemed to allow the President to set aside his preoccupation with Miss Gardiner, however. At twenty-four-years old she was thirty years younger than John Tyler. After giving birth to seven children, John Tyler's wife Letitia suffered a stroke in 1838 and never fully recovered. She lived in the White House for a year and a half before passing away. But Tyler's grief was spent by the time Letitia died. After four years of caring for an invalid he could not help but believe that she was better off in the hands of the God that she devoted so many of her waking hours to.

Four months after Letitia's death, Julia Gardiner attended a dinner at the White House with her father David Gardiner, a prominent New York millionaire. John Tyler still recalled his immediate fascination with the poised yet animated Miss Gardiner. After years of joyless marriage in the shadow of Letitia's infirmities, Julia Gardiner seemed to embody life itself. And John Tyler, despite being fifty-four years old, pursued her with the zeal of the most ardent schoolboy crush. As an outcast from both the Whig and Democatic parties, observers saw Tyler's behavior as proof positive of his shortcomings as a man and as a President.

Two weeks after meeting Julia Gardiner, the President maneuvered an invitation to a dance she was to attend with the direct purpose of asking her to marry him. When he proposed in the middle of their second dance of the evening, her eyes widened and she hurried away from him muttering "No, no, no, no. . ." To his own amazement, he was not deterred even after his daughter-in-law Priscilla scolded him about trying to woo a woman "young enough to be, well, frankly, your daughter-in-law!" For months, he availed himself of every opportunity to be in the presence of this dazzling beauty that men *much* younger and far more handsome than he were attempting to charm. It was, to say the least, an infatuation that held little promise of bearing fruit.

But John Tyler seemed to be beyond caring about whether his efforts bore fruit anymore. For the last three years, he was subjected to more criticism and overt threats than were visited upon all his predecessors combined. When Tyler took the view that he was to follow his own conscience rather than that of President Harrison's Cabinet, the Cabinet resigned *en masse* less than five months after he took office. Since that time, he was working with his second Secretary of State, his fourth Secretary of the Treasury, his third Secretary of War, his third Attorney General and his fourth Secretary of the Navy. His Secretary of State Abel Upshur and his Secretary of the Navy Thomas Gilmer were aboard the *Princeton* with him today. In Tom Gilmer and Abe Upshur he had two of the few friends that stood by him after the Democrats abandoned Tyler for his decision to be Harrison's running mate and then the Whigs abandoned him for his audacity in adhering to his Democratic principles upon succeeding Harrison.

John Tyler was a President without a party. Unlike John Adams and his son, however, both of whom disdained political parties, John Tyler understood the role that parties played and yearned for their support. But his loyalty to the primacy of States rights proved to be his undoing again and again. The Democrats proclaimed their belief yet worshipped at the altar of Andrew Jackson who repeatedly violated the sacred primacy of the States' right to be free from interference by the federal government. It was this hypocrisy that led Tyler to consent to running on the Whig ticket. It was only when Tyler began to routinely veto nationalist Whig legislation that the Whigs came to understand the extent to which they had bungled their chance to control the government. The Whigs finally understood that Tyler's disaffection with Jackson had everything to do with Jackson's departure from the Democratic platform and nothing to do with the planks in the platform itself.

After a year of Tyler vetoing every piece of Whig legislation that came before him, the Whigs were so enraged that a special committee was formed to study the veto power of the President. This committee was chaired by John Quincy Adams. Two ill-fated recommendations were made: 1. That a presidential veto be allowed to be overruled by both the House and the Senate with simple majorities rather than a two-thirds majority, and 2. That John Tyler's behavior bordered on treason and warranted impeachment.

The report issued by Adams' committee was scathing. But, at its essence, Tyler knew the report could not support an impeachment resolution. After all, the report said nothing more than that Tyler disagreed with the party that helped elect him Vice President. But the Constitution did not contemplate that a President's failure to abide by the wishes of his party was impeachable. Indeed, the Constitution's primary aim was to assure that the President guarded against the excesses of the Congress and vice versa.

On the other hand, Tyler was sure that Adams' real aim was to censure Tyler and embarrass him into compliance. And Tyler, who once resigned from the Senate rather than rescind his vote of censure of Andrew Jackson, *would* have been embarrassed by a censure. Adams and his fellow committee members went so far as to use the *identical* language used in the censure of Andrew Jackson in their report recommending, at a minimum, censure of Tyler. So, the President summoned the few political favors he still had coming to him and fashioned a defense that even the most fervent Whigs found compelling. Impeachment was narrowly averted and a censure was even more narrowly averted.

But Tyler's stubborn resistance to the Whig programs continued. Henry Clay, who originally favored impeachment but relented when it appeared that there was no mandate for such maneuvering, instead focused his attention on being elected President in his own right later this year. His whole plan to install the feeble Harrison and lay the groundwork for his own election by running Harrison's administration much the same way that Martin Van Buren did for Andrew Jackson disintegrated with Tippecanoe's death and John Tyler's unforeseen impudence. Without Clay trying to push his legislative agenda, Tyler could focus on the only two remaining goals he had for his administration, namely, the annexation of Texas and winning the hand of Julia Gardiner. But not necessarily in that order.

Texas was becoming the tenderbox of the country. One inflammatory move or spark in the heat of debate threatened to engulf the young republic in the flames of war. Northern states were concerned that the addition of such colossal territory as a state would give southern slave states unchecked power over national affairs. And, even more frightening was the specter of Texas being divided into three or four new slave states, each larger than any single existing state.

But John Tyler could not believe that the country would forego the opportunity to add millions of acres of bountiful western land assuring a virtual monopoly over the world cotton supply simply because it would tip the count of slave states ahead of free states. To Tyler they were separate and not insuperable issues. Advances in machinery were making slavery uneconomic and obsolete. On one thing he was in complete agreement with Andrew Jackson: Texas was the key to westward expansion and a country that would stretch from the Atlantic to the Pacific.

For the last few months Tyler and Abe Upshur were in secret negotiations with Sam Houston, the President of Texas, for terms that would annex his republic to the United States. Upshur was tenacious in not only wooing Houston but in swaying recalcitrant senators to the notion that the salutary economic benefits of adding Texas far outweighed any social concerns over the slavery issue. The slavery issue would take care of itself. At this point, Upshur and Tyler were confident of achieving the necessary two-thirds majority in the Senate to approve the annexation of Texas if a deal could be struck with Houston.

Upshur and Tyler's impending success in adding Texas to the United States emboldened Tyler. Despite an administration that was riddled with controversy and defections, Tyler saw Texas as his resurrection. As the opportunities that Texas afforded became known, Tyler was certain that his own fortunes would rise. The Whigs were hopelessly tied to the North and, increasingly, to radical abolitionist elements. The Democrats were still dominated by Martin Van Buren who would be the party's nominee in 1844. But Van Buren, despite Andrew Jackson's feelings to the contrary, *opposed* the immediate annexation of Texas. To a seasoned politician such as Tyler it was obvious that there were votes to be had for a candidate standing firmly in favor of Texas. And Tyler intended to be that candidate even if it meant forming a third party.

If his Texas plans played out and he was miraculously able to be elected President, Tyler knew that marrying Julia Gardiner would be the final ingredient to make his next four years the antithesis of the three years he just endured. But Julia Gardiner seemed content to stay at her father's side and charm her legions of suitors from a distance. From what Tyler knew of David Gardiner he did not seem to be a man who relied upon his daughter's support nor did he insist upon her allegiance, but Julia's devotion to him was complete nonetheless. It was figuring out how to pry her attentions from her perfectly self-sufficient father that Tyler believed was the key to winning her hand.

As Tyler rose from the table with intention of making his way over to greet Miss Gardiner he saw Tom Gilmer's feet and then Tom Gilmer himself hurrying down the steps from the deck. Gilmer excitedly inquired "Captain Stockton, may we have one more demonstration of 'The Peacemaker' before we dock? The crew has indicated that it is at the ready." Stockton nodded, surprisingly with a tinge of reluctance.

Gilmer scampered up the stairs followed by David Gardiner, Senator Benton and Captain Stockton. Julia started to move toward the stairs as she attempted to avoid further conversation with a young aspiring suitor. Tyler seized the moment to walk to the stairs timing his arrival to coincide with Miss Gardiner's. She smiled as he asked if she would like to endure one more thunderous cannon blast with him. "The Peacemaker" was the largest gun on the *Princeton* and its blast was impressive to say the least. Twice on their journey Captain Stockton "authorized" a demonstration and twice the guests were duly awed.

Just as Miss Gardiner alighted the first step, the tiresome and exceedingly drunk wife of one of the Democratic senators aboard the ship stood and slurred "I would like to propose a toast to the President" and then, after a moment's thought added "John Tyler." Julia Gardiner stopped and Tyler obligingly turned to be "honored." The other guests rose nervously and raised their glasses. Tyler did not hear the woman's comments for the first minute as he was lost in thought as how to best raise the topic of marriage with Julia again. As the woman began to gather herself for what was beginning to look like a long discourse on the virtues of this President that she had just met, the Peacemaker exploded with what seemed to be a more powerful blast than either of its prior detonations. The toastmaker was thrown to the floor due to her already precarious balancing situation while other guests grabbed chairs and one another to steady themselves.

Tyler turned to see Julia Gardiner running up the stairs to the deck. He followed and stepped into the bright glare and a nightmarish scene. The Peacemaker sat with a gaping hole and pieces of steel strewn across the deck. The President first saw Captain Stockton crawling on his hands and knees to reach Senator Benton who sat staring at the cannon, clearly stupefied by what hit him. He appeared unharmed. As Tyler came to understand what had transpired he realized that the faceless, bloody mass near the gun was what remained of Tom Gilmer, his Secretary of the Navy. He looked to the other side of the gun as Julia Gardiner screamed and swooned. Tyler leapt over Gilmer's body and caught her as she fainted. He lifted her extraordinarily light frame and, at the same time, saw the source of her distress. Her father's lifeless frame lay face down on the deck. His distinguished silver hair was awash in blood. It was clear that he was dead.

Tyler sat Julia in one of the chairs that were brought to the deck earlier to allow the ladies and more elderly to view the firing of the guns in comfort. He then returned to the carnage of the deck and helped Senator Benton to his feet to lead him to another of the chairs. As he did so he saw the sole of a shoe. He froze as he realized that the top of the shoe contained a foot held in place by a rope that was stretched taut across the deck. Tyler lowered the dazed senator from Missouri into a chair and returned to the foot. As he approached his dread rose to a fevered pitch.

As Tyler reached the railing he saw that this victim was caught in the rope which was all that kept him from dropping into the bay. He seized the leg and started to pull the man to safety but stopped. His legs trembled and his head went light as he stared at the vacant eyes and crushed skull of his Secretary of State and closest ally, Abe Upshur.

In what seemed like moments later, the *Princeton* was docked and John Tyler was carrying Julia Gardiner down the gangplank. In melancholy silence, she buried her face in the President's chest and wept silent, pain-seared tears. Tyler stared straight ahead. But all he saw was the death in Abe Upshur's eyes for their dreams of Texas and another term. And all he felt was the torpid body of the woman that he had only dreamed of holding this close.

***

Baltimore: May 1844

William Marcy poured another glass of madeira for himself and his friend Matt Van Buren. "Van, you're taking this news rather well I must say."

Van Buren shrugged and tipped his glass. "It's not as though I have not had the 'honor' of the Presidency bestowed on me before and found it to be a not altogether pleasant privilege. I suspect I will find things to busy myself. There are worse alternatives than President Clay."

Marcy smirked and said, "Discounting our candidate's chances fairly summarily aren't you?"

Van Buren replied, "With John Tyler and whatever it is he's calling his new party splitting the vote, Henry Clay will have no trouble winning this election."

The former newspaperman turned politician courtesy of Van Buren leaned forward and said, "But the people want Texas and Henry Clay won't deliver Texas."

Van Buren shook his head as he remarked, "No, he'll deliver Texas. Just not as quickly as Tyler and our candidate vow to. Henry Clay knows the importance of Texas but he also knows that most people don't want to send their boys off to die to get Texas. He'll negotiate to add Texas and work out a compromise on the slavery issue."

"Sounds like your plan, not Clay's."

"We're in agreement on how to proceed. We learned the price of war at the same time in 1814, back when Tyler and our candidate were more concerned with memorizing their Latin lessons than with the fate of their less educated peers."

Marcy's eyebrows arched, "I never knew you were a dedicated pacifist. That wouldn't seem like a practical stance for a politician."

Van Buren laughed lightly, "Maybe so Bill, maybe so. But we all start out as politicians only to discover that real people with real problems and real families are affected by what we do. The worst part of being President is that you no longer have the luxury of not taking a position. And when it comes to war, the zeal of youth for conflict long ago gave way to the reality that my four sons have been fortunate to not endure that type of hell and we should not be cavalier with the lives of other people's sons." His smile returned and he added "Maybe the madeira is making me a little more philosophical than appropriate."

Marcy only smiled. For all his years as a newspaperman and supporter of Van Buren he still never ceased to be surprised by the man. "No, the philosophy is appropriate. But this is a somewhat different approach than your letter to Mr. Hammet which, I think it is obvious to add, is the reason that you are not the Democratic nominee."

Van Buren closed his eyes briefly and sighed, "Probably true."

The "Hammet letter" was Van Buren's response just one month earlier to a Democratic Congressman from Mississippi named Hammet. Hammet was attempting to decide how to vote at the Democratic Convention in Baltimore and wrote to Van Buren seeking his view on the annexation of Texas. While many within his party knew that Van Buren was opposed to immediate annexation, given the fervor of most Democrats (and, particularly, Andrew Jackson) to add Texas, it was assumed that Van Buren would adopt a position in favor of immediate annexation. Or he would be sufficiently vague to leave it open to interpretation that he favored annexation.

But the Democrats were astounded and dismayed to realize

that the opportunistic and equivocal politician that engineered first the election of Andrew Jackson and then his own election had given way to a statesman. Van Buren replied very directly to Hammet clearly enunciating his objections to immediate annexation. He reminded Hammet that as Jackson's Secretary of State he attempted to purchase Texas from Mexico. If a valid and binding sale could still be negotiated, he was for annexation.

Van Buren demonstrated a deep understanding of the benefits that would flow from Texas becoming a member of the Union. But he was all too cognizant of the tension that Texas already engendered throughout the country. The addition of another gargantuan slave state or states had northern abolitionists up in arms. The addition of Texas could well be the impetus to civil war. But this was not the reason that Van Buren relied upon in his letter.

To Andrew Jackson's fury and even to the surprise of many Whigs, Van Buren's reluctance to openly court Texas was grounded in the obscure philosophy that John Quincy Adams penned for the fifth President: the Monroe Doctrine. Van Buren argued with uncharacteristic passion that the United States would be guilty of the most perverse hypocrisy if it violated its vow of fidelity and comity to Mexico by laying claim to Texas while Mexico persisted in its assertion of ownership. He recognized that Texas declared its independence and there was little chance of Mexico reconquering its wayward territory. But to Van Buren this was all the more reason for patience since Texas' leaders gave every indication that their ultimate desire was to join the Union. By waiting, Texas could be gained and, perhaps, Mexico would not be alienated.

Jackson and his followers were adamant that the British would seize Texas and form an alliance that would endanger the continued existence of the United States unless prompt action was taken. Van Buren negotiated enough with the Texans and knew their character well enough to know that the chances of them linking up with a European power were infinitesimal. From Europe's perspective, the logistics of such a conquest were prohibitive. No, the notion that the British would snatch Texas from under the United States' nose had more to do with Andrew

Jackson's lifelong paranoia about all things British than with reality. Most compelling of all to Van Buren, however, was the fact that the Texans were slaveholders and the Brits would never countenance such a practice. Van Buren's one allowance to politics in the Hammet letter was that *he* finally concluded that the United States should not countenance the practice of slavery either. But he did not inform Congressman Hammet or anyone else of his conclusion.

Van Buren's correspondence, with his permission, was published in newspapers first in New York and then throughout the country. The Democrats' alarm was palpable as they realized that the man who everyone assumed would be their candidate agreed with Henry Clay, the *Whig* candidate, on the issue of Texas. With the financial panic that sullied Van Buren's prior Presidential administration fresh in the public's mind, the Democrats were concerned that the only way to gain control of the White House was to appease the public's yearning for new western frontiers, namely, Texas. But the likely Democratic nominee was opposed to this plan.

The man the Democrats came to refer to reverently as "The Little Magician" proved unyielding on the issue of Texas. When John Tyler made it known that he intended to form a third party favoring immediate annexation of Texas and he intended to hold his convention in Baltimore at the same time as the Democrats, party leaders pled with Van Buren to recant the Hammet letter. But he declined. In private, he uttered the blasphemy that he would rather see Henry Clay in the White House than to create an enemy out of Mexico on the United States' southern border and tempt civil war by assuming the hopeless task of assimilating slaveholding territory the size of Texas into the country.

Andrew Jackson and other Democratic leaders were appalled at Van Buren's newfound fervor for conviction. But Martin Van Buren was not a new man. He was simply an older, wiser man. Since leaving the White House he spent his time in New York as the chief distributor of patronage all the while training his son John in the art of the spoils system. But his time as President taught him that as the boss of a political party machine he did not set policy, he merely set a general direction and assured that those who followed that direction were properly rewarded.

As President, however, Van Buren learned that the ultimate leader cannot afford to be equivocal. The financial panic set in motion by Andrew Jackson's withdrawal of funds from the second Bank of the United States crippled Van Buren's Presidency. To Van Buren's consternation, he discovered that the public did not blame Jackson, but blamed *him*. Despite taking steps to set the country on a sound footing economically for the first time in its brief history by establishing an independent government treasury that was divorced from private banking interests, it was too late. Van Buren's lifelong practice of avoiding taking a position did not serve him well.

He was certain that if the populace knew where he stood on most matters his chances for success were greatly enhanced. In explaining this conclusion to Marcy at the time of the Hammet letter he diagrammed his logic:

> *If I state my position and I am proved correct, the voters are pleased and support me.*
> *If I state my position but I am proved incorrect but all works out well, the voters are less likely to hold it against me.*
> *If I state my position and I am proved correct but all does not work out well, the voters are less likely to blame me.*
> *If I state my position and I am proved incorrect and all does not work out well, the voters will not support me.*
> *If I take no position and all does not work out well, I will be blamed no matter.*

The two friends laughed at Van Buren's analysis but both knew that it was the embodiment of the lessons learned by Van Buren as President. For one as disciplined as Martin Van Buren, it was a lesson that would not be ignored. From that point Marcy knew that attempting to dissuade Van Buren from the Hammet letter was fruitless. As would any attempt to obtain the

Democratic nomination by Van Buren.

Tyler, the President without a party but who found a rallying point in Texas, followed his audacious declaration of a third party by attempting to inveigle Van Buren into abandoning the fight altogether. In a move that was so transparently political that it almost offended Van Buren who prided himself on his ability to shrewdly yet discreetly manipulate the political system, Tyler offered Van Buren a seat on the Supreme Court. While Van Buren knew that the offer was fully intended to remove the primary obstacle to the success of Tyler's third party candidacy (and possibly even the Democrats resorting to Tyler as their candidate) rather than a profound respect for Van Buren's legal faculties, he was intrigued. The financial security of a lifetime judicial appointment coupled with the continued ability to impact the country's destiny was appealing to Van Buren. A lifetime of strategizing and scheming could be put behind him.

In the end, however, Van Buren politely declined without reproaching Tyler for his heavy handedness. Indeed, Van Buren found it amusing that he and Tyler who had been the Presidents for the last eight years save one month were vying for the privilege of returning to the position where each had endured more abuse and criticism than even the most despicable persons suffer in a lifetime. But he understood Tyler's attraction to the office. They both inherited the problems of ancient generals who really had no business being the Chief Executive but who the public adored as fearless warriors. When matters went afoul, career politicians like Van Buren and Tyler were easy to blame. And both wanted the chance to demonstrate that they were capable and competent leaders.

So, as the Democrats gathered in Baltimore with most northern delegates committed to Van Buren and while southern delegates were being instructed to disavow the Little Magician (including Congressman Hammet), Tyler and the most strident in support of annexing Texas met a few blocks away. But events soon conspired to bring the two congregations together.

Despite the Hammet letter and John Tyler's bid to split the party, Van Buren and Marcy arrived in Baltimore confident of being nominated. Once the nomination was secure, Van Buren was sure that he could dissuade Tyler from running. Tyler may have been passionate about Texas but he was even more passionate about his disdain for Henry Clay. When Van Buren pointed out that his futile candidacy would cause him to attend Henry Clay's inauguration, he knew that Tyler would capitulate. But treachery struck from an unexpected source.

The first order of business at the Convention was for the delegates to vote on whether a simple majority or two-thirds majority would be required to secure the nomination. That a simple majority would be required was a foregone conclusion until the Pennsylvania delegation voted in favor of a two-thirds majority. Van Buren's nimble political mind immediately recognized the game that was afoot. His suspicions were confirmed when James Buchanan's name was placed in nomination after several ballots failed to yield a nomination.

The Pennsylvania delegation arrived in Baltimore ostensibly committed to Van Buren and, with those votes and the requirement of a simple majority, Van Buren's nomination was guaranteed. But the Pennsylvania delegation's defection signaled that its members saw a weakness that it could exploit to place a candidate from Pennsylvania on ballot and wrench power from New York and Van Buren. Van Buren was perturbed but not surprised. Buchanan was a man of great ambition and, Van Buren had to admit, considerable political skill. While Buchanan protested that his friends were working without his blessing, Van Buren had his doubts.

In any event, Van Buren knew his candidacy was doomed unless he retracted the Hammet letter. This he would not do. He and Marcy retired to his room and opened the bottle of madeira that they now shared. Van Buren quickly calmed the agitated Marcy. As Marcy railed against the "double dealing sons of bitches from Pennsylvania" Van Buren waived his hand.

"Bill, what's done is done. I will not be able to gather the necessary votes so I will do the next best thing and control the outcome."

Marcy sat back and did not ask the obvious.

Van Buren continued. "With the two-thirds majority rule, Andy Jackson is controlling this convention. Buchanan won't be nominated because New York won't vote for him because I won't allow it and the southern states won't vote for him because Jackson won't allow it. Jackson has already made it quite clear that my position on Texas has cost me his support."

Marcy queried, "What about Cass?" referring to Lewis Cass, the former governor of Michigan and minister to France for Jackson.

Van Buren shook his head. "No. He's for annexation but against slavery. His view, of course, is right but hopelessly inconsistent. He is a good politician with strong support but not enough to get two-thirds."

Marcy joked, "But who can? The election is only five months away and there will be no Democratic nominee at this rate."

Van Buren looked at him, puzzled. "Well, isn't the answer obvious? Jackson controls the outcome and has already made clear who must be included on the ticket."

Marcy's eyes widened, "You're kidding."

"No, not at all."

"But he is so *dull*. He will never beat Clay!"

Van Buren laughed. "Right you are my friend but tomorrow morning after I withdraw my name from the Convention Andy Jackson's next set of instructions will be read. And those instructions will be to remove Jem Polk as candidate for Vice President and to run him for President. Since Polk will do Jackson's bidding, John Tyler will no longer be the champion of Texas, Polk will be. The Democrats will be united."

"I assume then that New York will get the Vice President then."

"Oh no, Bill, oh no. I'm sure they will offer it to me or Silas Wright knowing full well that neither of us would dare accept such a singularly insipid post. Then it will be given to Pennsylvania as its reward for helping Andy Jackson put me in my place."

"Seems pretty tricky for a decrepit old General. And besides, it plays right into John Calhoun's hands which I can't imagine Jackson doing."

Van Buren raised his glass. "But Jackson doesn't realize

that that is what he has done. I taught the General everything he knows Bill. *Everything* he knows. I apparently did not teach him enough though."

Marcy sat back with a troubled look. Van Buren knew that his once loyal friend was scheming just as Andrew Jackson had to win the nomination for Jim Polk. And that was because, just as Van Buren did with Jackson, Van Buren taught Marcy everything he knew.

PART IV

MANIFEST DESTINY AND
OLD ROUGH AND READY

(1845-1853)

Chapter 1:
James Knox Polk

James Buchanan sat at the mahogany table, his head tilted slightly to allow his farsighted eye to view the other gentlemen at the table. The gentlemen at the table constituted the officers of the new presidential administration. It was a Cabinet of novices. Except for the Attorney General John Mason, none served in a Cabinet position before. And it was not as though Mason was a veteran Cabinet participant. He served as Secretary of the Navy for the last few months of John Tyler's administration after Tom Gilmer died. Further, even Mason knew that the Attorney General post wielded little influence. Mason was here because he was from Virginia and that state traditionally was afforded a Cabinet position even if there were no qualified candidates.

Seated to Mason's left was the *new* Secretary of the Navy, George Bancroft of Massachusetts. Bancroft would seem to be oddly out of place in this gathering of Jacksonian Democrats. Harvard educated, founder of an elite Boston prep school, working on a definitive history of the young United States, with his perfectly groomed shock of hair and magnificent coils of sideburns, Bancroft looked, and was, the epitome of eastern snobbery. But he believed in Jeffersonian principles on a theoretical level and was a shrewd and loyal political strategist and organizer on a practical level. He did not deliver his home state of Massachusetts to the new President, which would have been nothing short of a miracle. But, working in concert with longtime ally Martin Van Buren, he did deliver Maine and New Hampshire, which made two more New England states than the

Democrats anticipated carrying. Bancroft's appointment was a political reward, but Buchanan had no quarrel with Bancroft's ability.

Cave Johnson, the new Postmaster General, was from Tennessee. A longtime supporter of the President, Buchanan was still amused by Johnson's appointment. The President did not carry his home state of Tennessee in the election and, despite Johnson's support, also lost the election for Governor of Tennessee in 1843. It seemed that the President could point to little success due in any way to Johnson's efforts. Apparently, friendship counted for a lot in this instance. Johnson could honestly state that he was a member of the administration and could distribute the multitude of jobs that the Postmaster held sway over as political rewards, but could do little substantive damage.

Buchanan looked across the table. Perhaps the most powerful member of the new Cabinet was by far its smallest. Robert Walker of Mississippi was the Secretary of the Treasury. He sat firmly erect and still his head was below the heads of the other men, most of whom slouched. Walker was intelligent and would be a solid Secretary, but his station, too, was a political dividend. While Mississippi was certainly not due the homage that traditionally was granted to New York, Virginia and the President's home state, Walker was second only to Andrew Jackson in assuring the President's election. It was Walker who flushed Martin Van Buren out on the subject of annexing Texas. Knowing that Van Buren opposed immediate annexation but, as usual, the former President was avoiding the issue, Walker published a lengthy article in February 1844 agitating for immediate annexation. He based his support of annexation first on the obvious economic benefits. But Walker went on to entice those northerners who were not abolitionists but who were, nonetheless, troubled by the existence of slavery by also arguing that the addition of such vast lands would necessarily lead to the dispersion of slaveholders over a wider area and sap their ability to work in concert.

To the amazement of Buchanan and countless others, Walker's article had a profound impact. Southerners and abolitionists both understood that adding Texas was bound to lead to statehood which would increase the representation of slaveholding states in Washington. And Washington was the only place where it mattered if they worked "in concert" anyway. Further, the idea that slaveholders would be disbursed over a broader area was preposterous. Slaveholders were not finite like Stradivarius violins; they already existed in Texas and, therefore, would only increase in number. But it seemed that Walker's editorial allowed many northerners to rationalize away the slavery issue and still gain the economic and national strength advantages of joining Texas.

Walker's article caused the tide in favor of Texas to swell and engulf the presidential campaign. It seemed to Buchanan that it was no coincidence that the letter seeking Van Buren's views on Texas came from Congressman Hammet of Mississippi. He had to acknowledge that Robert Walker was a politician to be reckoned with. The maneuvering was clever, but the fact that it was conducted at the expense of Martin Van Buren made it almost awe-inspiring. Walker's appointment over the objection of Van Buren established that the Little Magician was, indeed, out of tricks.

Next to Walker was the most unlikely Cabinet member of all, Bill Marcy. Van Buren's longtime confidant set to work for the President as soon as Van Buren's candidacy hit the rocks. Unlike his mentor, Marcy was not as prone to loyalty when it stood in the way of ambition. And as the man who first commented to Van Buren that "to the victor go the spoils," Marcy put himself in the position to share in the spoils after the President was elected.

Nonetheless, Marcy's open pursuit of a Cabinet position was unseemly to even Van Buren's political enemies. Marcy did not possess a remarkable intellect nor was he the type of tireless worker that made him indispensable. His appointment was, more than anything else, a reflection of the low regard that the President had for the North and New York specifically. Van Buren, it was reported, was furious over the President's failure to heed Van Buren's preferences for the Cabinet. Van Buren held the view that his withdrawal from the race, at a minimum, entitled him to some say in the structure of the Cabinet.

If Van Buren's view prevailed, Buchanan would not be sitting in this first Cabinet meeting as the United States' new Secretary of State. While Buchanan protested to the contrary, Van Buren was still suspicious that Jim Buchanan encouraged the defection of the Pennsylvania delegation from Van Buren at Baltimore. But Buchanan was very aware that the Baltimore Convention was dancing to Andrew Jackson's tune. The Pennsylvania delegation was just one part of the old General's carefully orchestrated plan to assure that the Democrats ran a candidate that was firmly behind annexation of Texas and westward expansion.

After the election, it was clear that the General continued to manage the decision making from his rocking chair in Nashville. After the President half-heartedly offered the Vice Presidency to Silas Wright of New York knowing that Wright would never accept, Buchanan's arch-rival for dominance of the Democratic party in Pennsylvania, George Dallas, was offered the second position on the ticket. Once Dallas accepted, Buchanan assumed that Pennsylvania was repaid for its role in ousting Van Buren. Apparently, Van Buren made the same assumption and, ever the political realist, harbored no grudge and commenced to offer "suggestions" to the President on appointments for the new Cabinet.

The President ran a campaign that was unique in its open pursuit of the office. The United States' early elections involved very little in the way of open campaigning. To openly seek the office of President almost automatically disqualified one from being worthy to hold the office. So, elections were more rooted in popularity since candidates did little to elucidate their position on any single issue. By the time John Quincy Adams and Andrew Jackson were vying for the office, campaigning was still not something that the candidates openly engaged in but newspapers became the voice that disseminated their views and that their supporters used to slander their opposition.

In the election of 1844, Henry Clay tried to slander James Knox Polk but found nothing to work with. With each effort to unearth some sordid episode from Polk's past, the Whigs found nothing more than a quiet, dull man with a seemingly infinite capacity for detail and work. The only slogan that they could come up with was meant to capitalize on Polk's lack of notoriety when compared with the garrulous and flamboyant Clay. The Whigs derisively asked in the weeks after the Baltimore Convention at rallies and in their newspapers, "Who is James K. Polk?" The candidate decided to answer the question.

For the first time, a candidate came out and squarely stated where he stood and why he wanted to be President. In addition to supporting John Tyler's efforts to annex Texas (which was the key to Tyler's abandonment of his efforts to form a third party) Polk let it be known that he would not run for a second term and that he would accomplish four goals during his administration:

1. Reduction of the tariff and the promotion of free trade.
2. Reenactment of the independent treasury bill first passed under Van Buren but then repealed by the Whigs under Tyler.
3. Settlement of the long simmering question of the exact boundary of Oregon with the British.
4. Acquisition of California.

These four goals were simple but all rang a similar theme: Expansion and economic opportunity. Polk painted a picture of a country spanning a continent with sound money and limited barriers to trade while Clay blanched for fear of running afoul on the issue of slavery. Polk ignored slavery and won the election by carrying the Deep South and pockets of the West. And Pennsylvania and New York.

Buchanan could not blame Van Buren for believing that his delivery of the New York vote to Polk warranted deference to Van Buren's opinion on Cabinet posts. But the underpinning of Jim Polk's whole career was allegiance to one man, Andrew Jackson. And Andrew Jackson was not pleased with Martin Van Buren's defection over Texas. Buchanan knew that the General could countenance disagreement over minor policy issues as Buchanan had done on occasion, but on a major issue such as Texas, adherence to the General's views was expected. In his extreme old age, Jackson could not tolerate even Van Buren straying from the fold.

Shortly after the election Van Buren virtually instructed Polk to appoint at least one of three New Yorkers to be either Polk's Secretary of State or Secretary of Treasury. With Polk's goals in mind, it was clear that there was likely to be a war with Mexico over Texas and California or with the British over Oregon. Van Buren knew, therefore, that the Secretary of State would wield great influence. To lower the tariff and establish an independent treasury, the Secretary of Treasury would likewise be an important appointment. Van Buren's nominees were Wright, Ben Butler or Van Buren's own son, John. The latter was laughable to Buchanan as he was surprised that Van Buren's judgment had regressed to the point that he believed that his intelligent but impetuous and bombastic son was mature enough to entrust with a key Cabinet position.

Wright and Butler, on the other hand, were extremely well qualified and deserving. Van Buren quickly abandoned his efforts to secure a post for his son, especially after John was elected Attorney General of New York. But as weeks went by with no response by Polk to his entreaties, Van Buren's letters in support of Butler and Wright and, ultimately, a long list of other candidates from New York grew more frequent and more urgent.

Buchanan figured that New York would receive either Treasury or State. He let his supporters know that he would accept the State post but thought it unlikely, principally because he and Polk's relationship was historically one of competition and antagonism. But, again, General Jackson interceded and directed Polk to appoint Buchanan. Buchanan had crossed Old Hickory enough times that he knew the General would never trust him as a presidential candidate but, apparently, Jackson viewed Buchanan's expertise on the Constitution as essential if Polk had to prosecute a war.

True to form, Polk's telegram offering the State department position to Buchanan was cold and formal. To Buchanan's dismay, Polk included a caveat in his offer that made it clear that Polk was following Jackson's orders but that he viewed Buchanan far more warily:

Should any member of my Cabinet become a Candidate for the Presidency or Vice Presidency of the United States, it will be expected that he will retire from the Cabinet. I will myself take no part between gentlemen of the Democratic party who may become aspirants or Candidates to succeed me in the Presidential office, and desire that no member of the Cabinet shall do so.

This restriction posed a problem for Buchanan. He desperately wished to be Secretary of State. But, he fully intended to spend the coming years coordinating efforts to elect him as President in 1848 since Polk promised to serve but one term and it would be a miracle of the highest order if Andrew Jackson was *still* alive in four years. He penned his response and held his breath:

I cheerfully and cordially approve the terms on which this offer has been made. I am not able to dictate the actions of my colleagues and constituents and cannot, in fairness to them, accept this office at the expense of self-ostracism. I cannot proclaim to the world that in no contingency shall I be a candidate for the Presidency in 1848. Should it become evident that that honor may be bestowed upon me, however, I shall retire from the Cabinet. If under these explanations, you are willing to confer upon me the Office of Secretary of State, I shall accept it.

In a terse reply, Polk accepted Buchanan's acceptance. Buchanan later learned that all Cabinet members received similar offers with the same restriction but he knew that Polk's suspicion of Buchanan's ambition was the origin of these odd offers to join the President's Cabinet.

Once Buchanan was slated to be Secretary of State, Van

Buren was not pleased but assumed that the Treasury Department would then go to New York. But unknown to Van Buren, Bill Marcy was conducting his own letter writing campaign touting *himself* for a Cabinet post. Polk was most concerned about appointing a capable fiscal manager to Treasury that he could trust since finance was not Polk's expertise. He also knew that he might be fighting a war but was less concerned about his ability to manage that effort. Besides, if Jackson was alive, Polk knew he would be receiving a great deal of instruction from Nashville on how to perform as Commander in Chief. Polk's solution was to appoint Walker to Treasury and then "rewarded" New York by appointing Marcy to be Secretary of War.

If Polk *ever* chuckled over anything, Buchanan sensed that it would have been sitting with the withered old Jackson and speculating over Van Buren's rage at the appointment of the self-seeking Marcy. Van Buren was double-crossed by Jackson at Baltimore and then by Marcy. Buchanan, who bore no animus toward Van Buren, felt some pity at how the fickle allegiances spawned by politics turned so cruelly on the Little Magician. But, by the same token, Buchanan knew that no one was as capable of understanding and accepting what befell him as Van Buren.

As he surveyed his new colleagues and ruminated about the tumultuous year behind him, Buchanan realized that the new President was staring at him. Buchanan cleared his throat and inquired, "Begging your pardon Mr. President, I am afraid I wandered off."

Polk scowled. "Perhaps training your energies on obtaining a wife like the rest of us would, in turn, help you train your attention to the task at hand Mr. Secretary." Nervous laughter emanated from the other Cabinet members.

Buchanan blushed. As the only bachelor among the Cabinet members he was used to jibes from other men and usually took no offense. But he knew that Polk was not given to facetiousness. If Polk recommended to Buchanan that he wed, it was because Polk believed that it would instill discipline otherwise lacking in Buchanan. Buchanan realized that this was not to be the last rebuke he would suffer at the whim of the new President. Buchanan's rapier wit victimized Polk too many times. Polk would use his new perch to his advantage.

Polk continued, "I was saying that I have made promises that I intend to fulfill. Mr. Walker is hard at work on the independent treasury and tariff matters. I wish to enlist your aid on the Oregon question. I know that many of our more enthusiastic supporters vowed that we should never accept less than the 54th parallel as our boundary for Oregon, but I would like you to explore the 49th parallel with the British minister."

Buchanan took note of the President's request. He asked, "And if they balk?"

Polk replied crisply, "We will terminate the treaty and force the issue. The only way to treat John Bull is to look him straight in the eye."

Buchanan nodded. The bluster about John Bull was typical Andrew Jackson contempt for the British. But there was little doubt that terminating the treaty negotiated by John Quincy Adams when *he* was Secretary of State in 1818 allowing for joint occupation of Oregon would precipitate a strong reaction. But probably not a war. England had more pressing matters than gaining a few degrees of land in the vacant, soggy woods of North America. Provided their access to the Pacific was assured the British were not likely to commit troops to the cause. The Oregon question was interesting and important but Buchanan knew that the warm ports of California and securing the benefits from the annexation of Texas were paramount. So, he ventured, "It will be done. What about Mexico, shall we be staring it down as well?"

Polk did not smile. In a matter of fact tone he replied, "Mr. Buchanan, a man with only one good eye should limit the number of things he casts his gaze upon."

With a simple yet brutal comment, Buchanan knew he was dispatched. And he knew that he would not occupy the same level of responsibility as Walker or even Bancroft. Polk saw Buchanan in the same light as he saw Marcy. Buchanan now understood that Old Hickory was responsible for his appointment but Polk had little intention of allowing Buchanan to show his mettle. The situation was intolerable but, for the time being, not alterable. He could hardly resign at this juncture without being labeled a quitter or, worse, difficult to get along with. Additionally, it would not help his Presidential aspirations to have it known that he did not enjoy the confidence of the head of his party. Finally, Polk had forced him to promise to not work for his own nomination for the Presidency while he was in the Cabinet. So, he was doing nothing on his own behalf while he did nothing for his country. Buchanan seethed as President Polk continued to methodically proclaim the work to be done in his administration without listing the task that he had already accomplished and in which Buchanan was sure that Polk took great pride: The political neutering of James Buchanan.

***

Corpus Christi: February 1846

Brigadier General Zachary Taylor ducked into his tent just in time to see an intruder slithering out. Taylor took one more step and grabbed his dress sword off his cot. Taylor had not worn his uniform since arriving at this camp and he certainly had not engaged in battle. Thus, the sword was reduced to snake killing duty.

Taylor stepped back out of the tent and around to where the rattlesnake was just completing its exit from the tent. Despite travelling from the Great Lakes to Florida to Louisiana to Texas and seeing more species of snakes than he cared for, Taylor still was in awe of the rattlesnakes of south Texas. They grew to mammoth proportions and, as snakes go, were exceptionally intrepid. Taylor judged this recent visitor at about six feet long and wider about than would allow the tips of his fingers to touch. It moved with that languorous ripple that typified the larger of its breed and gave even a man of Taylor's experience with the grotesque a momentary tremor. He raised the sword and severed the snake's head in one fluid movement. Killing snakes was easy provided the snake was deprived of the element of surprise, which, far more often than not, they were.

As he flicked the head away from the body and admired his work, Taylor smelled a rank cigar and knew that Lieutenant Sam

Grant was in the vicinity. His guess was quickly confirmed when a voice behind him said, "Good sign. Warm enough for the snakes to crawl."

Taylor didn't turn around but only nodded. After a moment he offered, "I'd ruther not have 'em crawlin' where I sleep all the same."

Taylor knelt to lift the snake. As he held it above his head the deceased reptile's rattles lay on the ground confirming Taylor's estimate of the snake's length since Taylor was well under six feet tall. Blood streamed down the sides of the snake and onto Taylor's hand. As he turned he was saying "Sam, we should probably put rocks or mud along the bottoms of the tents to keep this…Are you gonna be all right Lieutenant?"

Grant's face was pale as he stepped backward and waved Taylor off. In a moment, he was out of sight. Taylor smiled. He was fully aware of Sam Grant's squeamish nature. Odd for a soldier to become so repulsed by the sight of blood. Grant enjoyed bad cigars and, occasionally, bad whiskey. *So* bad that they made most of his men nauseated. But Grant was known to vomit when he caught a glimpse of dinner before it was fully cooked and insisted on bathing in the privacy of his tent rather than in the brown waters of the Nueces River as did most of the men, including Taylor himself. General Taylor was not sure that Lieutenant U.S. Grant was meant for a life in the military.

Taylor tossed the snake to a passing soldier and grunted "Dinner" which only elicited a return grunt. This was typical conversation for these men who had been camped on the banks of the Nueces for over six months. When they set out for Texas, Taylor knew that his troops could be in for a long wait before they saw action. If they ever did. So, Taylor sent advance scouts to find a warm spot to winter, and maybe even summer.

His scouts returned to Louisiana with word that Corpus Christi Bay (or Kinney Ranch as the locals referred to it) was described as enjoying very mild winters with an abundance of game in the woods and fish in the bay. In stifling heat Taylor led his troops across Texas to Corpus Christi where they arrived in August of the year before. The location was ideal once the summer heat, humidity and disease laden mosquitoes abated.

In his many years of being an officer in the United States Army, Zachary Taylor concluded that leading troops in a battle was a far easier task than maintaining order among troops that were waiting to fight. It was so difficult that Taylor long since stopped even trying to maintain order. A military camp that remained in one spot for any amount of time became a magnet for entrepreneurs of the basest variety. Tents and shacks soon surrounded the Corpus Christi camp where whiskey, gambling and whores with far worse diseases than the mosquitoes were all readily available. For the few devoted souls camped by this bay named for their Savior, the situation was the personification of hell. Sadly, for most, however, it was their fondest hope for heaven.

For a short time, Taylor's lieutenants prevailed on the troops' sense of duty and the need to remain prepared. But November brought freezing temperatures far below any that the locals ever recalled occurring. By December the Nueces was frozen in many places and dead fish rolled onto the beaches, bloated and spoiled. The humid air made the cold unbearable and the troops abandoned all pretense of dedication. They filled the makeshift bars, casinos and brothels to capacity. Swearing and drunken soldiers, fights and gunfire replaced the gentle lap of the ocean and cries of the gulls from dusk to dawn. The locals complained to Taylor but he knew there was little he could do. He merely speculated that it was likely that that he and his troops would soon be moving on.

In fact, Taylor's troops were ordered to move south to the Rio Grande River four months before. But Taylor ignored the Secretary of War's instructions. He knew movement would be nearly impossible until the weather warmed and the freezing rain abated. Additionally, his own intelligence contradicted Marcy's. According to Taylor's scouts, Santa Anna was not on the march to Texas although he was certainly preparing to do so. Marcy believed reports that the Mexican general returned to Mexico from his exile in Havana and immediately gathered a force twice the size of Taylor's army and set out for Texas.

Taylor was skeptical of Marcy's information. Santa Anna returned to Mexico City less than a year before--the same year that Texas consented to joining the United States and was quickly admitted to the Union as a state. While Santa Anna often boasted of his glorious triumph over a bunch of rag tag volunteers at a crumbling mission called the Alamo, Texas was, in reality, the scene of his most humiliating defeat. At the battle of San Jacinto, Santa Anna's troops were annihilated and Santa Anna himself was taken prisoner. The Texas volunteers were led by Sam Houston who followed his victory by prodding the Texans into proclaiming their independence from Mexico. In perfect synch with his own script, Houston was immediately elected as the first President of the new Republic. Samuel Houston, to his utter delight, was the George Washington of Texas. But, unlike Washington, Houston was an experienced politician, an adventuring opportunist and, frequently, a raging drunk. Houston now served as Texas' first senator in Washington after declining President Polk's offer of the command that Taylor now held.

Taylor knew little of Santa Anna other than that the Mexican general had some military training. But, again, unlike George Washington, Sam Houston, was not a military man. Santa Anna came to know Houston well during his captivity. Zachary Taylor was confident that Santa Anna must have berated himself many a time as he realized that he was not bested by a superior military mind but by a charismatic politician that just happened to attack when he was out of all other options and his troops were on the verge of mutiny. And now Santa Anna had to know that if he brought a force to Texas again that he would not be facing a rebel state led by an itinerant wanderer like Sam Houston. The United States would enlist every available military mind to protect its hard-won prize. No, Taylor reflected, it was not likely that Santa Anna was racing to meet his Waterloo in Texas, despite noise to the contrary in Mexico City. Beyond Santa Anna's own misgivings, Taylor also derided the thought of the one-legged Mexican President "rushing" anywhere.

Taylor continued to receive urgent telegrams from Marcy and, occasionally, President Polk directing him to move his troops south. He ignored most of these except to occasionally reply that preparations for the move were underway. Of course, this was a lie. Few among the troops had any idea that they were to go to the Rio Grande directly across from the town of Matamoros. Taylor knew that his soldiers' options were limited at Corpus Christi. But at Matamoros he envisioned endless patrols to fish soldiers out of the river while they tried to swim over to the senoritas that Taylor was sure Santa Anna already instructed to be more than obliging.

Taylor also was aware of the Jacksonian newspaper articles that equated Taylor's troops' lack of discipline at Corpus Christi with an inability on Taylor's part to lead men in battle. Taylor laughed as these articles made their way, from unknown sources, to Corpus Christi. If he didn't know that Andrew Jackson died almost eight months ago, Zachary Taylor would have ascribed the articles to Old Hickory himself. In Taylor's experience, the insistence on inflexible discipline was vintage Jackson. But having spent much of his life serving under General Jackson, Taylor observed that Jackson was never so popular with those who served under him as those who read about his supposed popularity among his men. Taylor tried Jackson's methods of fiery discipline as a young officer. The result was disastrous as Taylor came to understand that volunteer soldiers were not much inclined to trust the logic of a leader in battle who insisted on illogical rigidity when he wasn't fighting.

So, Taylor knew all too well that behind Marcy and Polk's cries for movement was, as always, Andrew Jackson. The old General's installation of Polk as President was consonant with his unswerving devotion to western expansion and securing Texas and California for the country. Polk was the one man whose fealty Jackson never doubted. An almost equally faithful disciple was the self-made Texan, Sam Houston. Houston could never vie with Polk for stability but he managed to punctuate his mercurial rises and falls from grace with moments of splendor.

Taylor had little use for Polk or, for that matter, Houston. Zachary Taylor spent most of his soldiering career clearing the path for white settlement in the West. Most of that time was spent under Andy Jackson who thought first of the political advantage to be gained from a military expedition and then, if necessary, justified his decisions. Old Hickory was adamant on the point of having his way as the first rule. Jackson followed this rule even if it meant resorting to less than savory means to meet his ends. While others, such as Polk and Houston and, truth be told, Taylor, did his bidding, Jackson took the credit. But unlike Polk and Houston, Taylor had no political aspirations and he registered his dismay about Jackson's manipulations sufficiently to discourage the type of rewards that Jackson arranged for Polk and Houston. While first Houston, and then Polk, both served as Governor of Tennessee Taylor managed to distance himself from the Old General. That gave him a sense of contentment that he was sure Polk and Houston would never know.

While Taylor knew that Polk and the witless Marcy were probably apoplectic at his inaction and that they were worried that a man as apolitical and unindebted to them as General Taylor was running *their* war, he also knew that they had no other choice. To recall Taylor at this point would set them back many, many more months while a new general arrived and surveyed the situation. If they wanted a war, it would be with Taylor or not at all.

And Polk wanted a war. Of that Taylor was certain. While Polk sent envoys to the Mexicans with miserly offers of cash for the millions and millions of square miles of land that stretched from Texas to the Pacific Ocean, Taylor knew that he was merely waiting for Santa Anna or some other Mexican official to respond with indignity in order to pick the fight. It was Jackson's way. Zachary Taylor saw it too many times to mistake the pattern. Jackson would start a war the same way he started a half dozen duels in his life. And the ever-loyal Polk was tracing the Old General's footsteps by proclaiming a desire for peace while berating his subordinates for not precipitating conflict. Once the battle was joined, however, Taylor figured Polk would be right there to take credit for all victories and equally absent to share in defeat.

As a soldier, Taylor accepted the peccadilloes of men like Jackson and Polk. He would make every attempt to reach the desired result of obtaining the southwest for this latest band of politicians. But with Old Hickory gone, Taylor had enough of following foolish orders from the amateur generals in Washington. To overrun a hapless country like Mexico to double the size of the United States was something Taylor found distasteful yet within the realm of his promise to serve his country. But to needlessly endanger the lives of the boys entrusted to his care by prematurely moving to Matamoros was something that Taylor could not abide.

Now, it was safe. The time had come to move the troops. As he wiped the snake's blood from his forearm Taylor agreed with Sam Grant. It was warming up and it was time to leave this once idyllic bay. And, he suspected, Santa Anna was beginning to think the time was right to head north to reclaim Texas.

***

<u>Mexico City: September 1847</u>

Franklin Pierce took a long swallow of whatever it was that one of his men brought him and strained to see out the window to the Square below. He could hear the bawdy revelry of hundreds of American soldiers as they paraded through the streets of Mexico City. For a "defensive mission" that was to end at the Rio Grande, it was not too much to say that the Americans had overshot their mark.

It started with Zachary Taylor's movement of troops to Matamoros on the Rio Grande a little over a year before. After Taylor's men finished despoiling Corpus Christi they finally moved on to Matamoros. As they settled into their new camp they took little time in noticing the Mexican senoritas beckoning from the far bank of the river. For men who only enjoyed the company of whores for the better part of a year, this was too much to resist. They poured into the river in droves swimming in pursuit of the fulfillment of their lust.

No sooner had they hit the water than the senoritas disappeared. Mexican soldiers emerged in their place with muskets and began shooting. The Americans doubled their swimming speed the opposite direction and Zachary Taylor commenced the Mexican War. Weakly worded messages were sent from Washington that Taylor should only use such force as necessary to "defend" his position. But Taylor construed his orders liberally and chased the Mexicans deep into their country. He routed them at Monterrey and, then, outnumbered 2 to 1 by Santa Anna at Buena Vista, he prevailed again.

After besting Santa Anna at Buena Vista, however, Taylor allowed the Mexican President to leave with his troops and agreed to a brief armistice. James Polk took advantage of Taylor's breach of political protocol and stripped him of all but few of his divisions and placed Winfield Scott in charge of the war command. Scott picked up where Taylor left off and led the Americans marching to the Mexican capital.

Frank Pierce's trip to Mexico City started in New Hampshire in the spring of 1846. Safe at home as a District Attorney appointed by the Polk administration, Pierce had a steady income and rarely had to exert himself in the quiet oasis of his home state. Polk offered him the opportunity to return to Washington as Attorney General in recognition of Pierce's work in delivering the New Hampshire vote to Polk. But Pierce declined for two reasons. First, Jane Pierce would never consent. Second, and even more important, the thought of working under the strict scrutiny of a compulsive taskmaster such as Polk made Pierce shudder. He was offered an appointment as Senator to fill an unexpired term. He again declined. He was offered the nomination for Governor of his home state. The thought of being a chief executive *really* perplexed Frank Pierce. It seemed to him that everyone envisioned great talents in him but him.

Yet, by early 1846, Pierce was bored. And, rather than delving deeper into his work, Frank Pierce did what he did so often when tedium won out. He drank. Unfortunately, he drank enough on the day that news of Zachary Taylor's victory at Matamoros reached Concord that he convinced himself to enlist.

At the age of 41, the Frank Pierce that the town of Concord adored for his pleasant manner and hallowed family name, despised himself. His name was synonymous with his legendary father, *General* Pierce, the Revolutionary War hero. His continued political well-being was inextricably linked to another legend, *General* Jackson, the hero of New Orleans. Pierce's seemingly comfortable and successful life was lived in the shadow of these *Generals*.

Although he made a competent showing of a productive life, Frank Pierce viewed himself quite differently. He saw his life as a charade hoisted on the reputations of a series of generous benefactors who saw no harm in promoting Benjamin Pierce's boy. He tried always to be appreciative and managed to avoid embarrassing anyone.

When Pierce heard about the events at Matamoros, however, he knew that James Polk would not tarry for long trying to negotiate with Santa Anna. And Pierce knew that Santa Anna only would be able to reclaim his mantle as the President of Mexico by promising to bring Texas back into the Mexican fold. There would be a war.

Frank Pierce's slightly inebriated enthusiasm led him to send a letter resigning his post as District Attorney and volunteering to raise a regiment to lead to Texas. He somehow rationalized that despite Zachary Taylor's early heroics, there was still time to make it from New Hampshire to Mexico and become a hero in his own right. By raising a regiment he knew that he would automatically move from being a private to a colonel and by the time he arrived in Mexico, with the help of his friends in the Polk administration, he was a brigadier general. For the first time in his life, Frank Pierce felt worthy of the two Generals. Never mind that he attained his commission in the same manner that he became a senator and district attorney.

But it wasn't just the fact that *he* was now General Pierce that buoyed Franklin Pierce. It was also that this war was extremely unpopular among the abolitionists. And Franklin Pierce was for anything the abolitionists were against.

The abolitionists, and everyone else for that matter, knew that along with the vast lands and economic potential of Texas and California came millions of acres of new slave territory. Frank Pierce disdained the abolitionists for fomenting disunion by antagonizing the southern states about their "immoral" institution. But, equally, Pierce was just annoyed by the abolitionists for all the times they upset his ability to exert minimal effort. Time and again when he was called upon to voice his opinion as a politician it was directly or indirectly at the behest of some rabid pack of abolitionists. When he would reiterate the traditional Democratic view that slavery would find its own limits and the states should be left to make their own decisions on the issue, he was painted in the most venomous strokes by the abolitionist press. For one such as Pierce who rarely had much to busy his day, such attacks were truly vexing. By riding into Mexico to secure the rights of the states to choose, Pierce felt a flow of adrenaline spurred by taunting his nemeses.

Pierce's sense of mission was cast in a radiant glow when he landed at Veracruz and reported to General Gideon Pillow (and, yes, the references to "soft" duty were legion). Pierce was directed to organize the movement of a couple thousand men west to Puebla where they would join General Scott and march to the Mexican capital. From the snowy and gray bleakness of Concord, New Hampshire, Pierce was transported to a sparkling bay with emerald waters. He drank in the warmth and sights and sounds of Veracruz with zeal bordering on avarice.

While he reluctantly left the comforts of Veracruz, his first impression of Mexico was of the proverbial end of the rainbow. He relished seeing more. He fantasized of simply disappearing in this wonderland. He probably would have but for his son Bennie who he missed despite not missing Jane or Concord. For the first time, threw himself into his work and, for the first time, had his troops marching inland ahead of schedule. He showed a genuine propensity for organization and logistics that the troops begrudgingly recognized and accepted.

But Pierce soon discovered that the splendors of Veracruz were pathetically absent as one departed the ocean. The peasantry was friendly but conditions were rank. Within days most of his soldiers were spending more time in the bushes evacuating their intestines than marching. Pierce himself was quickly stricken. His attempts to exhort his men with promises of the glories (and drink and women) that awaited them in Mexico City soon became more irritating than enticing.

Near a small village called Contreras, Pierce's illusion of glory dissolved. As his men trudged through the tropical heat dreaming mutinous dreams, rifle shots sporadically crackled and then began to rain down on the Americans. What would be called the Battle of Contreras commenced. Pierce's men rallied from their stupor and acquitted themselves well despite receiving no direction from their erstwhile leader.

After recognizing the first gunfire Pierce whirled in his saddle to instruct his men to fan out. Never much of a horseman in the first place, Pierce was truly vexed by the western saddle that he had only been in for a few days. As he turned, a shot whistled from the brush just ahead and startled his horse. It lurched forward sending General Pierce's groin careening into the saddlehorn. As he fainted from pain he tumbled from the saddle and spent the first fifteen minutes of the Battle of Contreras hanging upside down from a stirrup as the battle raged about him.

A lieutenant led the horse to safety and then helped Pierce to the ground where he lay until the fighting ceased. As his men glorified their exploits and momentarily forgot their dysentery and fatigue, Franklin Pierce lay in abject misery with his swollen testicles and knee being the least of his pain. He called for whiskey more to ease his mental rather than physical anguish. He was placed in the back of the cook's wagon and it was from there that he participated in the grand entrance of the American troops into Mexico City.

Winfield Scott had enough political ambition to understand that he owed a visit to Franklin Pierce even if Scott leaned more to the Whig point of view and was decidedly *not* a patron of Andrew Jackson. When "Old Fuss and Feathers" (as Scott's men affectionately and not so affectionately referred to him) appeared in Pierce's room and shared a glass of brandy, Pierce's humiliation was complete. Here was yet another general, literally larger than life at about six feet and five inches in full military regalia with minions scurrying about to assure that his bidding was done. By all rights, Frank Pierce belonged alongside this man reviewing troops and proclaiming the American triumph. With magnanimity that bordered on sincere, Scott informed Pierce that just as soon as he was able, arrangements were in place to transport him back to Veracruz and on to a ship bound for New England. Pierce wanly expressed his appreciation. But he knew that Scott's main concern was to assure that this political interloper could not stand in the light of Scott's military glory.

With rumors of the ragged Zachary Taylor ascending to the Presidency for his exploits, Scott knew that *anything* was possible.

When Scott rose to leave after once again wishing Pierce a speedy recovery (which Pierce, as a man, could not help but believe every man wished him with something of a stifled smirk given the nature of his injury) he stopped and said, "By the way, I assume you have heard that the Democrats in New Hampshire are awaiting your permission to nominate you for governor. You have declined in the past, have you not?"

Pierce nodded and answered, "Yes and I will again."

Scott looked perplexed briefly and Pierce knew he was attempting to calculate what this meant in terms of Pierce's role on the political landscape. He apparently concluded that it meant nothing when he abruptly smiled and waved his hand "Rest well General. Rest well." His tone was paternal yet somewhat mocking and made Pierce even more irritated with his lot.

Pierce followed his advice and for two more days drank this *tequila* that seemed to have little physical medicinal effect but was a grand elixir for his troubled mind. He rose and hobbled to the window fighting off the urges brought on by his lingering dysentery and stared out the window. The dusty street was filled with his men who seemed to bear him no malice for his failure to carry the fight with them. Victory made for charitable supposition.

Texas was now safely within the Union and for that Franklin Pierce felt some satisfaction, if not pride. He would be thankful to board a ship leaving this country which had come to symbolize the bowels of the earth to this now unemployed ex-senator from New Hampshire. He just wished that the ship was not bound for New Hampshire.

***

Washington: February 1848

From his seat in the middle of the last row of the United States House of Representatives, the thirty-nine-year-old representative from Springfield, Illinois reclined sideways in his chair to allow his seemingly endless legs to stretch into the passage between his desk and the next row of seats. Abraham Lincoln was less disturbed that his assignment to the last row reflected his lack of standing within the Whig party than by the arduous journey from the aisle to his seat. He didn't mind being in the back, but the middle presented logistical issues for a man of six feet and four inches.

Abe Lincoln conceded that his less than desirable seat did afford a good view of the comings and goings in the House, particularly given his height. He was currently watching one of the House boys slowly making his way toward the front of the chamber with the brittle former President of the United States, John Quincy Adams, clinging to his arm. Since Adams' return to the House after suffering a stroke in late 1846, these journeys to his seat had become a daily exercise in patience for the members of the House. Out of respect the House would stop all business when Adams appeared and would wait until he was safely deposited in his chair. On the first day of his return, Whigs and Democrats alike rose in ovation for the sixth President.

Lincoln did not know him well but was told, despite his emaciated physical condition, Adams retained his adroit mind. Adams struggled to form the words necessary to express himself and clearly was not the same firebrand that dominated the House for eight years in fighting the Gag Rule or who argued so eloquently to gain the freedom of Negroes aboard the slave ship *Amistad.* That was the John Quincy Adams that Abraham Lincoln would have relished seeing. It was hard to imagine being persuaded of anything by this old man with his drooping mouth foaming with spittle, disheveled white sideburns and tremulous hands.

The boy helped the decrepit gentleman to open a large envelope and placed a stack of papers before Adams and departed. Adams nodded to the gentlemen on either side. This was the signal that proceedings should continue. He then hunched over the papers and commenced reading slowly and laboriously occasionally dipping his quill and scribbling on the pages. This manuscript that held the former President's attention for the last several days intrigued Lincoln. Adams would blurt out a chuckle from time to time and an occasional "harrumph" but mostly sat and read with a sly smile and frequent nodding of his head that may have been from agreement or affliction.

The tales about Adams' ability to nap or read or stare vacantly while still absorbing every word spoken on the Floor were legion. Still, Lincoln wondered how much of the debate Adams was now able to assimilate. He had his doubts, even if Adams was as brilliant as claimed.

Lincoln knew enough about Adams to know that his legacy as the spokesman for the abolitionists was neither accurate nor desired by John Quincy Adams himself. The mundane squabbles of the North and South over the "rights" of the Negro probably mattered as little to Adams as they did to Lincoln. Lincoln was confident that Adams would agree with him that the Negro race was inferior. But, like Adams, a country founded on freedom that abided slavery troubled Lincoln. Lincoln was content that slavery should not be allowed to expand beyond its current boundaries. And he could not imagine a worldly man such as Adams being aligned with the zealous abolitionists of the North or, obviously, the more ardent proponents of the expansion of slavery in the South. After all, Adams' true legacy lay in the years he spent as a diplomat, Secretary of State and President who earned the grudging respect of the Old World powers. His history was one of negotiation and compromise, not extremes. While he apparently did little to cool the abolitionists' ardor for him, Lincoln suspected that Adams' war against the Gag Rule had more to do with a rigid view of House procedure than whole-hearted endorsement of the abolitionist cause.

Like so many of his colleagues, Lincoln was weary of the whole issue of slavery. It seemed that his entire term was spent trying to avoid the topic of Negro rights while the abolitionists did all they could to keep the question front and center. Their southern counterparts responded with equal vigor and, between the two, little else was confronted. For Lincoln and his colleagues' part there was very little "confronting" done with the problem of slavery. The abolitionists railed against it, the southern aristocracy cursed the abolitionists and the Senators and

Representatives did their best to stand firmly on the perimeters of the middle depending upon which group currently had their ear.

The abolitionists were about to embark on their most torrid campaign against slavery. With the addition of Texas and vast territories to the west, it was inevitable that the boundaries of Negro bondage would be a vexing quandary for years to come. One practical side of Lincoln believed that the Union could continue to prosper if 1) the South would only accept that slavery would be confined to states where it currently existed and 2) the abolitionists would accept such a restriction as some evidence of righteous victory. But the abolitionists were not ones to compromise and the leaders of the South were not likely to allow their representation in the national government to be diluted to the point where they had fewer votes than those who disdained them as immoral hypocrites.

Another practical side of Lincoln, however, saw that the slavery question was a political boon for the Whigs. Led by one of Lincoln's heroes, Henry Clay, the Whigs opposed President Polk's war against Mexico as a belligerent imperialist action intended to gain vast new slave territories and place Polk and Andrew Jackson's beloved South firmly in control of the Union. At the same time, however, the Whigs courted Zachary Taylor on par with the most lustful of young men chasing a debutante. In Taylor they had a war hero. That status, as shown by the election of Jackson and William Henry Harrison proved to be a virtual guarantee of victory. But given the very well-known fact (helped by numerous well-placed Whig newspaper articles) that Polk did all he could to undermine and usurp Taylor's power and glory, the Whigs could staunchly support Taylor as a soldier just doing his duty in an immoral war. Clay, Lincoln and their fellow Whigs knew the twelfth President would be Zachary Taylor.

Never mind that Zachary Taylor had not cast a vote for a public official in over thirty years and that the Whigs were not even sure if his sympathies lay with their party. Henry Clay was determined to wrest control of the White House from the Democrats one last time. And, hopefully, this time his man would not die in office as the disappointing Harrison did. But, if he did, Lincoln knew that Henry Clay had no intention of having anything other than a strong Whig as Vice President. Unlike John Tyler, a ticket headed by Zachary Taylor would have a northerner on it for balance. *Zachary Taylor* was from the South. And he owned slaves.

Lincoln warned his fellow Whigs to not underestimate "Old Rough and Ready" as a few of Taylor's troops called him and which the Whigs were all too happy to embellish upon. Lincoln recalled vividly Taylor's common sense and pragmatic intelligence as an officer in the Black Hawk War (Lincoln's memory of his military career was far more glorious than Taylor's recollection of Lincoln's military career). He suspected that once Clay made the magnanimous gesture of conceding the nomination to Taylor he would expect the General's unbridled allegiance. And, as with Harrison, Lincoln was sure that Henry Clay would be annoyed by Taylor's autonomy.

But Henry Clay was almost seventy years old and Lincoln was sure that he would not make the same mistakes that he made with Old Tippecanoe when he worked with Old Rough and Ready. Clay was now less politician and more statesman. He regarded the threat of disunion over slavery as real and would do all he could to assure that it was he who Taylor relied upon to avert such a calamity.

As for Lincoln, he knew that he could not bear another term of listening to the anti-slavery petitions of the abolitionists and, even worse, the lame arguments of the southerners attempting to defend their tyranny over the Negroes. He would return to Illinois to resume his law practice and, perhaps, run for governor or some other office that held no sway on the issue of slavery.

Lincoln gazed about the chamber. He was impressed with many of his colleagues in the House. Most were young like him. Most were handsome, unlike him. His gangly physique, large ears, swarthy skin and protruding lips were the subject of many taunts as well as his own self-deprecating comments. On a few occasions some of his more vicious Democratic opponents ascribed his sympathy for the Negroes to speculation that Lincoln himself had some Negro blood citing his physical make-up as evidence. To one as ambitious as Lincoln, these were the sort of jibes that went beyond humor and into slander.

But with few exceptions, most of the members of the House liked Lincoln. He adhered to his party but not in an obnoxious manner and he was not disagreeable even when he disagreed. This, more than any legislative agenda was Lincoln's real goal in coming to Washington. To forge and cement friendships that would allow him to pursue greater opportunities in the future. And the task had not been unpleasant for he genuinely liked almost all these men.

He again watched the gray and bald head of John Quincy Adams as it bobbed up and down. He noticed that Adams seemed to be drifting off again as his head slumped further toward the pages he was reading. His arm slipped from the table and swung listlessly. Lincoln smiled momentarily as he believed that the former President was engaging in a particularly vigorous nap. But then he realized that this was no nap as the old man's head thumped against the table and Lincoln could see his eyes fluttering to ward off some internal demon. Lincoln nudged Josh Giddings of Ohio and pointed at Adams. Giddings jumped to his feet and cried out, "Stop. Look to Mr. Adams!" There was a rush to the stricken man.

The boy who escorted Adams to his seat sprinted from the chamber in search of a doctor. Adams was stretched out on the Floor of the House of Representatives as some of the elder members knelt beside him and loosened his cravat. Lincoln stayed back and observed from his perch in the back of the chamber. The House physician arrived shortly and made his way to Adams. Lincoln could not hear his whispers but saw him shake his head. He motioned for assistance and Adams was hoisted aloft and removed. As he was carried out Lincoln could see that he was still breathing but at grotesque and irregular intervals.

Andrew Johnson, a representative from Tennessee who occupied Adams' chair in the House during Adams' absence the year before, waved his hand at the Speaker. When acknowledged he muttered in a low voice that it might be best for the House to adjourn. In a body that was scrupulous about formality there was nothing more than a uniform nodding of heads and the members began to file out.

As the last of his colleagues left the room, Abraham

Lincoln slowly rose and stretched. He buried his long, bony hands in his trouser pockets and made his way down the aisle to Adams desk. He looked about him and then turned to the first page of the stack that had so consumed the man who was just carried unconscious from the chamber. He was surprised to see that the writing was in French. On that page, he recognized the name of a Frenchman, Alexis de Tocqueville, who had come to the United States about ten years before. Lincoln knew little French but could translate this first page: *Democracy in America* by Alexis de Tocqueville. It looked to be a draft. There was a note to Adams from de Tocqueville in the upper corner that Lincoln could not decipher.

Lincoln flipped through the pages but saw nothing but French. As he laid the manuscript down he saw some writing on some of the pages in what had to be Adams' infirm scrawl. It appeared that Adams was entertaining himself by translating de Tocqueville's work. But as Lincoln read Adams' writings he realized that Adams *never* entertained himself. He was marshaling arguments. Lincoln read the passages that Adams had put inartful stars next to:

> *The state of Kentucky was founded in 1775 and that of Ohio as much as twelve years later; twelve years in America counts for as much as half a century in Europe. Now the population of Ohio is more than 250,000 greater than that of Kentucky.*
>
> *These contrasting effects of slavery and of freedom are easy to understand; they are enough to explain the differences between ancient civilization and modern.*
>
> *On the left bank of the Ohio work is connected with the idea of slavery, but on the right with well-being and progress; on the one side it is degrading, but on the other honorable; on the left bank no white laborers are to be found, for they would be afraid of being like the slaves; for work people must rely*

*on the Negroes; but one will never see a man of
leisure on the right bank: the white man's
intelligent activity is used for work of every
sort.*

*Hence those whose task it is in Kentucky
to exploit the natural wealth of the soil are
neither eager nor instructed, for anyone who
might possess those qualities either does
nothing or crosses over into Ohio so that he
can profit by his industry, and do so without
shame.*

*In Kentucky, of course, the masters make
the slaves work without any obligation to pay
them, but they get little return from their work,
whereas the money paid to free workers comes
back with interest from the sale of what they
produce.*

Lincoln flipped ahead to words that Adams circled in rough
fashion:

*What is happening in the South of the Union
seems to me both the most horrible and the
most natural consequence of slavery. When I
see the order of nature overthrown and hear
the cry of humanity complaining in vain against
the laws, I confess that my indignation is not
directed against men of our own day who are
the authors of these outrages; all my hatred is
concentrated against those who, after a
thousand years of equality, introduced slavery
into the world again.*

*Whatever efforts the Americans of the
South make to maintain slavery, they will not
forever succeed. Slavery is limited to one point
on the globe and attacked by Christianity as
unjust and by political economy as fatal;
slavery, amid the democratic liberty and*

enlightenment of our age, is not an institution
that can last. Either the slave or the master will
put an end to it. In either case great
misfortunes are to be anticipated.

If freedom is refused to the Negroes in the
South, in the end they will seize it themselves; if
it is granted to them, they will not be slow to
abuse it.

Lincoln laid the page down and retrieved the pages that fell during Adams' attack from the floor. He doubted that he would ever see John Quincy Adams at his desk again just as he doubted that Adams would ever finish de Tocqueville's manuscript. But Adams was steeling his fragile body to declare slavery wrong once more. Yet he was also going to say that de Tocqueville was right. The South was sowing the seeds of its own destruction. Adams, de Tocqueville and Lincoln all hoped that those seeds grew faster than the seeds being sown by the abolitionists that would destroy not just the South, but the Union.

***

New York: August 1848

Martin Van Buren laid the *New York Evening Post* down and leaned back. The *Post* printed his acceptance as nominee for the Presidency of the United States. He knew he should feel flattered and even honored, but instead he was simply weary and a little embarrassed.

For almost twenty-five years, Van Buren dominated the Democratic Party in New York with little to no resistance. Despite Thurlow Weed's impressive success in creating a Whig party that was occasionally successful in winning plum federal elections, Van Buren's Democrats generally remained firmly in control on matters within New York. Even as President, Van Buren managed to wield influence in New York as he cultivated his son John in the ways of the political machine. John performed well enough that when Van Buren returned from Washington after being defeated by William Henry Harrison, he may not have been President but he was still arguably the most powerful man in the nation. New Yorkers still had an abiding faith in the wizardry of The Little Magician.

Van Buren was not particularly disappointed in not receiving his party's nomination in 1844. Initially, he saw in Jem Polk the type of man that he assumed he could exert his influence over without having to endure the unpleasantness of *being* the President. Then, with Polk's Cabinet appointments and complete disregard for Van Buren's New York Democrats, Van Buren realized how precipitously his fortunes had fallen.

At the age of sixty-one, however, Martin Van Buren was no longer concerned with his personal lot. He cared about three things: His sons, his country and New York's Democratic Party. While he still had a penchant for strategy and political gamesmanship, he was no longer the shrewd and elusive politician of his youth. His politics were tempered by considerations of principle, something that he only allowed to occur under the most extreme circumstances in the days that he and Old Hickory were in their ascent.

His break with Old Hickory and with President Polk came over Van Buren's refusal to support immediate annexation of Texas until the question of the expansion of slavery in the new territories was settled. Van Buren was no abolitionist but his time as President afforded him a view he never enjoyed before. It was the view of the man on the highest peak who has no more cliffs to scale and so he is forced to finally survey what he has conquered. To Van Buren's alarm, he saw a country that was teetering on the brink of imploding.

To Van Buren, slavery was always an issue that would, by the sheer force of economics, resolve itself. But the abolitionists and many a northern Senator and Congressman were unwilling to wait for the economic inefficiency of slavery to manifest itself. Van Buren consistently took the Jeffersonian position that slavery was wrong but not an issue for federal intervention. In this way, he could express his displeasure but not alienate his southern political counterparts to the point that he was unable to negotiate other matters of interest to him and, more specifically, to New York.

But his time as President and, although he would never admit to it, the persuasive effect of the abolitionists' repetitive wailing about the immorality of Negro bondage, caused Van Buren to gradually conclude that Jefferson's rationalization was ill-conceived. Van Buren was not ready to join the abolitionist cause but he decided after leaving Washington that he could no longer be a party to passive acquiescence in the spread of slavery. He *did* believe that slavery could not survive as an economic proposition and, further, saw evidence all about that this was true. Despite this, he saw a movement of southern extremism rising up to meet the extreme tactics of the abolitionists rather than ignoring the Northern demagogues and realizing that the defense of slavery was not justified economically or *morally*. He decided to try to reason with both sides and issued his manifesto on slavery. For Van Buren, the master of taking the middle course, his pronouncements landed him squarely as an enemy in the eyes of the South and caused him to be viewed with suspicion in the North for his sudden penchant for blunt talk on the most controversial topic of the day. But Van Buren was simply trying to get the defenders of slavery to set aside their outrage at the slurs of the Northern extremists and to see reason. And he tried to cast his argument in terms of the harm being done to *whites* by the practice of slavery:

> *Free workers are unwilling to work side by side with negro slaves; they are unwilling to share the evils of a condition so degraded and the deprivation of the society of their own class; and they emigrate with great reluctance and in very small numbers to communities in which labor is mainly performed by slaves. With the exception of a few, and a comparatively very few, the white laborers, or in other words, the poor of those states where slavery is more extensively prevalent, are objects of commiseration and charity to the wealthy planter, and of contempt and scorn to the slaves.*

As the election of 1848 approached, there were, in reality, four political parties wrapped up in the Whigs and the Democrats. Within each of those parties there were southern and northern factions. The southern Whigs already successfully wooed General Zachary Taylor (who was really from the West but was a slaveowner). The South still did not have the voting power of the North so the South was obliged to find a candidate that would at least countenance slavery if not openly argue for its extension. Despite a great deal of contention, the southern Whigs also accepted Millard Fillmore as General Taylor's running mate. The Democrats saw the Whigs' strategy for what it was: Another attempt to get an indifferent general elected so that Daniel Webster and Henry Clay could run the government just as they intended to do with William Henry Harrison before John Tyler laid waste to their schemes.

Unlike the Whigs, to Martin Van Buren's dismay, the Democrats were unable to reconcile the northern and southern factions of their party. Even more troubling though was that it was Van Buren's own son, John, who fueled and braced open the schism. When the Democrats met in Baltimore in May to nominate their candidate, they selected Lewis Cass. The senator from Michigan was the classic compromise candidate. He steered a middle course, opposed slavery but supported annexation of slave territory and was irreparably dull.

Van Buren was not pleased with the selection of Cass but harbored no thoughts of betraying his allegiance to the Party. But his son John did and the majority of the New York delegation and the old guard of the Democratic party bolted from the convention. Dubbing themselves the "Barnburners", their sole basis for bucking Cass' nomination was his failure to support the Wilmot Proviso. David Wilmot of Pennsylvania thwarted all attempts at a negotiated peace with Mexico by inserting the caveat that all new territory gained in the conquest of Mexico would be free territory. The Northern dominated House passed Wilmot's amendment twice. But each time it failed in the Senate where the South was not under the same disadvantage due to the disparity in population.

A month later the Barnburners reconvened in Buffalo and

adopted a virtually identical platform as the Democrats did in Baltimore save support for the Proviso. It quickly became clear that John Van Buren had promised that he could get his father to carry the banner of this maverick wing of the Party. He grew more and more agitated as his father decried the lack of party loyalty. Ultimately, Van Buren decided that he could not embarrass his son and agreed to be the nominee of the party provided it was still called the Democratic Party. John Van Buren readily agreed and then turned right around and returned to the convention and proclaimed that the great Martin Van Buren would be the nominee of this new party that was dubbed "The Free Soil Party." To the naked eye, Martin Van Buren appeared to have become the darling of the abolitionists.

Ever fond of and yet ever exasperated by his son, he knew that his candidacy would only assure that Zachary Taylor would become President. But that did not bother Van Buren particularly. He held firm for William Crawford in 1828 even though Crawford was so debilitated that he could never have functioned as President. And even though Crawford was opposing the man whose career Van Buren intended to engineer, Andrew Jackson.

In the end, Van Buren saw little difference between Zachary Taylor and Lewis Cass. If his experience with Jackson was any indication, Taylor was probably being underestimated and Cass overestimated. Neither candidate was going to strongly oppose the spread of slavery. At this point in his career, Van Buren realized that he could not trade more bodies into bondage for political chips. His political chips were played and the days of fence-sitting the slavery issue were no longer viable. He only hoped that same ability to disagree pleasantly that earned him the sobriquet "The Little Magician" would still serve him in convincing citizens in the South that his moral indignation at the institution of slavery did not equate with a desire for disunion, just a desire that slavery not spread beyond where it currently existed while it gradually ran its economic course. It was a rationalization, but for Martin Van Buren it was a robust stance on principle.

The politician in Van Buren also saw an opportunity. Despite Van Buren's allegiance to the party even after it picked the colorless Polk as its candidate over himself, Van Buren still threw New York's support to Polk as only he could do. But Polk's own brazen lack of gratitude and slight of Van Buren's candidates for the Cabinet irritated Van Buren more than his affable demeanor would ever betray.

By running for President, he would reinforce his son's reputation for being able to deliver on a promise. While he knew he could not win, he knew that the country would be none the worse off with Taylor or Cass. But he did draw some satisfaction from knowing that he would strike a mighty blow for New York's Democratic Party. The next time the Democrats decided to ignore the wishes of Van Buren and his apostles, they would do well to remember that no party's candidate could succeed without accommodating New York. They might not fully understand it now as they read Martin Van Buren's acceptance as the Free Soil candidate for President, but they would in March of 1849 as General Zachary Taylor was being sworn in as President.

Washington D.C.

That night, President James Knox Polk wrote in his diary:

> *I learn to-night that the Buffalo convention of Whigs, Abolitionists, and Barnburners have nominated Charles F. Adams, the son of the late John Quincy Adams, who is an avowed Abolitionist, for the Vice Presidency on Mr. Van Buren's ticket, the latter having been nominated for the Presidency. Mr. Van Buren is the most fallen man I have ever known.*

Chapter 2:
Zachary Taylor and Millard Fillmore

James Knox Polk was dying. He was as confident of this as he was the rules of procedure for the House of Representatives or the prerogatives of the Executive branch of the government. For a man who spent his life burnishing a reputation for never being surprised because of his meticulous preparation, this was a surprise. The rare times he thought about death, he assumed that it was not something one ever saw coming. But the eleventh President could see his death looming with startling clarity.

From his frail youth Polk guarded his health knowing that he did not have the robust constitution of his father or his mentor, Andrew Jackson. That caution served him well as he weathered a political career and Presidency that established him as having a peerless work ethic. He took office vowing to serve one term and to dedicate that term to the accomplishment of four key objectives:

1. Reduction of the tariff and the promotion of free trade.
2. Reenactment of the independent treasury bill.
3. Settlement of the Oregon boundary with the British.
4. Acquisition of California.

These were all accomplished, and more, with time to spare. But the work was not easy. A war was fought with Mexico at the cost of many lives and leaving the United States with a hostile neighbor on its new southern border; the country came to the brink of war over Oregon before Britain decided that it had more pressing issues than a soggy forest on the other side of the earth (much to the relief of a Congress that could still see evidence of the last visit by British troops in charred buildings throughout Washington); and Congress smarted as Polk methodically had his way in passing a new tariff and establishing an independent national bank.

As his promises were met, Polk made few friends. Except for his Treasury Secretary Robert Walker, most of his Cabinet found him dogmatic, humorless and exhausting. Polk's impatience with those unwilling to work as hard as him became legendary. The Congress found him irritating as he used his vast experience in the legislative branch to bend the House and Senate to his will again and again. His military generals came to distrust him as he insisted on allegiance to his strategy for the battles he sent them to fight.

But the people, particularly in the South, were pleased. Just as few people knew very much about Polk in the campaign of 1844, they learned little more about him while he was President. He rarely appeared in public or engaged in the soaring rhetoric of a Webster or Clay. But he got results. The United States was larger, stronger and more prosperous. Ultimately, this was the aim of Polk's four goals. By the time he became President, James Polk understood that his fellow citizens valued prestige and economic opportunity more than virtue or harmony. So, while some wrung their hands over the sins of spreading slavery or fomented against the country's forays into imperialism, Polk ignored them as much as possible. By the time his one term was over he could say his work was done. None of his detractors could say the same.

As a result, cities throughout the South invited Polk to visit so they could honor him. Sarah Polk persuaded him to overcome his reluctance and his impatience to return home to Nashville and agree to a tour so his fellow citizens could express their gratitude. Now Polk was convinced that that tour was why he was now dying.

Not that he blamed Sarah for his plight. On the contrary, James Knox Polk knew with even greater certainty that his success was inextricably bound up with his choice for a wife.

From the age of 12, Sarah knew that her calling in life would be to help James make his mark in the world. While few doubted that Sarah was any man's intellectual peer (and, usually, superior), she was a woman and her options were limited. But in Jim Polk she found a man who not only respected her intelligence, but *valued* it. Sarah was content to debate the important topics of their country with her husband knowing that he would take her counsel before that of most of his advisors. In exchange, she helped him navigate a world of politics where charm and manners typically counted for more than ability and knowledge. The fact that the colorless, humorless James Polk ascended to the country's two most powerful positions, Speaker of the House and President, spoke volumes about *Sarah* Polk's achievement.

Sarah knew that her husband could never tolerate the informality and, indeed, chaos, that was typical of the President's Mansion when Polk became President. Thomas Jefferson established the precedent of making the house accessible to all citizens in his disdain for anything resembling monarchy. Andrew Jackson's followers did not just visit the Mansion seeking appointments and favors, but to party and toast their hero of the common man with some degree of regularity. Sarah could not shut the public out of the Mansion without compromising her husband's fealty to the principles of Jefferson and Jackson. Instead, in her own dignified but pleasant way, she introduced rules that did not exclude but instituted some degree of decorum.

Among her first rules was the banning of the serving of hard drink in the Mansion. While some grumbled, Sarah coupled her piousness with humble statements of the need for the President to be able to do the people's work with minimum distraction. Few could argue against the desirability of that.

Sarah saw two problems when her husband entered a room. For a man of little charisma such as James Polk, it was often awkward that few people noticed him or believed that he could be the President. On the other hand, when he *was* recognized, he was besieged by those seeking an audience and, usually, favors. She solved this problem by first making membership in the United States Marine Corp band a matter of distinction. Then she asked the band to play "Hail to the Chief" at any gathering of more than a handful of people. People came to associate the song with the President. Before long, he was entering rooms confident that he was recognized and able to get down to the business at hand reasonably unfettered. What some saw as pomp, James Polk knew to be his wife's way of saving him from embarrassment and annoyance.

Thus, when Sarah said her husband should indulge the desire of the country to express its appreciation, Polk, as usual, trusted her judgement. The Polks set out immediately after Zachary Taylor was sworn in as James Polk's successor.

Four years of constant toil left Polk ambivalent about Taylor's assumption of office. He was surprised by his affinity for Taylor. Polk never actually met Taylor prior to "Old Rough and Ready's" arrival in Washington even though the President relieved Taylor of his command and replaced him with Winfield Scott during the war with Mexico. At the time, Polk assumed that Taylor had the same affliction for glory and independence as Andrew Jackson and countless other military men. Polk was determined to manage the war his way and so he turned to Scott, who he knew he could control.

Yet, when Polk finally met Taylor he did not find a prima donna eager to seize the reins of power, but a simple and humble man as devoid of pretense as any man he ever met. Polk noted in his diary that night:

> *General Taylor is a well-meaning old man who is uneducated, exceedingly ignorant of public affairs and of very ordinary capacity. He will be in the hands of others, and must rely wholly upon his Cabinet to administer the Government.*

Polk was perplexed how a soldier's soldier such as Taylor was elected to an office he was clearly ill-suited to hold. He realized that his dismissal of Taylor had only fueled the public's imagination and craving for another military hero in the tradition of Washington, Jackson, Harrison and, now, Taylor. But Taylor had none of the gravitas of Washington, none of the ambition of Jackson or even the willingness to grovel of William Henry Harrison. His Presidency was created based on a fiction that Taylor clearly leant no hand in encouraging.

Polk confided to Sarah that he felt some responsibility for the position Taylor found himself in and of his fondness for the old soldier. Sarah arranged a grand welcome for the General complete with a reception and dinner with the most powerful men in Washington. At his inauguration, Polk earnestly, and sincerely, wished Taylor well. But the Polks left Washington troubled that all their hard work for the last four years would be wasted, not because Zachary Taylor opposed their work but because he could never understand it.

As they headed south on March 5, 1849, however, they dwelled little on what lay behind in Washington and more on what lay ahead. Once this tour of the southern states was concluded, the Polks would return to Nashville and to a new home. Polk purchased "Grundy Place" from Felix Grundy, his former tutor in the law, and promptly renamed it "Polk Place." For the last year, Sarah oversaw repairs and remodeling from Washington and both were anxious to see their new retirement home.

"Retirement" was a difficult concept for James Polk to grasp. He was 53 years old, the youngest President to leave office. While he genuinely relished relief from the grueling schedule he maintained as President, he knew he could not remain inactive for long. He anticipated that he would resume the practice of law and try to accumulate some of the wealth he had foregone in public service. While it was difficult to imagine staying away from politics for long, he was determined to avoid being a jaded nemesis like John Quincy Adams when *that* former President served in the House for many years after he left office.

With thoughts of a new home and new career on his mind, Polk embarked on the tour that his wife told him he owed the country. The trip began with a series of dinners, receptions and festivals that exceeded Polk's expectations considerably. At stop after stop through Virginia, North Carolina and South Carolina, thousands of people turned out to catch a glimpse of the Polks and to cheer. Even the taciturn Polk was forced to acknowledge that he was surprised and pleased to realize that his work was recognized and appreciated. On the way to Columbus, Georgia they made an unscheduled stop to stay at an acquaintance's home and recuperate. After settling into their room the Polks went downstairs to find hundreds of townspeople gathered in front of the house. Soon another grand party was underway.

It was in Alabama that Polk began his steady descent into his present condition. It started with a cough that developed into a cold (undoubtedly the same cold that Sarah was just recovering from). By the time they reached Mobile, there had been deaths from cholera among the passengers on their steamer. By New Orleans, Polk was violently ill with diarrhea. He was sure it was the early stages of cholera. He tried to beg off the rest of the tour but each city prepared festivities to exceed that of the last city. He was, literally, being loved to death.

By the time the Polks arrived in Nashville in April, James Polk was near death. Despite being administered opium regularly, his decline continued. By June, he knew that he had cholera, despite the denials of his doctor, wife and mother. The builders fixed a couple rooms in Polk Place for Sarah and James while the work on the refurbished mansion was completed.

None of that was what weighed on James Polk's mind now, however. As he looked at the troubled faces of his wife and mother, he thought about a young boy who never took the sacrament of baptism. His father's resentment against a preacher's rectitude left Polk adrift in a spiritual sea. He wrestled with the reality of a deity his whole life even as he regularly attended Sunday services with Sarah. But now he was dying and the two people who loved him unconditionally were the only ones with him. And it all became clear. These women were a reflection of Christ's love, the only love that ever really sustained him.

Polk lifted his hand slowly to touch Sarah's face. His next words stunned and thrilled her. "Sarah, I believe. I think it is time that I was properly baptized." True to form, Sarah quickly arranged for the Methodist minister to hurry to the former President's bed. Jane Polk, the life-long Presbyterian not only did not object, but thanked God effusively. Her greatest regret was resolved.

Driven to succeed in a way that his father could not understand, Polk worked his whole life at a pace that never allowed for humor or peace. Nonetheless, he never felt as though he met his long-dead father's nebulous expectations that were rooted in a masculinity Polk could never attain, even as he left the Presidency with a country that stretched from the Atlantic to the Pacific. But now, freshly baptized, Polk felt a peace and contentment he never knew. He again reached for Sarah's face and said, "I love you Sarah. For all eternity, I love you."

In a marriage defined by intellect, hard work and logic, James Knox Polk might be speaking the Latin he used to deliver the valedictory address in North Carolina all those years ago. But Sarah spoke both Latin and the language of the heart. She wept knowing that her husband had finally learned the latter language too as his hand dropped from her face and he died.

***

Washington: July 1850

Millard Fillmore was the perfect Vice President. He was an astute enough politician to know that the Whigs selected him not for his ability but because he was from New York and one had to win New York to be President. The Whigs already knew that Zachary Taylor would carry the South and most of the West. With Fillmore and the gift of Martin Van Buren choosing to run as a third-party candidate, the Whigs were very confident that their latest old General would be elected.

With Fillmore, the Whigs knew they had a man with little ambition who would not get in the way of Henry Clay and Daniel Webster as they exerted influence over the President. Taylor's Cabinet, to a man, bordered on contempt for the Vice President who they saw as another tool in the Thurlow Weed New York machine, whether true or not. Even the President who was constitutionally incapable of rude conduct seemed puzzled as to what to do with Fillmore and kept him at a distance. That is not to say that Taylor did not find Fillmore useful. Affable and handsome, Fillmore was an ideal representative of the President, particularly for those occasions that required some degree of polish rather than substance.

Remarkably, while Fillmore would occasionally smart from being excluded or even overtly derided, he was reasonably content to be Vice President, secure in his employment and the prestige that was denied him only by those who genuinely understood the vapid nature of the office. And there were very few of those people.

Fillmore also liked the President, even if they did not enjoy a close relationship. Zachary Taylor proved to be equal to the task of being President, much to the dismay of politicians like Clay and Webster who were disappointed by the appalling independence of the last Whig General, William Henry Harrison. Yet, unlike Harrison, Taylor was indeed his own man, not just a man intent on showing he was not Clay's and Webster's man. He disagreed with the Whig position on issues as often as he agreed. He was not petty but he did not brook a lack of respect for the office he held or for himself personally. At the same time, Taylor was folksy and charming in a very genuine way. His beloved stallion, Whitey, grazed on the lawn of the White House and Taylor often wandered out on the South Lawn to visit with his fellow citizens who were intent on seeing the famous General or on plucking a hair from Whitey's tail as a souvenir. Taylor sent letters to the editors of the Washington newspapers with syntax that was tortured, to say the least. He spoke bluntly and colorfully at formal events. In short, Fillmore found Taylor's assault on the stuffy environment of Washington refreshing and amusing, even if Fillmore himself was one of the most adept men in the Capital at operating in that very same environment.

The Vice President was not completely devoid of ego, however. Whatever the Cabinet and many in Washington believed, Fillmore's tenuous alliance with Thurlow Weed and his Albany machine was ruptured beyond repair. Weed and his man in the Senate, William Seward, conspired to utterly neuter Fillmore in terms of influence in New York and, worse, in the Administration. While Fillmore resigned himself to having little say in the direction of the government, he was using his political exile to plot his return to prominence. He reckoned that the best way to achieve his resurrection was through the President.

Fillmore knew that Zachary Taylor was, at his core, a man who valued integrity above all. While Jackson prized loyalty and Harrison, apparently, cherished esteem, *this* General valued honesty and candor. It was this characteristic that Fillmore hoped to appeal to in his quest for relevance. On July 3rd, Fillmore took his first definitive step toward that goal.

The country elected Zachary Taylor as the hero that won the Mexican War and delivered territories from Texas to the Pacific Ocean. The country's delight with its greatly expanded borders soon dissipated as representatives from California swiftly moved to seek statehood with a Constitution that forbid slavery. Passions over the issue of slavery threatened the Union again. The pro-slavery states saw admission of California as a free state as further eroding the South's strength in Washington. The anti-slavery faction wanted California admitted as a free state with no consideration for its effect on the current balance of power.

By January of 1850, the South had revived talk of secession. The President threatened to personally lead an army against any seceding state and to hang the instigators. This did not exactly calm the situation. It was at this point that Henry Clay rose from his seat in the Senate and changed the course of the debate. By this time, Clay was old and ill. His dream of becoming President Clay was a distant memory. Politics held no charm for him any longer. His only interest was in seeing the Union preserved until slavery ran its natural course. With this in mind, he proposed a compromise to allow California to enter the Union while the remaining southern territories would be granted the power to decide on the legality of slavery within their borders. To entice Texas, already a slave state, to join in the compromise, the country would assume Texas' debts from its war of independence with Mexico.

Clay's proposal was not immediately accepted but it redirected the country's attention from disunion to how to reach an accord on how to keep the United States *united*. Weeks of alternative compromises were debated within the Congress and between the Congress and the Administration. Stephen Douglas of Illinois worked tirelessly to craft a solution that could pass both houses and not be vetoed by President Taylor. Fillmore watched all of this from his perch as President of the Senate.

Then, on March 7, the other aged lion of the Senate, Daniel Webster, rose and spoke for three and one-half hours on the compromise effort. He started by detailing the history of slavery in the United States making it clear that the history of slavery was inextricably bound with the history of cotton. He pointed out that when the Constitution was being drafted, slavery was extant throughout the North *and* South of the new country. If anything, slavery was more reviled in the South than the North. At that time cotton yielded only $40,000 to $50,000 per year. But in a couple decades, cotton had become the backbone of the South's economy and slave labor was perfectly suited to the cultivation of cotton. Thus, despite James Madison assiduously avoiding the use of the term "slave" because slavery was universally seen as an evil to eradicate, the South gradually came to view slavery as essential to its prosperity.

Webster argued that slavery was irrelevant to the question of what to do with the new territories acquired in the Mexican War:

> *"California and New Mexico are Asiatic, in their formation and scenery. They are composed of vast ridges of mountains, of enormous height, with broken ridges and deep valleys. The sides of these mountains are barren--entirely barren-their tops capped by perennial snow. There may be in California, now made free by its constitution-and no doubt there are-some tracts of valuable land. But it is not so in New Mexico. Pray, what is the evidence which every gentleman must have obtained on this subject, from information sought by himself or communicated by others? I have inquired, and read all I could find, in order to acquire information on this important*

question. What is there in New Mexico that could, by any possibility induce anybody to go there with slaves? There are some narrow strips of tillable land on the borders of the rivers; but the rivers themselves dry up before midsummer is gone. All that the people can do, is to raise some little articles-- some little wheat for their tortillas-and all that by irrigation. And who expects to see a hundred black men cultivating tobacco, com, cotton, rice, or anything else, on lands in New Mexico, made fertile only by irrigation? I look upon it, therefore, as a fixed fact, to use an expression current at this day, that both California and New Mexico are destined to be free, so far as they are settled at all, which I believe, especially in regard to New Mexico, will be very little for a great length of time-free by the arrangement of things by the Power above us. "

Fillmore sat transfixed as the master of political oratory discoursed on the history of the nation and of slavery and, like De Tocqueville a decade before, saw the demise of slavery as an economic proposition, if events were allowed to run their natural path. His arguments were compelling and, to Fillmore's view, correct. But Fillmore was stunned when Webster then took his political life in his hands by calling out the abolitionists directly for unnecessarily fomenting disunion:

"Then, sir, there are those abolition societies, of which I am unwilling to speak, but in regard to which I have very clear notions and opinions. I do not think them useful. I think their operations for the last twenty years have produced nothing good or valuable. At the same time, I know thousands of them are honest and good men, perfectly well-meaning men. They have excited feelings; they think they must

do something for the cause of liberty; and in their sphere of action, they do not see what else they can do, than to contribute to an abolition press, or an abolition society, or to pay an abolition lecturer. I do not mean to impute gross motives even to the leaders of these societies, but I am not blind to the consequences. I cannot but see what mischiefs their interference with the South has produced.

"Sir, as I have said, I know many abolitionists in my own neighborhood, very honest good people, misled, as I think, by strange enthusiasm; but they wish to do something, and they are called on to contribute, and they do contribute;. and it is my firm opinion this day, that within the last twenty years, as much money has been collected and paid to the abolition societies, abolition presses, and abolition lecturers, as would purchase the freedom of every slave, man, woman, and child in the state of Maryland, and send them all to Liberia. I have no doubt of it. But I have yet to learn that the benevolence of these abolition societies has at any time taken that particular tum."

While most in Congress were not fans of the abolitionists and their unyielding stance on the principle of complete and immediate emancipation, Webster knew his vulnerability as he spoke these words. Webster was from Massachusetts and that state was the epicenter of abolitionist sentiment. The Massachusetts press was unabashedly at the beck and call of the abolitionist leaders.

All who sat in the Senate that day knew that Webster's days as a senator were numbered. Despite what Massachusetts might do to its famous statesman, however, Webster probably saved the Union with his speech. For outside of New England, the country was enthralled with Webster's logic and willingness to speak against his own personal interests. The efforts to reach a compromise reached a fevered pitch. By the beginning of July, an experienced vote counter like Fillmore saw the very real possibility that if the Compromise came to a vote, there was likely to be a tie and it would fall to the Vice President to cast the tie breaking vote. Fillmore stood ready to support Clay, Webster and Douglas and vote for the Compromise. He had only one problem: Zachary Taylor was against the Compromise.

Fillmore decided that this conundrum was to be his first step in gaining the President's trust and confidence. He had seen enough of Taylor to realize that he respected candor and straight talk more than charm or logic. He went to visit the President the day before the 4th of July holiday.

Ironically, the Vice President was shown upstairs by one of Taylor's slaves. Taylor chose to bring a few of his favorite servants from Kentucky to serve in the White House. The new President quickly realized it would be best to keep them out of sight as he grasped that passions ran much deeper on slavery in Washington than they did in Kentucky. Fillmore, who found slavery abhorrent, was always mindful of being respectful and courteous to these men and women who found themselves trapped inside the most famous home in the United States.

Zachary Taylor greeted Fillmore with his usual warm informality and, knowing the Vice President was a teetotaler, asked if he would like a lemonade. Washington in July was nothing short of stifling and Fillmore gratefully accepted. Once refreshments were served, Fillmore commenced.

"Mr. President, I have had a matter on my mind that I feel compelled to share with you out of courtesy to you and respect for your office."

Taylor smiled. "Then you best say your piece."

"The debates on Mr. Clay's and Mr. Douglas' omnibus bill have, as you know, engendered passions in the Congress. From my seat in the Senate, I have rarely seen tempers inflamed to the degree they have been the last few months."

The President leaned forward and stared at Fillmore slightly more seriously. The Vice President continued, "I am also fully aware of where you and the majority of the Cabinet stand regarding the proposed compromise. While I respect and, in many particulars, sympathize with your position, I have determined that, after weighing the merits of the bill, I intend to vote for the bill if it comes to that. As matters stand, I estimate that the Senate is very likely to deadlock on the Compromise leaving the deciding vote to me. I do not take this position lightly or to cause you any embarrassment, but I sincerely believe that it is the only way to avoid disintegration of our Union."

Taylor leaned back and stared out the window. Fillmore took a long drink of lemonade and silently prayed that he had read this man correctly.

The President turned back to Fillmore and said, "Well, I suspect the Cabinet won't be real pleased to hear this and, as you reckoned, I'm disappointed. But I respect a man who stands by what he believes and, Lord knows, you have more experience at this than me. If it comes down to that, which I hope it does not, I'll expect you to do what you think is right. And I appreciate you coming to tell me yourself." The President held out his hand and, after a bit more banter showed Fillmore to the door. For a few hours, Fillmore believed that his visit gave the President a greater sense of esteem for his Vice President that would allow Fillmore to have a more meaningful say in the Administration.

The next day was the 4th of July. The President sat outside in oppressive heat for hours on end watching parades and other festivities. By night he was ill. Five days later, he was dead.

The evening of July 9 a messenger brought Fillmore the news that he had expected for several hours: The President was "no more" and Fillmore was now President. After a sleepless night, he proceeded to the Capitol the next day where he was sworn in as the 13th President before both the House of Representatives and the Senate.

Now, back in the Willard Hotel, he reviewed the tendered resignations of Zachary Taylor's Cabinet members. None were missing. It was a courtesy on their part that they assumed the new President would decline. But President Fillmore wrote a single response to all the Cabinet. While he regretted the loss of the budding mutual regard he had with Zachary Taylor, he had no such ambitions for Taylor's Cabinet. He accepted all the resignations and took some solace in, what he was sure, would be several sleepless nights for the Cabinet members, William Seward and Thurlow Weed.

***

Pennsylvania: May 1852

James Buchanan served terms in the Pennsylvania Legislature, the House of Representatives and the Senate. He served as the United States' Minister to Russia and as the Secretary of State during the Mexican War under President Polk. In one month, his friends and supporters would travel to Baltimore to attend the Democratic Convention and, if all went well, secure his nomination by the party for the Presidency of the United States. He was, decidedly, an accomplished man.

Which is what his niece Harriet found so amusing as she watched the great man negotiate with James Henry, his nephew. The current bone of contention was James Henry's stalwart opposition to ingesting vegetables of any type. His uncle had less difficulty settling the Oregon boundary than prevailing upon James Henry to eat a green bean.

James Henry was just one of several wards living under James Buchanan's roof. As Buchanan rose to prominence, his siblings were all headed the opposite direction. Some were always on the brink of poverty and some, tragically, died. By the time Buchanan left the State Department and returned home to Lancaster, Pennsylvania in 1849, he had 22 nieces and nephews. Seven of them were orphans who came to live with their famous uncle. Many of the others lived in deprived conditions and escaped to Buchanan's estate whenever possible.

In the sad history of orphans, it could probably be said that none had it as good as James Buchanan's nieces and nephews. They lived with him on his sprawling estate that he called "Wheatland." Beyond the mansion that they all lived in, the orphans had 22 acres of countryside in which to frolic. All courtesy of their 60-year-old uncle who tried his best to instill discipline but was limited by his own easy-going, fun-loving personality. He adored them all.

One of those orphans was Harriet. She was undeniably beautiful with an infectious laugh and cheerful disposition. And, to Buchanan's dismay, she was a hopeless flirt. When her uncle, or "Nunc" as she called him, took her into town with him, young men emerged from all angles to "happen" into an encounter with Harriet. For her part, Harriet relished the attention leading Buchanan to lecture her about caution in her dalliances on numerous occasions. But his efforts were no more effective than in getting James Henry to eat properly.

Probably more than any of his other charges, Harriet Lane was closest to her Uncle. Despite being vexed by what he perceived as her occasional lapses in judgment, they were very fond of and, in their own way, looked after each other. For Buchanan, this was one of his many great blessings, for he was not just a 60-year-old man, he was a 60-year-old bachelor with a house full of orphans.

Harriet did not fill the role of mother for the other orphans but, in her own inimitable style, she was the one who they knew would enforce the discipline that their Uncle only threatened. Buchanan was cautious to not rely too heavily on Harriet's ability to corral her siblings and cousins since, in Buchanan's view, she was barely more than a child herself. But there were times, such as now, when she knew that her Nunc had weightier matters to attend to than James Henry's plant intake and she would deftly assume control and send Buchanan on his way.

Buchanan maneuvered his corpulent frame to his study to continue his preparations for Baltimore. His nomination by the Party was far from certain but, if he was candid, he was surprised to be considered at all.

While Buchanan could not be said to have been a figurehead as President Polk's Secretary of State, it was well known that Polk kept Buchanan on a short leash to manage what he viewed as Buchanan's overarching ambition. For his part, Buchanan transitioned from loathing James Polk to developing a firm respect for the eleventh President. He could never say that he liked Polk or even considered him a friend but, over their four years together, Buchanan could not help but be awed by Polk's capacity for work and his mastery of the mechanics of the Government. Instead of continuing to try to quietly extricate himself from the State Department, Buchanan changed course and studied Polk. He came to view his time as Secretary of State as his most rewarding time in government in terms of the development of his own character. Under Polk, Buchanan gained some sorely needed humility and an appreciation for what it truly meant to be a "public servant." At the start of his time in the Polk administration he (and most people in Washington) believed his prospects for the Presidency were irreparably damaged. Four years later, Buchanan not only gained vast experience in international relations but was a wiser and more patient man *and* politician. In 1845 he could not have predicted that his supporters would be carrying the mantle of "frontrunner" into Baltimore in 1852 even if it was by a slim margin.

As a veteran of Democratic conventions, Buchanan knew that a candidate must be prepared to address the issues of the day. Unfortunately, the issues tended to change daily so he was preparing positions on multiple topics for his supporters along with alternative positions in case circumstances or politics dictated a different approach. This evening he was wrestling with what to do about another Harriet and the need to mute his views on the *biggest* issue of the day: Slavery.

In the last year, the name "Harriet Beecher Stowe" was embraced in the North and reviled in the South, but known throughout the country. Her novel *Uncle Tom's Cabin or Life Among the Lowly* could not be printed fast enough to keep pace with demand. To the dismay of many, it was outselling the Bible in most cities. In Great Britain it was, if possible, even more popular.

Stowe was married to a theology professor at Bowdoin College in Maine. In her prior forty years she gave no inkling of the impact she was to have in the worlds of literature and politics. She wrote occasional short stories mainly for her own amusement and that of her family. But when Congress passed the Fugitive Slave Act of 1850 as part of the Compromise of 1850, Stowe joined the chorus of abolitionists who were outraged that the government would require its citizens to return escaped slaves to their "owners." Harriet Stowe sat down and wrote a novel telling the stories of slaves making their way north to freedom and slaves left behind in bondage (such as "Tom").

Uncle Tom's Cabin was not being confused with classic literature but it was undeniably affecting and had all the necessary elements of a great novel: heroes, villains, near-misses, surprises and redemption. In the North (and even a bit in the South), people who never gave much thought to the plight of southern Negroes became sympathetic to the abolitionist cause. In the South (and even a bit in the North), most saw Stowe's novel as insulting and grossly at odds with the true conditions under which most slaves lived in the South.

Buchanan despaired over the controversy. The country was divided by a debate over which part of the country debased the Negroes less: Southerners who fed and clothed them but granted them no freedom or Northerners who granted them freedom but who provided few opportunities for them to feed and clothe themselves. It was imbecilic yet both sides counted themselves righteous. And both sides seemed prepared to rupture the Union because of it.

The hardest for Buchanan to countenance were the New York merchants who denounced the evils of slavery but who relied heavily on cotton from the South to supply their manufacturing plants. These plants were abhorrent places to work but were largely closed to Negro laborers. Buchanan marveled at the industrialists' perfidy about all that they claimed to hold dear provided they were still able to turn a profit.

Buchanan was one of the few who did not laud the passage of the Compromise of 1850. Indeed, he saw it as short-sighted and certain to lead to the dissolution of the Union. Popular Sovereignty, a concept that was cooked into the Compromise, held that the states and territories could decide for themselves whether to permit slavery or not. More than any other part of the Compromise bills, Popular Sovereignty troubled Buchanan. He agreed with Daniel Webster's March 7 speech that slavery was only conducive to the large scale raising of cotton and, therefore, naturally limited to the southeastern part of the country. Given the "natural" limits of slavery, he was afraid that delegating the right to decide would simply spread the feud unnecessarily.

As the economics of slavery became less and less attractive and the scorn of the rest of the country for the institution became more widespread, Buchanan was confident that slavery would die a quiet death. Indeed, most of his friends in the South shared this same view but were unwilling to part with their slaves in the absence of another source of cheap labor. Buchanan expressed the view to one southern congressman that it might be cheaper to pay the workers a wage and grant them freedom rather than paying to feed and board them. The southerner responded, "If you promise they won't murder my family for holding them as slaves and they will show up for work every day, that might work."

In November 1850, Buchanan penned a letter to the Democratic Party of Pennsylvania. Like Daniel Webster, Buchanan took aim at the abolitionists. He argued that the Fugitive Slave Act portion of the Compromise was the same act passed in 1793. Now, however, it was to be enforced by the Federal government rather than the States. So, the abolitionist outcry was directed at an act that had been part of the country's law for over a half century. He also agreed with Webster that the Negro race was worse off because of the abolitionists. Southern farmers worried that they would be deprived of their source of labor so they held the bonds of slavery ever tighter. Meanwhile, white northerners worried that, if the abolitionists prevailed, their jobs would be taken by black men willing to work for much lower wages. The southern leaders went from working with their fellow countrymen to find a graceful exit from slavery early in the century to distrusting and despising the North for its haughtiness.

Buchanan's letter was warmly received in the South and in some parts of the North. The nomination of his party that he long sought was within reach. But, now it appeared that *Uncle Tom's Cabin* would thwart his ambition. With each new reader, amateur abolitionists were born. The sentiments expressed in Buchanan's letter were no longer fashionable and were, indeed, derided as heartless logic in the face of the suffering of fellow humans.

Buchanan knew the electorate well enough that he despaired of persuading a majority that breaking the Union over slavery would undoubtedly lead to a collapse of the South's economy. That might lead to the freeing of the slaves but where would they go in an economy without work? If they moved north their situation would be no better. The black men there already struggled to find work. Further, the Northern plants would suffer and many shuttered in the absence of raw materials being imported from the South. So, the southern blacks would be both unwelcome in the North and unable to work in the North *or* South. What brand of "freedom" was that?

James Buchanan made his fortune through his ability to persuade a judge or jury with unassailable and eloquent logic. He desperately wanted his fellow citizens to understand that the Union, with all its current flaws, was better for the Black Man now and in the future than if there was a rupture. But, unlike the courtroom, Buchanan had been a politician long enough to know that his argument would be recast by the abolitionists with James Buchanan in the role of Simon Legree, the reprehensible and sadistic master in Mrs. Stowe's book. And no one would ever vote for Simon Legree for President.

All of which made Harriet Lane's Uncle fatalistic about the chances of actually being nominated by the Democratic Party in Baltimore. He was pessimistic about the Compromise of 1850 while most of the country was declaring it the "final" solution to the slavery dispute. Worse, he wrote very publicly about the folly of the abolitionists, just as the people he needed most to vote for him were deciding that they were abolitionists.

His primary competition for the nomination would undoubtedly be Lewis Cass of Michigan, the same man who the Democrats nominated in 1848. Cass, by all rights, should have been elected over Zachary Taylor but for the treachery of Martin Van Buren. After Van Buren ran on the "Free Soil" ticket and, in effect, assured Taylor's election, Buchanan knew that many would feel that Cass deserved another shot. Buchanan was not overly fond of Cass but he would have little trouble supporting him if he were the nominee. Buchanan knew that he and Cass were of the same stripe: ideologically aligned but both too ambitious to step aside for the other. Buchanan had not changed *that* much.

Neither Buchanan nor Cass would receive sufficient votes in the early stages of the Convention, of that Buchanan was sure. His route to the nomination depended on the patience of his supporters. They needed to allow several alternatives to be floated and rejected while holding on to the delegates that were committed to "Old Buck", as Buchanan's friends referred to him. Eventually, it would come back to Cass and Buchanan and he just had to hope that the Democrats decided to try a new horse.

Buchanan also knew that, aside from the tradition of not appearing to openly pursue the nomination, he would need to keep a low profile. To the extent they were known, his views were not currently popular. He was left with a strategy that relied heavily on people knowing his name but not what he stood for. It was everything that politicians were condemned for but, in the end, it was usually good politics. And James Buchanan was not just a gifted lawyer, he was a gifted politician. Particularly after four years under that most unforgiving of taskmasters, James K. Polk.

***

Massachusetts: January 1853

The President-elect of the United States, Franklin Pierce, settled into the seat in the carriage next to his wife Jane for the short train trip from Andover, Massachusetts to Concord, New Hampshire. Their eleven-year old son Benny sat behind them. Benny was named for Pierce's father, Benjamin Pierce, Revolutionary War hero and a founder of the nation his son was soon to lead. As seemed to happen with confounding regularity in Frank Pierce's life, he was mystified by how he arrived at this point.

The last four years were the most content of Pierce's life. His adventure of being a General in the Mexican War gave him a sense of accomplishment and confidence that he did not enjoy previously, notwithstanding his service on behalf of New

Hampshire in both the United States House of Representatives and Senate. He resigned from the Army after the Treaty of Guadalupe Hidalgo, returning to New Hampshire more popular than ever. While he was sure that his heroics did not measure up to the adulation that was heaped upon him, unlike his time in the House and Senate, he believed he made a difference during the War.

The "adulation" also translated into a thriving law practice in Concord. Before entering politics, Pierce was, at best, an indifferent lawyer who largely traded on his father Benjamin's legendary name. Now, however, Pierce found himself enjoying the practice of law. Indeed, his new-found confidence revealed a talent for the law that he was surprised and pleased to discover. That talent was also generating a lucrative income that Pierce was relieved to finally be earning. In four short years, Pierce transformed from being prominent because of his famous name to being prominent as the most sought after lawyer in New Hampshire.

The prosperity included his family life. Pierce resigned from the Senate a decade earlier as a concession to Jane's disdain for Washington and her desire to return home to New Hampshire. Restless and bored back home, Pierce signed up for the War on a drunken whim. He returned a year later to a wife that was still given to bouts of prolonged illness, real and imagined, but who was pleased her husband was safe and that their only child was thriving.

Benny's name was intended to honor Franklin Pierce's father but was, in equal measure, superstitious. Having lost their first two sons who were each named Franklin after *their* father, Jane and Frank decided to not tempt fate by using the name again. Frank knew that Benny was the primary reason for both his and his wife's contentment and renewed affection for one another.

Unlike many only children of well-to-do parents, Benny was possessed of a cheery disposition but also an unusually selfless interest in the well-being of his parents. For the last few years, father and son developed a routine where Benny would meet Frank at his law office at the end of the day and walk home together. Just as routinely, Benny would ask "Papa, how was your day?" and inquire about interesting developments in Frank's practice since their last discussion. Frank cherished these walks both for the time with his son but, in truth, because he could review significant events in his busy day which allowed him to prioritize for the next day. When he would hear about Benny's day, he never doubted that he was listening to a faithful recounting of events. Benny seemed incapable of exaggerating or behaving in a way that did not leave them both proud.

Benny adored his parents. He was patient and caring with his mother when she was ill and reveled in their learning and play together when she was well. Yet, despite the family's mutual devotion, Benny was popular with other children and a welcome guest in their homes.

In the last two months, Frank wondered many times how he was lured back into politics and whether he was not making a mistake in trading the tranquility of his life in Concord for a return to Washington that neither his wife nor son favored, even if it was to be President of his country. Somewhere in the last six months, he lost control of events.

It all started in earnest two months before the Democrats met in Baltimore to nominate their candidate for President. Since 1848, many of Pierce's Democratic friends in New Hampshire convinced themselves that a relatively open field in 1852 might finally be the Granite State's chance of being represented on the National ticket. The obvious first choice was Levi Woodbury, New Hampshire's former Governor and then a member of the Supreme Court. Just as the Democrats began to solidify a strategy for Woodbury's nomination, he died in September of 1851.

The New Hampshire Democrats then turned to Pierce. At first, they made sure to propose him as Vice President at every turn. At 47 years old, he would be the youngest President to date so the assumption was that it would be better to run Pierce for Vice President and perhaps position him for the Presidency in 1856 or 1860 which would have the added benefit of having a New Hampshire man on the ticket for close to a decade. But then Pierce's friends saw an opening that made them reconsider their strategy.

George Sanders was the editor of the popular *Democratic Review*. He was also openly campaigning for Stephen Douglas of Illinois for the Presidency. Sanders ridiculed all the expected competition for the nomination referring to James Buchanan, Lewis Cass and William Marcy as retreads and "Old Fogeys." It was time for some fresh blood in Washington and Sanders recommended Douglas. Pierce's friends Edmund Burke and Benjamin French were amazed to see the sentiment in Sanders' argument spread and soon talk of passing over the "Old Fogeys" was common. To Burke's and French's minds, however, Sanders overplayed his hand in one critical respect.

Stephen Douglas was certainly a future contender for the Presidency. But, in 1852, he was 38 years old. Whatever the country's appetite for new blood, Burke and French were confident that it was not prepared to give the Presidency to someone *that* young. Suddenly, Franklin Pierce was perfect: Young enough to meet the desire for a fresh face but not so young to make it simple for Whigs to attack his maturity and experience. Burke and French set to work quietly making it known that New Hampshire would bring forward Franklin Pierce as the Party's nominee.

There was only one problem with Pierce's friends' plan. Franklin Pierce did not want to be President or Vice President. When New Hampshire held its Democratic Convention early in 1852 in preparation for the National Convention in June, a resolution was offered to place Pierce's name as a candidate for President. Pierce replied politely but firmly that the resolution "would be utterly repugnant to my tastes and wishes." He shared the letter with Jane before sending it and both were satisfied that they were sending a clear message that the Pierces had no desire to live in Washington again.

But Burke, French and other devotees of Pierce, remarkably, took the letter as the typical coy response of a politician. As they continued to press, Pierce reminded them that he had not been a politician for close to a decade and was very content in Concord. Every week brought another request for the delegation to place his name in nomination. As this figurative war of attrition persisted, in April Pierce finally relented, to a degree. He said that his name could be used in the event of a deadlocked convention, but *only* in that event.

Jane wept when her husband told her of his instructions to the New Hampshire Democrats. But he assured her that he was certain that James Buchanan would prevail at the Convention so he was not concerned that the delegates would draft him. He was not even being considered among the top dozen candidates. He was being loyal to his party but, more importantly, he believed he found a way to dispense with what was a distraction from his busy law practice. Jane seemed mollified but, as the Convention in Baltimore approached she grew more and more apprehensive and, of course, ill.

Pierce did not share the real reason for his willingness to allow consideration of his name: Winfield Scott. Pierce knew Scott well from their service together in Mexico. While Pierce did not take issue with Scott's ability as military leader and strategist, that was where his regard for Scott ended. During his time serving under General Scott, Pierce concluded that all the stories maligning Scott as arrogant and vain understated the nature of Scott's character by a great deal. "Old Fuss and Feathers", as he was called by friends and enemies, was one of the most insufferable braggarts that Pierce ever encountered. Given Pierce's extended tenure in Washington, that was saying something.

It appeared that the Whigs were intent on following the same successful script in 1852 that they did in 1840 and 1848, namely, to nominate a war hero. It was an ironic habit of the Whigs given their history. The Whigs primarily existed due to their antipathy for Andrew Jackson and what they perceived as his dictatorial methods. To combat Jackson's followers and his legacy, they turned to War heroes like Jackson with regularity. Unfortunately, the two war heroes that they could elect, William Harrison and Zachary Taylor, both died early on in their terms. But in their brief terms, the political neophytes emulated Jackson's penchant for demanding adherence to their directives.

Frank Pierce knew that if humble men like Harrison and Taylor were prone to issuing edicts, Winfield Scott would undoubtedly impose martial law upon assuming office. Pierce might have earned the title of "General" during the War but, unlike Scott, he was a General for less than a year before resigning and returning to civilian life. With tensions in the country alarmingly high and the word "secession" being bandied about by southern leaders with increasing frequency, Pierce was genuinely anxious that the self-absorbed and insensitive Scott would cause the Union to finally split without ever knowing what he did or said. It was not a time for amateurs to lead the country.

There was some hope that Scott would not be nominated by the Whigs but Pierce thought it unlikely. Scott's competition would be President Fillmore, who was not being bashful about seeking to be elected in his own right after succeeding Zachary Taylor, and Daniel Webster. Webster was the perennial candidate for the Whigs but could never muster quite enough votes to secure the nomination.

Millard Fillmore rose to prominence loosely associated with Thurlow Weed and his New York political machine. But it was no secret that Weed and Fillmore had fallen out. Weed and his chief political lackey, William Seward, were backing Scott. Fillmore appeared to have convinced himself that most voters would see his split from Weed as evidence of his integrity and independence. Pierce knew that Fillmore was delusional. The stain of sin was very hard to wash out for a politician. In short, Pierce would be very surprised if the Whigs gave Fillmore another chance.

As to Daniel Webster, while Pierce respected the Massachusetts Senator, he could not see why the Whigs would nominate a sick and dying Daniel Webster when they passed so many times on nominating a *healthy and vibrant* Daniel Webster. Further, Webster was Fillmore's Secretary of State and Pierce knew that many in the Whig Party felt it unseemly that Webster would so blatantly attempt to unseat the President he was serving, even if Fillmore was not the most inspiring leader.

Pierce's normally keen political instincts told him that the Whigs would turn to Scott. Those same instincts told him that if it was Scott, a country that was clearly tired of the old guard would not find a man referred to as "Old Fuss and Feathers" particularly appealing. The Democrats would need a nominee that exuded youthful energy and optimism to counter the latest old Whig General. Even the self-effacing Pierce understood that he could fill the bill. If his nomination was what it took to keep Winfield Scott from becoming President, the patriot in Pierce felt compelled to make himself available no matter how much he hoped the nomination would not come to pass.

What struck Pierce was how little political party meant in his decision. With Andrew Jackson long dead, the Whigs were devoid of a rallying principle. Consequently, there were not many issues that divided the Democrats and Whigs. With both parties supporting the Compromise of 1850, even the most prominent issue in the country, slavery, would not be hotly contested in this election, except when abolitionists turned out in force in the Northeast. But, even then, there would be little profit in either party choosing to take a decisive stand on the issue.

The Whigs had an abolitionist wing and a larger Compromise of 1850/Popular Sovereignty wing. The Democrats had few abolitionists in their ranks and a larger Popular Sovereignty wing than the Whigs but even the most passionate States rights proponents saw value in keeping the Union together. As a result, while Pierce would never admit it to his Democratic colleagues, he would not have given permission to put his name in the mix for the nomination if he had any faith that the Whigs would nominate Fillmore or Webster. But he did not.

What Pierce did not reckon on was the political skill of his New Hampshire supporters. Once assembled in Baltimore, they quietly began touting Pierce's name to other state delegations. Referring to him as "General Pierce" and "Young Hickory of the Granite Hills", they patiently built the story of a youthful, handsome war hero who gave up politics to serve his country in Mexico and then to serve those seeking justice as a fabled lawyer.

To the extent the frontrunners' campaigns paid any attention to the growing talk about Pierce, they assumed that the New Hampshire delegation was trying to position Pierce for second place on the ticket as the Vice Presidential nominee. To most participants, that seemed like an idea well worth considering when the time came. But they were engrossed in trying to figure out how to get their respective men nominated first.

It was not proving to be easy. For the first two days, Buchanan and Cass traded positions but neither received anything resembling a commanding majority. Stephen Douglas held a firm but small number of candidates proving that Burke and French read the response to Sanders correctly—Stephen Douglas' day would have to wait. By the third day William Marcy was gaining delegates but, again, just barely outpacing Buchanan and Cass. It was during that day that Buchanan's supporters made a fatal error.

After polling the states over thirty times with eight or nine candidates continually getting one hundred or fewer votes, Buchanan's faction decided to educate the Convention that it was time to start coalescing behind a single candidate by showing that no candidate could acquire the necessary majority of votes. To do this, they would release delegates for a few states from their commitment to support Buchanan. Their notion was that those states would swing to one of the other candidates but there would still not be enough momentum to rally behind a single candidate. They would then retrieve the delegates from those states and redouble their efforts to convince delegates that it was time to throw their votes to Buchanan.

This was the opening Burke, French and the other New Hampshire men were waiting for. What Buchanan's men failed to grasp was that the New Hampshire men were not referring to Pierce as Vice President when they spoke to delegates of a "second choice" but of Pierce as the next best alternative for President. By the time Buchanan's group launched their ploy, many delegates in the hall were thinking that a dynamic, youthful Pierce might be someone to turn to in a deadlocked convention. Once Buchanan's men demonstrated unequivocally that the Convention was deadlocked, they were stunned when the name of Franklin Pierce started receiving votes. Suddenly, the momentum they were seeking to generate was gaining speed but not for their man. Instead, Franklin Pierce, who had not received a vote or a thought for the first 35 ballots, was the toast of the Convention. It took 14 more ballots but Pierce gained votes with each new poll and, on the 49th try, he was nominated unanimously.

Buchanan's supporters were stunned, then angry and then resigned. There was no evidence to be found that Pierce himself engineered the coup and the other campaigns realized they were outwitted. Most quickly concluded that their futures in politics would not be aided by prolonging the story of this Convention.

However astonished the other candidates and their supporters might have been by the turn of events, their surprise paled beside that of Franklin Pierce. He never imagined that his small coterie would be able to outmaneuver the veteran political operators for Buchanan and Cass and even Marcy. Jane was aghast. Even Benny, who was staying with his Aunt and Uncle in Andover when he heard the news, sent his mother a letter saying that he hoped his father would lose so they would not have to live in Washington.

Two weeks later the Whigs gathered. It took even longer to break the deadlock at their Convention than it did at the Democratic Convention. But, as Pierce expected, Winfield Scott was ultimately nominated. Pierce was quietly thankful that at least he could tell his wife with a straight face that he felt the country would be better off if they occupied the White House.

The campaign did nothing to allay Jane's fears. The Whigs were vicious toward Pierce, taking full advantage of his lack of notoriety by planting stories in the press designed to define Pierce before his supporters could. An early article accused him of being anti-Catholic, a drunk and much less of a war hero than his campaign was leading gullible voters to believe. Pierce wrote the editors of the Concord newspaper that reproduced the story. Knowing that the editors knew the story to be slanderous, Pierce wrote to them:

> *"Is it not sad that scoundrelism can obtain access to the columns of respectable papers? That those whose very breath taints this air they breathe with falsehood can be received anywhere where a respect for truth is maintained. Above all is it not singular and singularly disgraceful that the Town of my residence should contain the chief fountains of*

malevolence, detraction and abuse poured out against me!"

The editors sheepishly retracted the story but, unfortunately, civility never did feature in the campaign. Pierce vacillated between defending himself and trying to protect his wife from the political life he once again plunged her into.

In due course, election day arrived. Pierce was not just elected. He was elected in a landslide. The, *finally*, humbled Winfield Scott carried just four states. In five whirlwind months Franklin Pierce emerged from relative anonymity to President-elect. A nation craving new leadership hoped he could steer it away from the forces that were pulling it apart. In Pierce, they believed his support for the Compromise of 1850 coupled with his pragmatic views on slavery and diffidence toward the abolitionists would calm the passions that seemed to keep sweeping the country.

By this day in January Pierce was beginning to adapt. His wife was none the happier about moving to Washington and intended to delay her and her son's departure as long as possible. But she was at least solemnly resigned that they would, indeed, be moving to Washington although she made it clear that reelection was not an option.

At first, Frank Pierce was perfectly aligned with his wife's insistence that this was a four- year commitment. Once the calamity of Winfield Scott being elected President was averted, Pierce realized that, beyond his desire to prevent Scott's election, he had not spent much time contemplating his own election. Immediately after the election, Pierce's first thoughts were to question whether he was any better suited to lead the country than Old Fuss and Feathers. His initial conclusion was that he most certainly was not.

He toyed with taking the oath and then, within a few months, resigning and allowing his Vice President, William R. King, to become President. King was from Alabama, a political veteran and well respected by the members of Congress. He would have no problem absorbing the responsibilities of the Presidency. For his part, Pierce would simply excuse himself on the basis that his wife's health would not permit them to remain in Washington which, after a few months of a Washington summer, would probably be true.

But soon after the election, King was seized with tuberculosis and left for Cuba to try and recuperate. His closest friends, including James Buchanan who shared a room with King in Washington for ten years, advised Pierce that he would probably serve without a Vice President because they did not expect King to make it back from Cuba alive.

At that point, Pierce realized that he must embrace the trust the country placed in him. He began to plan his administration and, gradually, the political skills that lay dormant for so long started to resurface. As he assembled his Cabinet and created his lists of priorities he came to an illuminating realization. His time in Mexico did not just give him the confidence to be an effective lawyer, both his time in Mexico *and* his enthusiasm for the law gave him poise, organization and courage that he did not possess as a young Congressman in Washington. He may be the youngest President to ever be elected but Pierce was not inexperienced. He came to relish the challenge.

So, the train started his journey home. Once there, Pierce would pack up some belongings and take Benny with him for a short tour of cities wanting to fete the new President on their way to Washington. Pierce steeled himself to rise above his wife's dour resignation and to be a leader worthy of a meaningful legacy. He would set an example for his son of hope, hard work and optimism.

He looked out the window as the train pulled into the frosty countryside. Patches of snow dotted the landscape. As the train traversed a curve, Pierce noticed the rocky embankment that the track was perched upon. At that moment, a deafening sound burst through the train as it lurched to Pierce's right. He threw his left arm around Jane and pulled her close. He tried to reach behind and grab Benny with his right hand but the boy was just out of reach. The train shook violently and tipped further and further until it was tumbling down the embankment. Inexplicably, it landed upright.

The President-elect saw that Jane, like himself, was not

seriously hurt. He turned to check on his son. Benny was two rows further back and appeared to have been knocked unconscious. Pierce bounded over the debris in the carriage. As he placed his hand behind Benny's head, he felt the moisture that he felt too many times in Mexico. As panic took hold, Pierce saw that the back of Benny's skull was crushed and soaked in blood. His son was dead.

Frank Pierce looked up at his wife. She knew. The horror on her face reflected his own. His legacy was meaningless.

PART V

THE IRREPRESSIBLE CONFLICT

(1853-1861)

Chapter 1:
Franklin Pierce

Rome, Italy: November 1853

Pope Pius IX smiled at the odd-looking old man before him. The translator extended greetings on his behalf. The Pope was fascinated that this rotund gentleman with impressive sideburns and who spoke with a unique combination of clicking and a lisp was allegedly the most skilled politician in the short history of the United States. The Pope was particularly intrigued that this man was considered a political genius but he was only able to be elected President once. Even more remarkable was that he willingly stepped aside after four years to allow a withered old soldier (who did not even stage a coup!) to take over. This new country was peculiar to most people in Europe.

Martin Van Buren was even more intrigued by the man who he was paying homage to despite Van Buren's loose association with religion. Van Buren was Dutch Reform, not Catholic. But the Pope was popular throughout Europe with a reputation for kindness, intelligence and generosity toward all, not just those in his flock. As leader of the Papal States, a region cutting across the heart of Italy and which included the grand sites of Rome, the Pope bore great influence not just in the Catholic Church but in Italy itself. The Italian monarchs long vied with the Popes to reduce their power but their alternatives were limited in a country where most people viewed the Pope as God's chosen spokesman.

Van Buren commented to the Pope that they were both emissaries of sorts. The Pope was the first Pope to be able to say he visited the American Continent. Van Buren learned that, before he ascended to the Papacy and when he was still Giovanni Maria Mastai-Ferretti, the Pope worked as a missionary in Chile and Peru. Van Buren, on the other hand, was the first man to have served as President of the United States to visit Europe.

The genesis of the former President's visit was not diplomacy or even to represent the United States in any fashion. His son, Martin Jr. suffered from tuberculosis and Van Buren was advised to take him to see doctors in London and Paris. Once they arrived in Europe, Martin Jr. was put under the care of preeminent physicians in London and Paris. His father commenced a tour of Europe that soon caused Martin Sr. to forget the political tumult back home and to revel in the curiosity that Europeans had about all things American.

President Pierce provided Van Buren with a letter of introduction to Lord Aberdeen prior to Van Buren sailing for the Old World. Van Buren was greeted warmly in London and found himself being whisked from reception to reception where he was lavished with gifts and laudatory speeches. Given his close affiliation with the notorious Anglophobe Andrew Jackson and his own reputation as architect of the Democratic Party with its roots in Jefferson's disdain for the British and adoration of the French, Van Buren was taken aback, to say the least. He joked to his fellow travelers that he was almost certain that the Brits must be mistaking him for someone else.

In the little free time that Van Buren's hosts left him, he soaked up London. Like every visitor to the city for years hence, he was humbled to realize how extensive London's history was, particularly when compared with that of his own country which was not quite eighty years old. He strolled through Trafalgar and St. James Squares and thought how Washington should make a point of setting aside areas for rest and reflection as the United States' history proceeded. He received a personal tour of the almost completely reconstructed Parliament that was destroyed by fire in 1834. It was, he had to admit, much more impressive than the U.S. Capitol. Of course, the Capitol in Washington was continually being refurbished after these same British tried to burn *it* in the War of 1812. He enjoyed bantering with members of Parliament about how they balanced their legislative duties with the dictates of Queen Victoria, a strong monarch that Van Buren was quite confident would not have countenanced the American Revolution the way George III did. By the end of his visit, he decided that Parliament's relationship with the Queen was not much different than trying to work constructively with Andrew Jackson, although he would be careful to never say that among Democrats back in the States.

He saw Ireland and Scotland and was charmed by the people and the pubs. More receptions were held. The locals were fascinated that the former President was content to wander in their midst without an entourage or any sign of pretense. As he moved across the channel to Belgium and Holland, Van Buren was little aware of the impression he made on the British Isles. They concluded that, perhaps, the rumors of democracy actually working on the other side of the Atlantic were true.

In Holland, Van Buren delighted in the opportunity to speak the Dutch tongue of his youth. He was pleased with how easily the language came back to him and comfortable among people who did not find his manner of speech strange, as so many in Washington and the Pope did. He could have stayed much longer researching his lineage and enjoying the Dutch hospitality. But the itinerary called for him to head for Paris and on to Italy.

After enjoying the sites and especially the food and drink of Paris, Van Buren went on to Rome where he was to spend several weeks. He was astounded with his new-found energy since arriving in Europe. For the last twelve years since leaving Washington, it seemed that Van Buren's time was wrapped up in salvaging the history of his political accomplishments and his Presidency. His friends and his sons were of the same mind as they tried to get him re-installed as President in both 1845 and 1849. They finally relented with the election of 1852 as Van Buren convinced them that his time had passed and that Franklin Pierce was worthy of their full support.

Before he left for Europe, Van Buren had his first doubts about Pierce's worthiness. He had always been fond of the much younger Pierce and had, for a time, tried to mentor the New Hampshire man. But Van Buren soon realized that Pierce would never possess Van Buren's political skills. Pierce was intelligent enough but no one would describe him as cunning. *Everyone* would describe Martin Van Buren as cunning.

Nonetheless, Van Buren supported Pierce as a good Democrat whose affable nature and instincts for compromise would serve him and the country well. Both Van Buren and Pierce supported the Compromise of 1850 and both believed it would be the end of the slavery debate.

What Van Buren perceived before leaving for Europe was not that Pierce had changed his views on the Compromise or was departing from the Democratic platform that helped elect him President. Rather, Van Buren saw a man that was broken and not ready for the battles that inevitably came to a President. It was clear that Pierce's son's death exacted a toll on him that left him eviscerated of the will that vexing political issues required.

Not that the former President was not sympathetic. His four sons were a greater source of joy to him than any of his political accomplishments. Both Abraham and Martin Jr. served as their father's personal secretary at different times after establishing themselves as respected professionals and John was a successful lawyer who inherited his father's mantle as one of the chief strategists for the New York Democrats, along with being a gifted orator. Only Smith, the youngest, caused his father some consternation due to his son's lack of ambition. But Smith Van Buren was not a debauched person, just an unproductive one. He married a lovely heiress and the young couple seemed content to live off her inheritance. They doted on the elder Van Buren and all who knew them were charmed. So, the Patriarch held his tongue and tried to encourage Smith when the occasion presented itself.

Van Buren could not imagine life without his sons much less life with no children at all as the Pierces were being forced to endure. More to the point, he could not imagine attempting to serve as President after such a devastating loss. From all that he heard from his own sons and friends in Washington, Jane Pierce was not making it any easier on her husband. She had not appeared at a single White House function since his inauguration, living as a recluse in a small room upstairs at the Executive Mansion. She spent her days talking to the deceased lad and writing letters to him as though he was still alive.

Pierce would have been justified in resigning the Presidency in favor of his Vice President. But William King died shortly after Pierce took office. King was sworn in as Vice President in Cuba where he was convalescing from tuberculosis and died two days after returning to the United States. King's demise was part of Van Buren's reasoning for not heeding advice to take his own son Martin south to Cuba to try and heal.

Van Buren was not sure that a healthy William King would have been desirable as President. Putting the Alabaman on the ticket with Pierce was obviously intended to ensure geographic balance for the Democrats but it was also an obvious sop to James Buchanan. Buchanan was prepared to lose the nomination in 1852 to Lewis Cass or possibly William Marcy but he was apoplectic about the maneuvering of Pierce's New Hampshire lieutenants at the Convention. Van Buren thought this said more about Buchanan than Pierce. A veteran politician like Buchanan should be prepared and know his vulnerabilities. The fact that his supporters were outwitted told Van Buren that Buchanan was still long on ambition and short on preparation, a career-long malady.

Buchanan was placated by the nomination of King as Pierce's running mate. Conversely, Van Buren was alarmed. There were rumors prior to the Convention that Buchanan would name King as his running mate or likely Secretary of State if he was nominated. While Van Buren had nothing against King as a statesman, he found Buchanan's instincts naïve. Buchanan and King were both old bachelors who shared a one bedroom apartment in Washington for close to a decade. They appeared at social events together so often that Andrew Jackson called them "Miss Nancy" and "Aunt Fancy." Whatever their relationship, Van Buren, who tolerated (if not abetted) the slanderous nature of the Presidential campaigns from 1828 onward, thought Buchanan was foolhardy to think that the Whig press would not delight in printing embarrassing and damaging innuendo daily from June to November.

Few people gave much thought to who a President named as his Vice President. If there was some benefit from a geographical perspective and the nominee was not a distraction, the office of Vice President was of little consequence. But Martin Van Buren did not enjoy a reputation for political mastery by overlooking details. What the nomination of King indicated to Van Buren was that Pierce was willing to placate Buchanan. In Van Buren's calculus, James Buchanan did not have the political weight to merit being placated. He was generally well-liked and reasonably intelligent but prone to abandoning whatever principles he had for the sake of a friend or to maintain harmony. In other words, he was malleable. Further, whatever demands he may have made of Pierce, Pierce *was* the nominee and Buchanan needed to get along with his Party's popular nominee if he was ever to fulfill his long-held ambition of being the President himself. Van Buren deduced that if Franklin Pierce was willing to accommodate James Buchanan, he was not likely to stand up to politicians with greater will and gravitas than Buchanan, of whom there were many.

Van Buren rarely thought of these things since coming to Europe though. He was enthralled with history, architecture, great wines and madeiras, beautiful women and fawning dignitaries. He was due to leave Rome soon and go south where he planned to write his memoirs where he would rehabilitate his Presidency and pass along his political wisdom and genius. There seemed to be many important reasons for this work when Van Buren boarded the ship to Europe months ago. Now, as he bowed to take his leave from Pope Pius IX, he was hard-pressed to remind himself what those reasons were.

***

Virginia: May 1856

John Tyler named his estate near Williamsburg, Virginia "Sherwood Forest." Visitors who knew the former President as sober and serious, were perplexed as to whether Tyler truly likened himself to Robin Hood. Tyler did think the comparison was apt since he left the White House with neither the Democrats or Whigs claiming him as their own. Like Robin of long ago, Tyler was an outlaw.

Tyler's guests were relieved to find that the ex-President did not name his home in a fit of pique or to make a point as he might have during his political career, but in jest. By the time he and his young wife Julia settled at Sherwood Forest, they were much too busy to be troubled by Tyler's political woes. Julia kept him too busy renovating their new home and entertaining to dwell on politics. She also kept him busy with a steady supply of new children. At 36 years old, Julia was giving no signs that the latest addition was likely to be the last in the Tyler line.

The "latest addition" was Robert. Tyler held his newest son on his lap now as Julia issued orders to her children and her slaves. Sherwood Forest was not a serene southern plantation but a chaotic jumble of comings and goings that the 66-year old Tyler found it hard to keep pace with. But he would not change a thing.

While the well-to-do of Virginia were scandalized by Tyler's marriage to the *much* younger Julia and by his fathering of multiple children in his seventh decade, Tyler ascribed their condemnation to nothing more than petty jealousy. John Tyler may not have left Washington a popular man but, here at home, he was popular, well-loved and completely content. He doubted that many of his peers could say the same.

Robert was John Tyler's thirteenth child. His first wife Letitia gave him seven children, three of whom died in the last five years. So far, Julia had given him six children. Robert's oldest half-brother was forty years old and was named…Robert. Several youths currently visiting the Tyler household were greeting their newest "Uncle Robert." On their trips into Williamsburg Tyler was routinely congratulated on his latest grandchild by those who did not know him well.

As Tyler read the newspaper before him, he intermittently bounced Robert in his arms. A female slave that had been with the former President for many years saw him becoming engrossed in his reading and knew that it was time to scoop the baby up before his absent-minded father did any damage to the child. Tyler smiled wanly at her momentarily before turning back to the newspaper.

The article that Tyler read today left him melancholy and

deeply troubled. In 1854, the South's fading attachment to the institution of slavery was given new life. To Tyler's surprise, the source of this renewed hope for the South was Illinois Senator Stephen Douglas.

Douglas was backed by the railroad interests that used Chicago as their central rail terminus. In exchange for their support in making him one of the most well-known politicians in the land, they simply wanted Douglas to push for settlement of the vast lands between Iowa and the Rocky Mountains. Knowing that these great plains were well-suited for farming, the railroad barons had grand visions of trains full of crops and cattle unloading in Chicago at their freight yards. The two biggest impediments to settlement were the existence of several Indian Reservations in the territories and, of course, the question of slavery

The young Senator was not one to run from controversy. He introduced a bill for the settlement of Kansas and Nebraska. The "Kansas-Nebraska Act" reignited the passions that animated the debates over the Compromise of 1850 and called for the repeal of the Missouri Compromise. Those two compromises were steered through the Congress by the mastery of Henry Clay and Daniel Webster with an aim of preserving the Union. Clay's and Webster's respective prestige and commitment to peace were essential to the passage of both bills. By 1854, both Clay and Webster were dead. And the railroad interests did not care one whit about Senator Douglas' prestige or even that much about the Union. They wanted a rail line to the Rockies and on to the Pacific.

Because he was not Clay or Webster, Douglas soon lost control of the bill and the Kansas-Nebraska Act became a free-for-all of amendments, filibuster and bargaining. President Pierce was incensed that his own Party brought forth a bill that would disrupt the tenuous peace purchased by the Compromise of 1850. The South felt short-changed by the 1850 Compromise and relished the opportunity to re-trade the deal. It welcomed 1) the *de facto* repeal of the Missouri Compromise and its prohibition of slavery north of Missouri and 2) the further assimilation of the concept of Popular Sovereignty.

No one believed that slavery would be viable in the northern climates of Kansas and Nebraska, just as it had withered in Ohio, Indiana and other cold weather states. But those in the South who saw their political power eroding in a federal government that was more and more in the thrall of small Northern states and their industrial interests were willing to send enough settlers to Kansas to vote in favor of slavery to maintain the relatively equal split between slave and free states.

The problems went from theoretical to dangerous as New England abolitionists sent their *own* settlers to Kansas. Before long skirmishes were breaking out all over the state between pro-slavery and anti-slavery forces. When an anti-slavery zealot named John Brown rode into Pottawatomie and murdered five supporters of slavery in the territory it appeared that Kansas would degenerate into civil war. The ever-opportunistic abolitionist press dubbed it "Bleeding Kansas."

After Brown's massacre, Tyler realized that his support of the Kansas-Nebraska Act may have helped lead to the demise of his beloved South. Talk of secession in the South was no longer idle frustration expressing itself. It was the inevitable reaction to the increasing number of people that sympathized with abolitionist sentiment that slavery had to be stopped. And it had to be stopped *now*.

Several northern senators ascribed to this position but few as fervidly as Charles Sumner of Massachusetts. The article that was consuming Tyler described a speech by Sumner on the Senate floor four days earlier. William Seward, Thurlow Weed's prize New York politician, introduced a bill intended to pre-empt Popular Sovereignty as part of the Kansas-Nebraska Act by admitting Kansas as a Free State immediately. Stephen Douglas opposed the amendment. Douglas knew that the only appeal that his Act had to the South was the chance to gain pro-slavery ground.

To underscore the benefits to the South of the Act, Douglas persuaded Senator Andrew Butler of South Carolina to co-sponsor the Act with him. On May 19, Charles Sumner rose and delivered a speech he entitled "The Crime Against Kansas." Sumner spoke well into the next day deriding and insulting both

Douglas and Butler in the most graphic terms. Casting his gaze upon the empty seat of the aging and courteous Butler, Sumner said

> *"The senator from South Carolina has read many books of chivalry, and believes himself a chivalrous knight with sentiments of honor and courage. Of course, he has chosen a mistress to whom he has made his vows, and who, though ugly to others, is always lovely to him; though polluted in the sight of the world, is chaste in his sight -- I mean the harlot, slavery. For her his tongue is always profuse in words. Let her be impeached in character, or any proposition made to shut her out from the extension of her wantonness, and no extravagance of manner or hardihood of assertion is then too great for this senator."*

Sumner proceeded to ridicule Butler's stammering speech and numerous other personal characteristics of both Senators. In a body that prided itself on gentlemanly conduct, it was agreed by all in the Capitol that Sumner exceeded the bounds of decency by a wide margin. He was roundly criticized by Senators from the North and South as well as the press. But what he did not reckon on was the Southern pride of Senator Butler's family.

Preston Brooks was a cousin of Senator Butler and he idolized his Uncle. Mr. Brooks was also serving South Carolina in the House of Representatives. On May 22 after reading the text of Charles Sumner's speech, Congressman Brooks crossed the Capitol, entered the Senate floor and went directly to the desk where Senator Sumners sat. Before Sumners could speak or rise, Brooks beat him with his cane until Sumner was a bloody, unconscious mass on the Senate floor. Brooks only stopped after he broke his cane on Sumner's motionless body.

As he read the account of the thrashing of Charles Sumner at Preston Brooks' hand, John Tyler knew instinctively that a line had been irretrievably breached. He was sometimes accused of being naïve, even in his old age, but Tyler believed that his young country was unique in world history. Almost all its institutions of government were experimental in nature and still developing. But civility and peaceable debate were as well-entrenched as any precepts that American politicians held dear. And the United States Senate was the temple where these precepts were worshiped.

Tyler thought it odd that, for all intents, the Whig Party was dead. Born out of enmity for Andrew Jackson, the Whigs grew into a party similar to the Democrats albeit with a greater number of abolitionists in their midst. With little to differentiate themselves and an inability to attract votes, the Whigs were finished after Franklin Pierce routed Winfield Scott in 1852.

For Tyler, this was a relief. Both while completing William Harrison's term and after leaving the White House, Tyler was subjected to the humiliation of neither political party wanting to claim him. With the demise of the Whigs he could at least say that he had outlasted one of the parties. But given the fissures in the Democratic Party he was sure that another party would soon replace the Whigs. His fear was that the new group with distinctly anti-slavery sentiments might be that party. They called themselves "Republicans." If they made the election in November close, Tyler was fatalistic. In that event, the United States' experiment in governing would be, like the Whigs, finished.

***

Illinois: December 1856

To his surprise, Abraham Lincoln was a Republican. One of the most prominent Whigs in the country, despite his inability to convince the Illinois legislature to send him to the United States Senate, Lincoln found himself adrift with the demise of the Whigs after Winfield Scott's trouncing by Franklin Pierce in 1852.

Pierce took office with buoyant expectations that his charm

and youthful energy would neutralize the issue of slavery and get the country to train its sights on the economic boom that it was enjoying. The nation's borders ran from the Atlantic to the Pacific. Mechanization and industrialization were sweeping the cities, especially in the North. Few countries in history could match the prospects that lay before the young Republic. But prosperity seemed ephemeral with slavery taking center stage at every turn.

Franklin Pierce proved unequal to the task. With the tragic death of his son, it took the young President two years before he seemed to warm to the office. By then it was too late. Lincoln's nemesis, Stephen Douglas, pushed through the Kansas-Nebraska Act setting off a string of skirmishes in Kansas and laying bare how deep the chasm over slavery ran. Lincoln was horrified as he read daily newspaper accounts of lawlessness and bloodshed in Kansas. If the country was headed for Civil War, certainly Kansas portended that many were willing to shed blood for their principles.

As the Democrats gathered earlier in the year, there was little doubt that Pierce would not be re-nominated. He was well-regarded in Washington for his hard work but managed to alienate both the abolitionists in the North and the pro-slavery forces in the South. He made no secret of his hostility to the abolitionists but the South regarded too many of his appointments as sympathetic to Northern interests. Lincoln was not sure what Pierce could have done differently to make the Democrats believe that he could win re-election.

Instead, the Democrats turned to the perennially available James Buchanan with little enthusiasm. It was telling that the most persuasive argument in favor of Buchanan was that he spent most of Pierce's term as Minister to Great Britain. He managed to make a hash of that mission but he avoided taking a stand on Kansas and the Kansas-Nebraska Act since he was out of the country as the Congressional and physical battles raged. His veteran lieutenants quietly lined up his delegates and, in their fourth Convention where they were working to nominate their man, they finally succeeded. Pierce undoubtedly sent the ever-ambitious Buchanan off to England to eliminate him from the political landscape. The strategy failed miserably.

Unlike Pierce four years earlier, few people were expecting much from the aging and cautious Buchanan. His campaign was subdued and remarkable mainly for its silence. With little in the way of competition given the demise of the Whigs, Buchanan stayed as quiet as possible rather than taking a position that could chase away votes. An uninspired electorate expected him to win and he did.

Lincoln was no more enthused than most about Buchanan's election. But he *was* enthused about the election *results*. Abraham Lincoln was one of the finest lawyers in the State of Illinois. He spent the last five years cashing in on that skill but he craved a return to politics. He was already preparing to run against Stephen Douglas for his Senate seat in 1858 but he knew defeating a sitting senator was against the odds. He also knew that Douglas had more friends in the Illinois Legislature than Lincoln and, ultimately, it was the Legislature that chose the senators from Illinois.

Until he reviewed the final tallies from the Presidential election, Lincoln was despairing of getting back to Washington. But the results of the election of 1856 made Lincoln believe that he may not be aiming high enough. In those results, Lincoln saw a path to the White House in the election of 1860...for a Republican.

Optimism was not high for a Buchanan Presidency. At least Franklin Pierce tried to bring parties together and took strong stands for what he believed would hold the Union together. Most people who knew James Buchanan could not imagine him taking a strong stand on anything or leveraging agreement out of opposing factions. Buchanan had a romanticized vision of the South (influenced by William King, his decade long "roommate" from Alabama), despite never having traveled south of Northern Virginia. Buchanan's caution and vacillation would be his undoing.

Not that Lincoln could not equivocate with the best of them when politics called for equivocation. But Lincoln was not running the country at its most perilous turn since conception.

The people would want strong leadership. Lincoln knew James Buchanan as a smooth orator, a Constitutional scholar and a skilled lawyer. He got along well but never at more than a superficial level. He would not be a "strong" leader.

Lincoln did not intend to leave Buchanan's failure as President to chance. As Lincoln figured it, he had three years to undermine Buchanan in a manner sufficient to ensure that the Democrats would again reject a sitting President as their nominee. Lincoln knew the Democrats and knew that they liked to reward those who waited their turn. The next turn would undoubtedly go to Stephen Douglas. Douglas was still a young man but was now a veteran of two close Democratic Conventions at the age of 43. In 1860 he would be 47—the same age as Franklin Pierce when Pierce was elected.

While he might be destined to lose to Douglas for the Senate in 1858, suddenly Lincoln realized the magnitude of that campaign. He would probably be running against the next nominee of the Democrats for President. Lincoln may not be able to defeat Douglas for the Senate but he was confident he could beat him for the Presidency based on the results of the last election.

The page that Lincoln was reading said

BuchananFremontFillmore
Electoral Vote1741148
Popular Vote1,836,0721,342,345873,053

As Lincoln scanned the next few pages that showed the individual state tallies he realized that Buchanan, the candidate that all expected to win handily, *barely won.* Indeed, but for about 7000 more votes for Fillmore spread across Louisiana, Kentucky and Tennessee, the election would have gone to the House of Representatives for lack of a majority victor. Even though Buchanan would have been chosen by the House, Lincoln was certain that Buchanan would not have failed to note his near-miss, notwithstanding his supporters and fellow Democrats congratulating him on his impressive victory. For one as used to having victory snatched away from him, the fact that his predicted victory was not as dominating as expected would cause Buchanan to *remain* cautious in his Presidency.

Millard Fillmore was another Presidential candidate that benefitted from being out of the country during most of the Pierce administration. Less than one month after leaving the White House his wife Abigail died. A crestfallen Fillmore eventually decided to travel in Europe after the example of Martin Van Buren. Lincoln heard how Fillmore was honored and feted throughout Europe which Lincoln could not imagine happening for Fillmore in his own country. When Fillmore returned to New York after over a year of travel, he discovered that most American of phenomena—former Presidents seemed to inexorably gain in popularity after leaving office, no matter how loathed they were *in* office.

Fillmore was the last Whig President. Former Whigs were desperately trying to reform under a different banner. They split into two starkly different parties, thereby all but assuring Buchanan's victory. One group called itself the "American" Party, a suitably patriotic name that might be expected to attract a significant number of voters. For a while, it did.

The American Party stood on a platform of being anti-immigrant. As industrialization took hold in the North, waves of immigrants, mostly from Ireland and Germany crossed the Atlantic to come to the United States and work in the new factories. Most of the immigrants were Catholic. As Americans in the North began to fear that the immigrants would take their jobs, anti-Catholic sentiment rose in the working class to a point where a politician could gain several votes by denouncing the "Catholic scourge."

The American Party was more commonly known by its nickname the "Know Nothing" Party. When members would meet to contrive their next anti-immigrant event or stance, their password or common greeting was "I know nothing." Obviously, they preferred to be called the American Party but many who knew them as the Know Nothings voted loyally for them. Paradoxically, and perhaps inconsistently in Lincoln's mind, the

Know Nothings claimed to be against slavery and in favor of female suffrage.

After winning several seats in Congress in 1854, the Know Nothings took aim at the Presidency. Realizing that their primary message of stemming immigration to a nation full of immigrants might not resonate outside of the major eastern cities, they attempted to portray themselves as the Whigs' logical successor party. When Fillmore returned from Europe he was told that the American Party, the Whigs' new banner, nominated him as their Presidential candidate. Again, Fillmore had no stain from Kansas on him and had the added benefit the American fondness for nostalgia.

Fillmore accepted the nomination to the delight of the Know Nothings. They were soon dismayed to realize that Fillmore did not share their aversion to immigrants or Catholics and was not in favor of regulating the new industries that were bringing prosperity to the country. It was the beginning of the end for the Know Nothings.

Lincoln had little trouble rejecting the American Party version of the Whigs. Asked by a friend what he proposed to do in the absence of the Whig Party, Lincoln wrote

> *"I am not a Know-Nothing – that is certain. How could I be? How can anyone who abhors the oppression of negroes, be in favor of degrading classes of white people? Our progress in degeneracy appears to me to be pretty rapid. As a nation, we began by declaring that 'all men are created equal.' We now practically read it 'all men are created equal, except negroes.' When the Know-Nothings get control, it will read 'all men are created equals, except negroes and foreigners and Catholics.' When it comes to that I should prefer emigrating to some country where they make no pretense of loving liberty – to Russia, for instance, where despotism can be taken*

pure, and without the base alloy of hypocrisy."

Lincoln was not just glad for the Know Nothings' demise for philosophical reasons, however. Their architects could not build a political organization in the next three years which meant that the next President would be another Democrat...or a Republican.

John Fremont was the first Presidential candidate of the new Republican party. The party was unequivocally anti-slavery, something the Whigs nor the Democrats ever claimed to be as they tried to straddle the line between extremists and partisan press in both the North and South. The Republicans did not expect Fremont to win the election this year but they hoped to stake out a platform to build on in the future. When Fremont swept the entire northeast, many ambitious former Whigs, like Lincoln, took notice.

Fremont was not even a strong candidate. Known for exploring the Western Frontier more than anything else, Fremont was intended to be in the mold of a war hero when both parties had run out of war heroes to run for President. Fremont's passionate abolitionism cost him votes in the South and border states and nullified any chance of him being nominated again.

This was where Lincoln saw his chance. He appreciated that he was not alone among former Whigs in sensing that a Republican who moderated his views slightly might have a chance to be elected President in 1860. He would express the view that slavery should be left alone where it already existed but not be allowed to spread further. He would proclaim his deep enmity for slavery at all opportunities but also make sure that it was known that he viewed the negro class as inferior. Inferior, but still entitled to freedom. By adhering to these positions, he would keep most of Fremont's victories in the North and certainly add some Western states that grew more sympathetic to abolitionist views with each passing year. Lincoln knew he would not fare well in the South but, while his positions would make the South nervous, his hope was that his stated intent to not interfere with existing slavery would stem the momentum for secession.

Even these carefully constructed positions would not be

sufficient to differentiate him from other candidates vying for the nomination. None of the other candidates, however, were running against Stephen Douglas for the United States Senate in 1858. For the next two years Lincoln would make it clear that he wanted to take Senator Douglas' Senate seat from him and would debate him every chance that he could. But he would use those debates to assure that James Buchanan's failings were as much on display as those of Senator Douglas. Lincoln would try to win the Senate seat but viewed preservation of Senator Douglas as a viable candidate to replace James Buchanan as being even more important.

Unlike James Buchanan, Stephen Douglas had been in the country the last four years and led the way for passage of the Kansas-Nebraska Act which now had the Union tearing at the seams. As a Northerner who tried to appease both sides during the Kansas debates, he was not entirely trusted in the South. Lincoln was fairly certain that a Douglas candidacy would spawn a third-party effort or two, most likely by individuals sympathetic to the South or trying to broker another compromise to save the Union. But he doubted that any party would come out stronger against slavery than his Republicans. Lincoln suspected that his victory would be closer than Buchanan's. Nonetheless, if he executed his strategy of undermining the already vulnerable Buchanan and keeping the damaged Douglas viable, he was confident that he would have the votes to become President. Yes, indeed, he *was* a Republican.

Chapter 2:
James Buchanan

President James Buchanan was lonely. He missed his long-time companion William King. He regretted not marrying the many women over the years who made their willingness to wed known. As only an aging bachelor can be, he became more set in his ways and more critical of the ways of others. His niece Harriet recently left the White House after serving as hostess for two years. She grew tired of her "Nunc's" constant inquiries as to how and why she was doing whatever it was she was doing.

Not that Buchanan did not continue to have opportunities to cure his loneliness. He grew infatuated with Elizabeth Craig, a beautiful widow from Georgia who he invited to be his guest in the White House. She stayed for two months, with many assuming she would soon be the First Lady. And, while that was certainly her goal when she arrived at the White House, after prolonged exposure to the President's fussiness and witnessing his family's weariness with his quirks and moodiness, the widow Craig pled homesickness and fled back to Georgia.

For all his youthful charm and political astuteness, Buchanan realized that his life's ambition of leading his country was proving to be a pyrrhic victory at best, an epic failure at worst. His irritability intensified as he watched the only family he knew put distance between themselves and the Uncle that raised a house full of orphans. More and more he relied on his enormous stock of wine and madeira to dull the pain of the choices he had made. It was often remarked at social events just how much the President seemed to be able to imbibe without ever appearing inebriated. Buchanan was only glad that they did not understand just how much he *did* drink. Especially as he watched his beloved country spiral beyond his control toward civil war.

As he sat in the Oval Office he finished reading the latest speech of William Seward, the Senator from New York:

"It is an irrepressible conflict between opposing and enduring forces, and it means that the United States must and will, sooner or later, become either entirely a slave-holding nation or entirely a free-labor nation. Either the cotton and rice-fields of South Carolina and the sugar plantations of Louisiana will ultimately be tilled by free labor, and Charleston and New Orleans become marts for legitimate merchandise alone, or else the rye-fields and wheat-fields of Massachusetts and New York must again be surrendered by their farmers to slave culture and to the production of slaves, and Boston and New York become once more markets for trade in the bodies and souls of men.

It is the failure to apprehend this great truth that induces so many unsuccessful attempts at final compromise between the slave and free States, and it is the existence of this great fact that renders all such pretended compromises, when made, vain and ephemeral. Startling as this saying may appear to you, fellow citizens, it is by no means an original or even a modern one. Our forefathers knew it to be true, and unanimously acted upon it when they framed the Constitution of the United States. They regarded the existence of the servile system in so many of the States with sorrow and shame, which they openly confessed, and they looked upon the collision between them, which was then just revealing

*itself, and which we are now accustomed to
deplore, with favor and hope. They knew that
either the one or the other system must
exclusively prevail."*

Buchanan rolled his eyes and leaned back in his chair. The
Albany Evening Journal, not surprisingly, decided to print, in its
entirety, the latest speech by Senator Seward. The *Journal* was
owned by Thurlow Weed, boss of the Republican New York
political machine. Senator Seward was Weed's latest protégé for
the Presidency. Buchanan had little time for Weed or Seward but,
even so, he was mystified as to what they thought this speech
would do to enhance Seward's outlook for election.

James Buchanan was confident that the next President
would be a Republican. Even if he wanted to run for re-election,
which he did not, Buchanan knew that the Democrats would not
fare well in 1860. Despite his and Franklin Pierce's best efforts at
compromise and their belief that the demise of slavery was
inevitable, the abolitionist press was perfecting its story that the
Democrats were the party of the slave owners. And while the last
President and the current President may have hailed from the
North, they were southerners at heart.

The Republicans were still getting organized in 1856 as
they rose from the ashes of the defunct Whig party. Additionally,
they lost votes to the short-lived Know Nothing party. But in
1860, the Republicans would stand alone and, for the first time in
a generation, the two major parties would be clearly different.
The Republicans would range from ardent abolitionists to
members who were anti-slavery but advocating limitation of
slavery to existing states with no further expansion. Democrats
would range from believers in the principle of Popular
Sovereignty where each state or territory decided for itself
whether to be slave or free to pro-slavery zealots who not only
wanted to see the expansion of slavery but could not brook the
notion of full citizenship rights for the African race. The area that
used to overlap between Democrats and Whigs was gone, as were
the prospects for compromise.

Buchanan was equally sure that the Democrats would

splinter into two or three parties, if not forever, then at least for the 1860 election to accommodate the various perspectives within the Democrats' range of positions on slavery. The Republicans, however, would not split because they were too new. The more extreme abolitionists in the party would tolerate a less extreme candidate for the simple reason that they were getting nowhere with Democrats in the White House. Thus, between a fractured Democratic party and the fact that the North was increasingly sympathetic to the abolitionist cause *and* there were simply more people in the North, Buchanan thought it would take a monumental *faux pas* by the Republicans to not take over the White House in 1861.

Seward's speech came dangerously close to such a mistake. Prior to his speech, Senator Seward was one of the leading candidates for the Republican nomination, if not *the* leading candidate. But Buchanan suspected that, at some point, Seward would do exactly what he did. He would come out in language that would offend the increasingly prickly South and eliminate himself as a viable candidate. What caused Buchanan to roll his eyes was his certainty that Seward *believed* he was steering a middle course on the slavery issue. But Seward could not resist use of phrases like "trade in the bodies and souls of men" or "sorrow and shame" when referring to the slave-holders. Not that most of the South would find less direct language problematic but, more importantly, those in the North who wanted to see the Union stay together would see Seward as the catalyst for the civil war that was poised to ignite at any moment. And they were right. Most voters in the North would be looking for a candidate that would be against slavery but able to hold the Union together. This was particularly true of Northern merchants that needed Southern cotton and other raw materials for their factories and continued prosperity.

Seward's and Weed's other problem was that another Republican candidate clearly understood what was needed to carry the North. Abraham Lincoln was proving to be one of the shrewdest politicians Buchanan observed in his long political career. Lincoln had not made a single public statement expressing an interest in becoming President. He was running to unseat

Stephen Douglas as the Senator from Illinois. Yet, their debates were receiving press coverage far out of proportion to the office being sought. Indeed, Buchanan guessed that Lincoln assumed that he would lose to Douglas in *this* race.

The President grudgingly admired Lincoln for identifying a brilliant strategy. Buchanan surmised that Lincoln was making sure that his debates with Douglas were reported on religiously and that Lincoln's views on slavery were repeated with sufficient frequency that all would know where he stood. After Lincoln lost to Douglas next month, Lincoln and his supporters would start the work of getting Lincoln nominated by the Republicans in 1860 as the anti-slavery candidate that was pragmatic enough to not seek immediate abolition and courteous enough to not insult his fellow countrymen in the South. That message might not carry the day in Illinois but, to most of the North, Lincoln would appear reasonable. Finally, unlike the New Yorker Seward, Lincoln would not be suspect given his Kentucky and Illinois roots. Absent a colossal misstep, Buchanan thought Lincoln would be his successor. And Abraham Lincoln did not seem the type to misstep.

Nonetheless, Buchanan was not sanguine that Lincoln would avert secession or civil war. Buchanan himself knew that he did little for the last two years to stem the gathering storm. It started two days after he was sworn in as the fifteenth President in March of 1857. On that day, the Supreme Court handed down a decision in the *Dred Scott v. Sandford* case.

For James Buchanan, a renowned lawyer with a reputation for being an expert on the United States' Constitution, the *Dred Scott* case was to be the final word on slavery. For most people in the North, however, the case was a leap forward toward civil war. It took Buchanan close to a year to realize how naïve and insular he was.

Dred Scott was a slave who was taken north with his family into the Minnesota territory. There, his "owner," Sandford, would lease Scott and his family out for labor. Under the Missouri Compromise, Minnesota was free territory. Dred Scott sued for his freedom. After losing in the lower court, the Supreme Court agreed to hear the case. James Buchanan knew that the case could be decided about the time he took office and he knew that the result could have immense ramifications for the slavery debate raging in the country.

Before taking office, Buchanan contacted Justices on the Court to inquire when the decision might be announced and to offer unsolicited legal advice on the Constitution. He was informed that the decision would be announced shortly after his inauguration and would correlate with the President-elect's views on the Constitution.

Buchanan was elated and tailored his inaugural speech to comport with the expected outcome. He embraced the concept of "Popular Sovereignty" despite his belief that every new territory that debated slavery would just inflame the national quarrel again. He used the word "happy" so many times that many of his closest friends wondered if the new President indulged his fondness for strong drink before giving his speech. Indeed, the speech seemed so oddly optimistic when the country was so passionately divided that even the Democrats were left wondering about their new leader.

As a lawyer and a politician who marveled at the durability of the Constitution and the United States' unique history of peaceful transitions of power, Buchanan assumed that once the Supreme Court spoke, the country would recognize the matter of slavery as settled and "the public mind shall be diverted from this question to others of more pressing and practical importance." Abolitionists at the Inauguration and reading the speech in newspapers over the following days were agape that a President from a northern state would find the lot of the slave to not be of pressing and practical importance.

Rather than preparing the citizenry to accept the *Dred Scott* decision, Buchanan's speech gave the abolitionists time to prepare if the Court's opinion coincided with the views expressed by the new President. When Chief Justice Taney issued the Court's decision, they were ready. Taney ruled that, as a black man, Dred Scott could not be a citizen and therefore had no right to sue for his freedom. From this premise Taney concluded that a slave owner held a property interest in his slaves and that that interest was protected by the Constitution. Buchanan was pleased to see that Taney went on to rule that since slavery was protected under the Constitution, the Missouri Compromise, which outlawed slavery in northern territories, was unconstitutional. It was the first time the Supreme Court ruled that a law was unconstitutional since John Marshall used the failure of James Madison and Thomas Jefferson to deliver William Marbury's commission to expand the Court's power.

Buchanan's conviction that the slavery question was resolved and the country would move on was short-lived. Far from concluding the issue, the case became a rallying point for abolitionists who agitated against an immoral Administration *and* Supreme Court. Buchanan soon realized how badly he misread the mood of the country and its willingness to abide any law that conflicted with the entrenched positions of both sides. For one as dedicated to the rule of law as Buchanan coupled with a predisposition to compromise, the situation was almost incomprehensible.

Kansas was the reason why Buchanan thought the *Dred Scott* case would dispose of the slavery battle. After *Dred Scott*, Buchanan figured that the territory would vote on its proposed constitution for statehood and, given that the majority of citizens in the territory were opposed to slavery *and* the fact that Kansas was not at all suitable for raising cotton, the Kansas exercise of "Popular Sovereignty" would yield a free state. He was stunned when the free state advocates in Kansas refused to vote since the election was being run by the pro-slavery government that Franklin Pierce installed. As a result, a pro-slavery constitution that was supported by virtually no one in Kansas was sent to Washington for approval. Burnishing his reputation for being a stickler for law and procedure, Buchanan sent the constitution to Congress for approval. It was not approved.

As Buchanan headed into his second year in office he had managed to convince the North that he was firmly in the pro-slavery camp without gaining any great admiration in the South. To compound matters, many Northern manufacturers were on the cusp of financial ruin as a Panic swept the financial markets. The Southern cotton growers proclaimed it just desserts for the haughtiness of the North toward them. Unable to appease or persuade anyone, Buchanan was counting the days until he could leave this miserable office.

The perennial candidate, Buchanan never imagined that the disintegration of the country would be the legacy of his Administration. He wanted no part of remaining in office and, yet, returning home to Wheatland held very little appeal. He reflected often these days on James Polk's derogatory comments to Buchanan about Buchanan's "old lady" habits and his failure to find a suitable wife. Polk could be cruel. But, even worse, Polk was proving to be right.

***

Washington D.C.: February 1861

When he was asked to preside over a "Peace Conference," John Tyler was flattered. He felt, at long last, that his country finally appreciated his service and wisdom. He left "Sherwood Forest" with Julia and arrived in Washington with cautious optimism. Indeed, their first few nights in Washington reminded Julia of how she missed the lavish balls and receptions of her short time as First Lady.

The Conference was the product of business and political leaders trying to find one more compromise to save the Union. When Tyler entered the Conference hall he saw many familiar faces that he had not seen in many years. Most, like him, were faces that aged significantly in the interim. The "Peace Conference" soon was being called the "Old Gentlemen's Conference" to Tyler's dismay and slight embarrassment. Now, after three weeks of bargaining and arguing, Tyler and his fellow old men were going home having failed in their mission.

Seven southern states seceded since November of 1860. That was the month that the Republicans elected their first President, Abraham Lincoln. True to his campaign speeches, Lincoln immediately made it clear that he did not intend to interfere in states where slavery already existed but would draw the line at any new slave states or territories. In other words, "Popular Sovereignty" was dead. First South Carolina and then six more cotton states decided that Lincoln's restriction nullified all prior compromises and would ultimately cause them to live subject to the North's dictates. By the time of the Peace Conference in early February, the seven states were forming a government under the banner "Confederate States of America."

Virginia had not seceded yet but was considering it. In preparation for possible secession (and to create pressure for the Peace Conference), Virginia was forming an alternative Confederate government. John Tyler was elected to serve in the Confederate House of Representatives. He came to Washington praying that he might avoid serving any government other than that of the United States.

Seven southern border states attended the conference along with fourteen northern states. None of the states that seceded were in attendance. But all states knew that Virginia was critical to the success or failure of the Conference.

The Commonwealth of Virginia was essentially the host to Washington D.C. and, in so many respects, the birthplace of the nation. Tyler's father was one of the founders of the country and a contemporary of Washington, Jefferson, Madison and Monroe. John Tyler himself grew up at the knee of these luminaries. He may not have been a popular President himself, but he was one of the last lingering ties to the state that was home to the most popular of the Founding Fathers. Those sponsoring the Peace Conference knew that if Virginia seceded, the Union would be no more.

That is why John Tyler was invited to preside over the Conference and to give the keynote address. Even the most vociferous of his former political enemies (and there were many) had no quarrel with Tyler's leadership of the Conference. As the Conference progressed, however, Tyler confirmed what he was afraid of when he set out for Washington. The dye was cast for secession and, undoubtedly, war.

The proposal from the Peace Conference was yet another variation on the Missouri Compromise. When Tyler and other leaders of the Conference carried it to Congress it died a quick, merciful death on the floors of both the House and Senate. Tyler was assured by the Congress that further work was pointless and

Tyler adjourned the Peace Conference. He had no further illusions and planned to recommend secession to his home state when he returned home.

Knowing that he was soon to be a member of the House of Representatives for the Confederate States of America, Tyler decided that he was duty-bound to try and prevail on the outgoing President and the incoming President to let the Confederate states leave in peace. It was his failure in that mission that left him even more despondent than the futility of the Peace Conference.

First, Tyler visited President Buchanan. The former President made it clear that secession of more Southern states was inevitable and that Buchanan should do what he could in his few remaining days in office to assure that their exit was peaceful. Small skirmishes already occurred near Ft. Sumter in South Carolina. Tyler advised the President that it would be best to withdraw Union troops from the Fort and bring them back north.

With his head cocked to the side as it always was, Buchanan replied, "If I withdraw those troops, I'll be burned in effigy all over the North."

Tyler was exasperated. "Old Buck" was one of the few Presidents that could contend with Tyler in terms of unpopularity. He, literally, had a few days left in office. Yet he was concerned with how he would be perceived by a part of the country that treated him with utter contempt anyway rather than seizing an opportunity to spare the lives of both northern and southern young men.

Tyler shook his head and, in a trembling voice weakened by age and emotion said, "What of it? I have been burned in effigy more than any of your other predecessors. That has nothing to do with doing your duty."

Buchanan shed all pretense. "I have to live in the North. That's my home. And my conscience is clear that I have done all I could as President *and before,* to accommodate you *gentlemen* of the South. Perhaps too much. Is there anything else you wish to discuss Mr. Tyler?"

Tyler left the White House wondering why James Buchanan only seemed able to muster courage when confronting a seventy-year old man who held no meaningful political power. John Tyler had heard that Buchanan was a talented orator and lawyer prior to entering politics. Perhaps that was true but Tyler believed that Buchanan had long ago squandered any gift he had for advocacy. Instead, he serially denuded himself with compromises, all in service of ambition.

As Tyler stepped into the windy streets of Washington, he headed toward the Willard Hotel, temporary residence of the President-elect, Abraham Lincoln. Still as reed-thin as in his youth, Tyler was finding the gales sweeping Pennsylvania Avenue harder to navigate than two decades earlier. It was just one more sign of his advanced age. The Peace Conference had not just taxed his patience, it demonstrated how much his stamina had withered.

The former President had never met the President-elect. A Pinkerton agent met Tyler in the lobby of the hotel. Tyler heard that Lincoln arrived under cover and in a disguise after he received several promises of harm if he traversed areas sympathetic to the South on his journey to Washington. Tyler never imagined the need for protection from a Pinkerton agent when he was President. It was further evidence of how deep passions now ran, and how much more divisive a figure Lincoln was than Tyler.

When Abraham Lincoln opened the door, Tyler was momentarily taken aback. At six feet tall, Tyler always considered himself tall and slender. Lincoln, however, towered over him. But he was even thinner than Tyler. He had a scraggly beard that Tyler deduced must have been part of his costume to avoid discovery. Tyler concluded quickly that the man before him was one of the homeliest people he ever saw.

Lincoln seized on Tyler's momentary incredulity to grab the former President's hand and draw him into the hotel room.

"President Tyler, I am privileged to make your acquaintance and humbled that you would pay me the honor of a visit."

Tyler, the Southern gentleman to his core, was, he had to admit, impressed. Lincoln was not polished but had an infectious earnestness and warmth that was hard to resist.

"Mr. President-elect, the privilege is mine. I appreciate you extending me the courtesy of an audience at, what I am sure, is a busy time."

Lincoln smiled. Tyler thought that, unlike most people, even a smile did not help diminish Lincoln's homeliness. Yet, Tyler could see how Lincoln succeeded both as a lawyer and a politician. There was something incongruously attractive about him.

Lincoln joked, "Well, if a few more states secede, I might be the least busy President ever."

Tyler had also heard that Lincoln had a disarming sense of humor. As they spoke, Lincoln made several attempts at jokes that mostly fell flat with the serious-minded Tyler. While Tyler could not help but like this man from Illinois, he was certain that there were probably never two more different men than he and Abraham Lincoln.

Ultimately, Tyler came to the point of his visit. Gingerly, he suggested that it might be best if the North allowed the seceding states to go peacefully with the hope that reconciliation might be effected in the years to come. Lincoln's face grew longer and he was visibly sad.

"Sir, with the utmost respect, it is my intention to fulfill my oath and protect the Constitution of the United States. That document does not allow for secession or treason."

Tyler slumped slightly in his chair. His voice quivered as he tried to grasp the reality that was now confronting he and all secessionists. "You would allow blood to be shed to grant the Negro equality?"

Lincoln fixed his gaze on Tyler. "Equality is not the issue. Fealty to the Union is the issue. The inferiority of the Negro race is not where we disagree. It is whether their inferiority excludes them from the human race and whether that is a sufficient reason to violate the Constitution that your father helped to become the law of our land."

Reflexively, Tyler stood. "Mr. Lincoln, I wish you God's speed as President. I believe you will find it a job requiring an ability to occasionally yield in order to avert harm."

Lincoln slowly rose. "Thank you for your visit President

Tyler. I truly am honored."

Tyler made his way downstairs to the lobby. He stopped and stared out at Pennsylvania Avenue. This was likely to be his last visit to Washington for a long time. Possibly forever. If Lincoln meant what he said, and Tyler had no reason to doubt him, then John Tyler was about to be dubbed a traitor. The son of John Tyler, one of the most prominent of the Founding Fathers would return to their common home of Virginia, recommend secession and risk being hanged if he returned to Washington D.C. "Civil War" was no longer an abstract phrase. It was extant in the form of Abraham Lincoln.

Tyler made his way back to his room where Julia was waiting. He opened the door to find her nursing eight-month old Pearl. He pondered for a moment, thinking that Pearl deserved better than a seventy-year old father who was about to be branded a traitor to his country. But Pearl also deserved a father who stood for what he believed to be right. Tyler smiled weakly and said to Julia, "It is time to go. I can do nothing more here." Julia nodded and eased the child from her breast.

***

New York: March 1861

The "Little Magician" was no longer little. At 78 years of age, Martin Van Buren was certainly no taller but was much, much larger than in his youth. Years of gourmet meals replete with expensive wines and madeiras left him unable to stand without considerable effort and with a laborious asthmatic wheeze.

Winters were long at Lindenwald, Van Buren's mansion south of Albany. His sons Abraham and Smith and their lovely wives saw that Van Buren was cared for and doted upon, to his delight. Six years earlier his third son, Martin Jr., succumbed in his long battle with tuberculosis. The former President was living in Italy working on his memoirs when the doctors in Paris sent word that his son was declining rapidly. Van Buren hurried back to Paris, arriving just in time to hold his son's hand as he died.

The agony of losing his son was worse than Van Buren

could have ever predicted. He lingered in Paris long enough to settle his son's affairs and then set sail for New York, his three other sons and home. Since returning to Lindenwald, he had not written another word of his memoirs. Nor did he intend to.

For the last two months, Van Buren was sure that he would soon join his son in Heaven. Shortly after Christmas he came down with a cold that progressed to influenza and pneumonia. Racked with fever for over two months and rarely leaving his bed, the rarely ill Van Buren despaired of recovering. Indeed, his family came to believe this as well and arrangements began to quietly be made.

By the end of February, however, Van Buren was surprised to find himself feeling much better. Over the last few days he stayed up most of the day and prowled the halls of Lindenwald watching through the windows for a sign of winter abating. Today, he settled himself in a chair next to a small table where he could look out at the snow-covered grass that made up part of the 220 acres that he called home. Mail was piled up on the table from the last two months, awaiting Van Buren's attention.

He thumbed through the envelopes looking for anything out of the ordinary. A postmark from Concord, New Hampshire caught his eye. He carefully sliced the top of the envelope open and pulled out a short letter. He glanced at the return address and saw, as suspected, that the letter was sent by former President Pierce. After lamenting the corrosive relations between the North and South, Pierce concluded with an invitation:

> *"The Lincoln administration seems intent on holding the southern states in the Union by force. Before matters deteriorate further into pointless deaths, I propose that those of us who have confronted these issues most prominently convene a peace conference in Philadelphia, where our forefathers first brought the states together under our blessed Constitution. Please give this favorable consideration. I have extended this invitation to Presidents Tyler, Fillmore and Buchanan."*

Martin Van Buren shook his head and sighed. As fond as he was of Frank Pierce, the New Hampshire man did not seem to understand that it was *his* failure to "confront" these "issues" that helped bring "matters" to their current state.

It was March 4. Today, Abraham Lincoln would be sworn in as the sixteenth President of the United States. Already, Lincoln was making it clear that he would blame his Democratic predecessors Pierce and Buchanan for coddling the South and making secession a reality. Van Buren was sure that Pierce did not seek Lincoln's concurrence in the idea of a "Past Presidents Peace Conference" just as he was sure that Lincoln would do all he could to doom such a meeting.

While Lincoln was not nearly as socially adept as Martin Van Buren, he was every bit as shrewd. Lincoln was the standard bearer of the young Republican party and, through dispensation of patronage and election organization, Van Buren could see many of the same patterns that *he* followed in building the Democratic party. The Democrats were nominally constructed on Jeffersonian and Jacksonian notions of States rights until Martin Van Buren spun a web of favors, patronage and backscratching that caused the Democrats to become less ideological and more pragmatic. But they never wholly abandoned their adherence to States rights. When slavery bloomed from an irritant to a potentially fatal issue for the Union, Van Buren's machine and methods were so well entrenched throughout that country that his Party could not risk the loss of southern votes by standing firmly against Negro bondage.

Nonetheless, to a lesser extent, the Whigs were in the same position. For two decades, the supposedly opposing parties crafted compromises and preached Popular Sovereignty to keep Washington D.C. above the fray.

For "The Little Magician," however, staying out of the fray proved difficult. Assembling a political machine was second nature for him. But, as President, the inconsistency of slavery in a "free country" became impossible for him to ignore. After perfecting a reputation for political sharpness that caused Democrats across the country to seek his counsel on how to win and hold office, Van Buren lost his bearings. Unable to reconcile an idle central government that allowed the states to vie with one another over the spread of slavery, Van Buren first lost usefulness and then trust. He was not little, nor was he magic anymore.

He took some consolation that there was little he could have done to prevent the present crisis. The magnitude of the slavery battle that was upon the country was not fully apparent when Van Buren became President in 1837. The Missouri Compromise of 1820 seemed to temper passions by creating the State of Maine at the same time Missouri entered the Union as a slave state. But the Compromise also forbid further slavery in the northern territories acquired in the Louisiana Purchase. Thus, when he was President, Van Buren was not consumed by the vexatious issue of slavery as much as his successors. Nevertheless, it was during those years in the White House that he first began to struggle with the paradox of slavery in the United States. By the end of his term his conscience was besieged by the specter of southern slaves.

So, while Van Buren sympathized with his successors who still lived, all could have done more. Of that, Van Buren was bitterly sure.

Van Buren wondered how Pierce proposed to entice John Tyler to a peace conference. Tyler already hosted a "Peace Conference" a month earlier in Washington and failed miserably. As Van Buren understood it, Tyler was now back in Virginia preparing to take his seat in the Confederate States of America House of Representatives. Not only would John Tyler not be interested in another peace conference, he probably knew that he would not make it to Philadelphia and back alive.

Not that many would care about Tyler's welfare. His recommendation of secession to the Virginia legislature was just his latest act of treachery. Van Buren lost any affinity for Tyler when the Virginian ran as a Whig with General Harrison in 1840, denying Van Buren a second term. Martin Van Buren could endure an election loss, but an election loss to a *Democrat* who joined the Whig ticket was an abomination. For Van Buren, party came first. The product of Tyler's disloyalty was the refusal of *either* party to nominate him for a second term. Martin Van

Buren was not one to hold a grudge but he could not envision a reconciliation between the North and South that involved John Tyler, nor did he wish to be party to such a reconciliation.

Nor did he find the notion of Millard Fillmore brokering a peace agreement inspiring. Fillmore claimed credit for helping negotiate the Compromise of 1850 but, despite his support for that Compromise, Van Buren thought Fillmore's "help" was not much more than allowing the Compromise to pass once he became President. Zachary Taylor would not have been so accommodating. The Whigs seemed incapable of finding Vice Presidents that were of the same mind as their old General running mates.

Both Fillmore and Van Buren were from upstate New York so Van Buren knew the thirteenth President well. It was easy to like Fillmore. He was distinguished, mild-mannered and exuded sophistication. Unfortunately, Van Buren found Fillmore to be a bit of a plodder. He took Fillmore more seriously when he was loyal to Thurlow Weed. Van Buren admired Fillmore's willingness to break with the odious Weed. But Van Buren found Fillmore alarmingly naïve in thinking that he could be elected on the strength of his reputation alone. Ultimately, Van Buren lost whatever respect he had for Fillmore when he ran for President as the candidate for the short-lived but utterly distasteful Know-Nothings. He knew that Fillmore knew little about the organization and made no pretense of campaigning on its platform. That did not assuage Van Buren's dismay in the least. Again, party came first. If it did not, then a candidate was seeking office under false pretenses.

If Tyler and Fillmore were hapless in attempting to be elected President in their own right, the same could not be said for Pierce and Buchanan. Franklin Pierce was elected with Van Buren's full support. For the first time since he left the Presidency, Van Buren was optimistic that the country might avoid destruction over slavery given Pierce's popularity. But first Pierce's son died before he was even sworn in as President and then he supported the Kansas-Nebraska Act forfeiting whatever goodwill he had with most of the North. Pierce was a disappointment of tragic proportions to Van Buren.

After Pierce handed over a country teetering on the brink of civil war to Buchanan, Van Buren had little appetite for politics or even his beloved Democratic Party any longer. Van Buren was not an admirer of James Buchanan but he thought that an experienced politician like Buchanan was unlikely to compound Pierce's mistake of encouraging the South's desire to spread slavery even further. But Buchanan proved him wrong by embracing the *Dred Scott* decision and declaring the whole question of slavery moot in his first week as President.

Martin Van Buren was so confounded by the *Dred Scott* decision that he did something he had not done since he was a young lawyer. He read the briefs submitted to the Supreme Court and the decision itself. It was only then that he came to an inescapable conclusion, at least for him.

The Missouri Compromise was not at issue in *Dred Scott*. Justice Taney ruled that Dred Scott had no standing to sue because he was a Negro. As a Negro, he had no citizenship rights. That was where Van Buren and many others believed the decision should have ended. But Taney went on to rule that the Missouri Compromise banning slavery in the territories was unconstitutional. As Van Buren studied the opinion he realized that the constitutional argument had to be the product of a nimbler legal mind than Roger Taney's. That mind had to be that of the new President.

James Buchanan's reputation as a lawyer and then a politician was inextricably linked to his expertise on the United States Constitution. Van Buren was certain that, even if Buchanan did not write the words himself, he made sure that the Supreme Court adopted his reasoning, including an issue that most lawyers saw as superfluous.

Van Buren's legal analysis was much different than Buchanan's. The Missouri Compromise was a political creation. The Supreme Court was duty bound to stay out of politics. This was especially true when the political issue was not even necessary to the disposal of the case. Van Buren was incredulous that Buchanan, the Constitutional scholar, would lose sight of such a rudimentary tenet. It was so rudimentary that Van Buren was sure Buchanan did not lose sight of it. He simply decided to ignore it.

Why would Buchanan breach the sacred separation of powers enshrined in the very Constitution that he claimed to hold dear in such an overt manner? Van Buren knew that James Buchanan was much more enamored with the prestige of being President than with the conflict, controversy and, indeed, hard work, that came with the job. Van Buren concluded that the *Dred Scott* case was Buchanan's chance to institutionalize "Popular Sovereignty" and foist the issue of slavery on the States to decide. *That* would allow Buchanan to wash his and the federal government's hands of the slavery debate and to indulge his inclination toward international affairs. As the father of the concept of a "political organization," Van Buren was disheartened by Buchanan's amateurishness, naiveté and, indeed, cowardice.

Of course, Buchanan's scheme yielded none of the desired effects. The President spent four years trying to broker the very compromises he sought to avoid. Given his proclaimed support for the *Dred Scott* decision as "the law of the Land," the North disowned Buchanan and, for the first time, sent a Republican majority to Congress in the elections of 1858. For two long years, the Republicans blamed Buchanan for every step that took the country closer to civil war. By the end of his term, Buchanan was utterly impotent.

The party that Martin Van Buren created and nurtured into the most dominant political force in the country was now barely intact. For that, Van Buren held Franklin Pierce and James Buchanan responsible. Rather than standing firm that slavery should not be allowed to spread outside of its current borders, they opened the door repeatedly for the states to cannibalize one another as the more extreme citizens of the North and South bludgeoned their counterparts with self-righteous indignation. Van Buren loathed slavery but was certain that, if confined, it would die a death brought on by economic obsolescence. "Popular Sovereignty" would do nothing to hasten that death.

Van Buren folded Pierce's letter, placed it back in its envelope and then slowly tore both in two. He would not respond to the invitation because he could not think of a polite way to do so but also because he was suspicious that Frank Pierce did not even recall sending the letter. Between the grief of losing his only son, the failure of his Presidency and the rejection by the Democrats to even be considered for a second term, Pierce was reported to be in a perpetual state of inebriation. Van Buren suspected that Buchanan would soon be in a similar state.

More than his disenchantment with Franklin Pierce and James Buchanan and their almost lethal impact on Van Buren's Democrats, the Little Magician was disturbed by another thought. As he pondered the mistakes that Pierce and Buchanan made and the pronouncements of Abraham Lincoln, Van Buren could barely comprehend his own thoughts. The new President's views seemed to square almost perfectly with his own. If that was true, then Lincoln deserved Van Buren's support, which Van Buren would readily give. At what point, however, did his support transform him from the architect of the Democratic Party into the unthinkable: A Republican?

EPILOGUE: July 4, 1861

Senator Andy Johnson of Tennessee stood in the doorway of the chamber of the United States Senate. His fellow senators were slowly making their way to their desks, greeting one another graciously but mostly in subdued tones. At least *some* of his fellow senators. The row where Senator Johnson sat was still empty. It would remain that way during this 37th Congress of the United States.

The last few weeks were the most harrowing of Johnson's life. On June 8, Johnson's home state of Tennessee voted to join the ten states that already seceded from the Union. Consistent with his stance for years, Johnson campaigned against secession, arguing that not only was secession impossible under the Constitution, the South was better off in the Union than out of it. What Johnson did not say aloud but believed fervently was that the South would be destroyed in a war with the North.

When Tennessee voted, that war was already underway. South Carolina, which threatened secession for over forty years, was the first to secede and the first to draw blood. The Union garrison at Fort Sumter was attacked in April. Within a couple days, the Fort was in the hands of a South Carolina militia. As the federal soldiers stationed at Fort Sumter fled, the long-dreaded Civil War was a reality.

In the South, Johnson marveled at how jubilant his southern brethren were to *finally* be at war. When he pointed out that the North had a decided advantage in manufacturing, manpower, weaponry and wealth, Johnson was attacked, sometimes physically, for being disloyal to the South. The South's plan was, apparently, to open direct trade with Great Britain swapping cotton for weapons. As to manpower, the argument seemed to rely on the belief that it took three Yankees to equal one Rebel. Johnson saw only disaster ahead for Tennessee and its Confederate allies.

It was not that Andrew Johnson was unsympathetic to the South. He was a slaveowner who could not fathom being a fellow citizen with a Negro and, like most of his fellow Democrats, a firm believer in Popular Sovereignty. He did not relish the prospect of four years under Abraham Lincoln who Johnson was sure was intent on annihilating the Confederate States, now that South Carolina had given the North an excuse for doing battle. In short, he believed that the South was right about everything except its ability to and the wisdom of seceding from the Union. Johnson predicted economic ruin to go along with scores of pointless deaths.

But war fever had taken hold in the South and Johnson's refusal to celebrate secession left him, suddenly, unpopular and, more importantly, in grave danger. Johnson's unpopularity was incredible for a man who, just a year earlier, was the most admired man in his home state. He was a Congressman and then Governor before being elected to the Senate. His supporters in Tennessee were almost successful in persuading the Democrats to nominate him for President in 1860. If this nascent war could have been averted, Johnson would have been the likely candidate in 1864.

In Johnson's home district of Eastern Tennessee, secession was not supported, in part because of Johnson's earnest pleas against it. But within 24 hours of the secession vote, Confederate troops swarmed into Eastern Tennessee intent on crushing any opponents. Andrew Johnson was at the top of the list to be crushed.

Johnson began receiving warnings to cast his lot with the Confederates or suffer the consequences. The "consequences" clearly involved beatings at best and, at worst, death. Johnson was sure they did not involve due process and started carrying a pistol. By June 12, Johnson's friends loaded him in a covered stage and set off for Cumberland Gap where they hoped to smuggle Tennessee's senator safely into Kentucky.

They reached the Gap and stopped just before the state line.

When Johnson emerged from the coach where he was secreted away throughout the journey, a bullet whistled past his head. He jumped back in and the party raced to the border where he set out on his own.

As he traveled to Washington, Johnson made speeches supporting the Union but begging for leniency for the South in the same breath. As he made his way North, he was surprised by the empathy he solicited. When he arrived in Washington, he was being cast as the last statesman of the South and drew adoring crowds wherever he appeared. He made it clear that he intended to continue to represent Tennessee's interests in the United States Senate and would be assuming his rightful seat on the Senate Floor.

As Johnson shuffled to his desk, senators rose and applauded. The Senate Gallery soon followed suit. Old Hannibal Hamlin, the Vice President from Maine even stood. Senator Johnson smiled momentarily and nodded to acknowledge the spontaneous tribute. As he eased into his seat, however, he choked back tears. To his right sat the empty desks of John Slidell of Louisiana, Jeff Davis of Mississippi (and new President of the "Confederate States of America"), Clement Clay of Alabama and William Sebastian of Arkansas. To his left sat the empty desks of Trusten Polk of Missouri and, finally, Alfred Nicholson, Johnson's fellow Senator from Tennessee. All around him were the empty desks of senators from the South. Senator Johnson of Tennessee was the only southerner present.

The Senator fingered the Resolution that he would present to the Senate on this 85th anniversary of the Declaration of Independence. He was sure the Resolution would pass because it was just words. But, it was a start.

> *"Resolved, that the present deplorable civil war has been forced upon the country by the disunionists of the southern States now in revolt against the constitutional government, and in arms around the capital. That in this national emergency, Congress, banishing all feelings of mere passion or resentment, will recollect only its duty to the whole country; that this war is*

not waged on their part in any spirit of oppression, or for any purpose of conquest or subjugation, or purpose of overthrowing or interfering with the rights or established institutions of those States, but to defend and maintain the supremacy of the Constitution, and to preserve the Union with all the dignity, equality, and rights of the several States unimpaired; and that as soon as these objects are accomplished the war ought to cease."

As Andrew Johnson read the Resolution, he prayed that his southern brethren would be with him on the Senate Floor for the 86th anniversary of the United States. Until they *were* reunited, Johnson would speak for them and, hopefully, save them from their folly. If necessary, God forbid, he would beg for mercy on their behalf.

Author's Note

This is a work of fiction based on *many* factual events. Most of the significant events described occurred. On the other hand, almost none of the quoted conversations occurred. Where events did occur, each President's proximity or attitude toward those events is roughly accurate. *All* conversations, views or events are based on historical record or a well-informed guess as to what each President would have done or thought at the time.

Why write an essentially biographic book that takes some of the liberties of a novel? For fifty years I have read dozens of books on the United States Presidents, including at least one biography of each President (and, for most Presidents, several). As I have accumulated knowledge about the Presidents I learned the history of the United States from the unique perspective of the Chief Executives who, for better or worse, shaped so much of that history. I came to appreciate their strengths, their weaknesses, their victories, their potential, their passions and their tragedies. Most of all, I am fascinated by their humanity.

It was this humanity that I wanted to capture. *Each* President, in his own way, plays an outsized role in shaping the country that, unfortunately, high school and college history books simply cannot convey. I wanted to introduce these lesser known Presidents between Washington and Lincoln in a way that gives a sense of who these men were and why they are important (and interesting) to know.

While this book is not as much of a "novel" as Gore Vidal's *Burr* and *Lincoln* or William Safire's *Freedom*, those works were my first exposure to attempting to relay large doses of history through a work of fiction. I, of course, am no Gore Vidal or William Safire, but do hope to have honored their genre.

Finally, for many years I have heard flat declarations that a contemporary President is the "best" or the "worst" President "ever." Or people will reflexively declare Washington, Lincoln, Roosevelt or Kennedy the greatest because those are the only Presidents they can remember. Rather than asking them to compare their chosen President with, for example, John Quincy Adams, I usually remain silent knowing that the last thing they intended their comment to elicit was a boring discourse on Presidential history.

This book is my effort to make those evaluations a little more informed. Ultimately, an understanding of *all* the Presidents who have led us will tell us more about where we have been, where we are and where we are going. It should be both humbling and encouraging to recognize that many of the dilemmas a President confronts today are not unique or new, they are just the latest chapter in our collective story. Our story is, more than anything else, a Presidents story.

Brad McKim
March 2017